Robert Pickett

Oxford?
6.60297

Fundamentals of
College Algebra

Fundamentals of College Algebra

WILLIAM H. DURFEE
Mount Holyoke College

New York
THE MACMILLAN COMPANY

Second Printing 1963

Library of Congress catalog card number: 60-5484

The Macmillan Company, New York
Brett-Macmillan Ltd., Galt, Ontario

Printed in the United States of America

Preface

A course in college algebra is a stepping stone between high school and college mathematics. Its purpose should be to fill the gaps in the student's preparation and to introduce him to the spirit and objectives of mathematics as it is taught in colleges today where the emphasis is increasingly on fundamentals and careful reasoning. Because of the many new concepts that have come to the fore, time should not be spent on topics that are outmoded or of little relevance to later work; the student should move on to other things as quickly as possible.

This book is written with these considerations in mind. It covers those aspects of classical algebra that are important in present-day mathematics and that I have found particularly useful in later courses in analytic geometry and calculus. I have treated them in a careful, up-to-date manner that will give the student not only useful mathematical tools but also a sound algebraic foundation for later work. More important, perhaps, I have endeavored to instill in him an appreciation of algebra as a logical subject. Basic principles, deductive reasoning, and precision of statement are stressed rather than the development of manipulative skills, although there are many problems to test the latter. In addition, I have tried to orient the student to the modern view of algebra as a study of structure by emphasizing sets, axioms, and the various subfields of the real number field. This point of view, together with many of the topics covered, should provide a good background for a subsequent course in modern algebra. I have tried to be as rigorous as possible for a book at this level. I believe, however, that rigor can be overdone to the point of deadening the student's interest in mathematics and obscuring for him the beauty and scope of the subject. The role of proof is stressed, and assumptions and omissions in proofs are carefully pointed out.

The review of algebraic operations is incorporated in Chapter 2 in an axiomatic development of the field properties of the real numbers. I hope that this approach will make elementary algebra more meaningful and interesting to the student than before. Many routine exercises as well as problems of a theoretic nature are given here. The presentation is flexible so that the instructor need not emphasize the theory but can treat the material as a review of technique and proceed as quickly as he wishes through this long chapter. On the other hand, he can omit the review and, by concentrating on the theory, develop the elementary algebraic properties of a general field.

Equations are carefully studied, the basic principles underlying their solution being discussed rather than a listing of various tricks to effect a solution. Complex numbers are developed axiomatically, and their role as elements of a field with certain desired properties brought out. Later, a brief outline of their construction by means of pairs of real numbers is given. A knowledge of polynomials is especially useful in the calculus, and I have included a treatment of their elementary properties. Most of the material on the theory of equations can be found here. Inequalities, an increasingly important subject, are discussed at some length. Those in one unknown are solved algebraically, and sets of inequalities in two unknowns are treated graphically. Since it is the theoretical rather than computational aspect of logarithms that is important today, I have emphasized the logarithmic function and its graph.

In accordance with my objective of treating only those algebraic topics of immediate use in later courses, I have omitted many topics traditionally found in college algebra texts. Some of these are outmoded and of little value today; others for which there is a later need are best postponed until such need arises; still others are on the edge of the main stream of algebra and are better replaced by the study of newer and more interesting ideas in mathematics.

Of these omitted topics, perhaps determinants and probability need special mention. The only *immediate* use for determinants is in the solution of systems of linear equations. Since their applicability is limited even there, I have chosen instead to solve such systems by the elimination method. This method is faster if there are more than three unknowns and provides complete solutions for all types of systems. Moreover, when performed systematically it is similar to tests for the independence of vectors and equivalence of matrices and hence has some generality of application.

The older concept of probability with its assumption of equally likely cases is inadequate for today's applications and developments of the subject. The modern axiomatic approach using set functions, together with the necessary background, cannot be presented to beginners in a few pages. Since the subject is not necessary for the calculus, I have omitted it in order to keep the book within the desired length.

The problems in each set are arranged in approximately increasing order of difficulty. Those marked with an asterisk develop theory used later in the text. The exercises within the text are intended to test the student's comprehension of newly introduced concepts, an understanding of which is necessary if he is to follow what comes afterwards. Chapter 5 on polynomials and Chapter 8 on sets of equations can be omitted without breaking the continuity of the book.

I thank Professor Carl Allendoerfer for his critical reading of the manuscript, my colleagues Professors Fred Kiokemeister and Grace Bates for their interest and suggestions, and Mrs. Donald McAuslan and Mrs. William Durfee for their help with the preparation of the manuscript.

South Hadley, Mass.   W.H.D.

Contents

Index of Special Symbols

Chapter 1

Sets and Numbers

1.1 Sets

Until the seventeenth century mathematics was primarily concerned with two fields: algebra, which is the study of numbers, and geometry, the study of geometric objects. Since that time, as new concepts were introduced and developed, mathematics has expanded until today it is a large subject with many subdivisions. Some of these ideas are so fundamental that they have had a profound effect on all of mathematics, not only providing material for further advances, but, equally important, casting additional light on its older aspects. One of the most important of these concepts is that of a set. We shall find that the notion of a set will be helpful in many parts of algebra, and so we begin our study of that subject with a brief examination of this idea.

A *set* is nothing more than a class or collection of objects. The concept is so basic that it is impossible to give a useful definition of what is meant by it. Instead we shall have to rely on the reader's experience and intuition and merely list some examples of sets as a guide:

(a) The set composed of the six New England States.
(b) The set of all books in the Library of Congress.
(c) The set of all books with red covers in the Library of Congress.
(d) The set of all numbers between zero and two, inclusive. (Don't forget that fractions and $\sqrt{2}$ are numbers too.)
(e) The set of all trees in the world.
(f) The set of all positive integers: 1, 2, 3, 4, 5, etc.
(g) The set of all cities in the United States with populations greater than 7,000,000 in 1960.

Obviously there are many different sets. The objects constituting a set are called its *elements*. A set may have a finite number of elements, as in (a), (b), (c), (e), and (g) above, or an infinite number, as in (d) and (f).

1

The number of elements in (e), although very large, is still finite. Note that the set in (g) has just one element. When we are interested in a set solely as a collection of objects, the order of the elements within the set is immaterial. The set composed of all books in the Library of Congress is the same regardless of the arrangement of the books on the shelves. The set (f) of all positive integers is not affected by a rearrangement of the integers from their usual order into the ordering 2, 1, 4, 3, 6, 5, 8, 7, etc.; it is still the same set. Mathematics studies many different kinds of sets, but we shall be interested primarily in sets, such as (d) and (f), whose elements are numbers.

Some sets are themselves contained in larger sets. The set of all books with red covers in the Library of Congress is contained in (that is, is a part of) the set of all books in the Library. Such a set is called a subset of the larger set. The set of all books in the Library with more than one hundred pages is another subset having, incidentally, some elements in common with the first subset. The set (d) is a subset of the set of all numbers. The interval consisting of all numbers between zero and one, but not including zero or one, is a subset of (d) as well as of the set of all numbers.

It is customary to use letters as a convenient means of referring to sets in much the same way that letters are used in algebra to denote numbers. Naturally, the context should make clear whether a given letter refers to a number or a set. If X stands for the set described in (b) and Y for that in (c), we can indicate that Y is a subset of X by the notation $Y \subset X$. We shall now give a precise definition of a subset.

Definition.   The set B is a *subset* of the set A if every element of B is an element of A. We indicate this relationship by the notation $B \subset A$.

Illustration 1.   Let A be the set composed of the seven numbers 1, 2, 3, 4, 5, 6, and 7. We shall use the notation $\{1, 2, 3, 4, 5, 6, 7\}$ to indicate this set. Let B be the set of the four numbers 2, 7, 5, and 3, indicated by $\{2, 7, 5, 3\}$, and C the set $\{2, 6, 7, 4, 9\}$. Then $B \subset A$, since every element of B is an element of A. However, C is not a subset of A (notation, $C \not\subset A$), since the element 9 of C is not in A. It is not enough that some elements of C be in A. According to the definition, C is not a subset of A unless every element of C is in A.

Illustration 2.   Consider the following sets:

$$A = \text{set of all animals,}$$
$$V = \text{set of all vertebrates,}$$
$$F = \text{set of all flying animals,}$$
$$M = \text{set of all mammals,}$$
$$B = \text{set of all birds,}$$
$$W = \text{set of all bats,}$$
$$I = \text{set of all flying insects,}$$
$$H = \text{set of all horses.}$$

Then $V \subset A$, $M \subset A$, and $I \subset F$. But $I \not\subset M$ and $F \not\subset V$.

Exercise A. In Illustration 1 find two sets, one containing a finite and the other an infinite number of elements, each of which contains A. Find a subset of B and one of C. Which set is the largest common subset of B and C?

Exercise B. In Illustration 2 find five more examples of set inclusion and two of set non-inclusion. Of which sets is B a subset? Which sets have none of the other sets as subsets? Is there any set that has all the other sets as subsets?

The relation of the subsets of a set to each other can often be represented by means of a line diagram, as in Figure 1.1, which refers to Illustration 2. Each set is represented by a point. If a set is a subset of another, its point is joined to the other by a rising line or series of such lines. Thus, W is a subset of V and F but not of B.

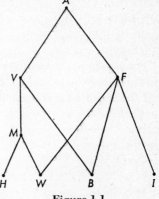

Figure 1.1

PROBLEMS

1. Give an example of a set with a finite number of elements. Find two subsets of this set that have no elements in common. Find two subsets that have elements in common.

2. Give an example of a set with an infinite number of elements. Continue as in Problem 1.

3. Give an example of a set consisting of just two elements.

4. Which of the following numbers are members of the set of all positive numbers: $3, \dfrac{16}{5}, \dfrac{4}{-7}, \pi$?†

5. If S is the set of all positive numbers whose squares are less than 9, which of the following are elements of S: $2, 6, 1\frac{1}{2}, -7, 9, 3, -1$?

6. Let $A = \{-\frac{1}{2}, 0, 25, 13, 8, 1, \frac{4}{3}\}$, $B = \{0, 24, 13\}$, $C = \{13, 8, \frac{4}{3}, 0\}$, and $D = \{0, 13\}$. Indicate which of these sets are contained in the others, and draw the corresponding line diagram.

7. List the set inclusions among the following sets and draw the line diagram showing their relationship:

    R = set of all numbers,
    P = set of all positive numbers,
    N = set of all negative numbers,
    A = set of all numbers greater than 3,
    B = set of all numbers greater than 2.9,
    C = set of all numbers between 1 and 5, inclusive,
    D = the set consisting of the number 4.

8. List the set inclusions among the following sets and draw the line diagram showing their relationship:

    I = set of all isosceles triangles,

†A positive number is a number that is greater than zero; a negative number is one that is less than zero. Zero is neither positive nor negative.

A = set of all triangles with area greater than 3,

D = set of all triangles with one or more sides greater than 4,

T = set of all triangles,

C = set of all triangles similar to the isosceles triangle whose base is 6 and altitude 5,

B = set of all triangles with area greater than 17,

F = set of all triangles with base 6 and altitude 5,

E = set of all equilateral triangles.

9. Give an example of a set that has five or more subsets. List some of the set inclusions and draw the line diagram.

10. List all the subsets that can be formed from a set of three elements; from a set of four elements.

11. If A, B, and C are any three sets such that $A \subset B$ and $B \subset C$, show, using the definition of a subset, that $A \subset C$. State in words what this means.

12. If for the sets A and B, $A \subset B$ and $B \subset A$, what more can you say about A and B?

13. Show that every set is a subset of itself. (*Hint:* Interpret literally the definition of a subset.)

14. Some sets have elements that are themselves sets. Give an example of such a set.

15. Let F be the set of all integers divisible by 4, S the set of those divisible by 6, and T the set of those divisible by 24. Are any of these sets contained in one of the others? What is the largest set contained in both S and F?

16. Let S_1 be the set of all numbers between 0 and 2, inclusive; S_2 the set of all those between 0 and $1\frac{1}{2}$; S_3 those between 0 and $1\frac{1}{3}$; and, more generally, S_n the set of all numbers between 0 and $1 + \dfrac{1}{n}$, inclusive, where n is a positive integer.

   (a) Describe S_4 and S_{37}.

   (b) Does either of S_3 or S_5 contain the other?

   (c) If n is greater than m, does either of S_n or S_m contain the other?

   (d) Is there any set in this collection of sets that contains all of the others?

   (e) Show that no set in the collection can be a subset of all the others.

   (f) Find a set, which of course will not be in the collection, that is a subset of every set in the collection. If there is more than one, find the largest such set.

1.2 Integers

Since elementary algebra is concerned with the study of numbers, it is perhaps worthwhile to examine some of the important components of our number system.

The set of numbers is divided and subdivided into several categories. This is partly for historical reasons, and partly because the various classes are themselves of interest. Certainly the first numbers of which man was aware are those used for counting: 1, 2, 3, 4,···, the so-called *whole numbers*.† These are the foundation on which our system of numbers rests in

†The three dots stand for the phrase "and so on."

the sense that all the other numbers can be built up out of them by certain techniques too advanced to be considered here.

Although fractions were the next development historically, the category we shall consider next is the one composed of the whole numbers together with their negatives and the number zero, that is, the set $\cdots$, -3, -2, -1, 0, 1, 2, 3, 4, $\cdots$. These numbers are called *integers* and the set of integers is one of the most important in mathematics. They have many useful and interesting properties and are such a fertile field for study that new properties are continually being discovered. Since we shall be making frequent reference to the set of integers, it will be convenient to have a symbol to denote it. Throughout this book the letter I will stand for the set of all integers. Note that, since every whole number is an integer, the set of whole numbers is a subset of the set of integers.

A basic property of integers is that the sum of two integers is again an integer; one never, for example, obtains a proper fraction. We express this fact by saying that the set of integers is closed under addition. There are other sets of numbers with the property that the sum of any two numbers of the set is again in the set; for example, the set of all positive numbers. It is convenient to formulate this basic property of closure under addition as a definition.

Definition.   Let A be a set of numbers. A is *closed under addition* if the sum of any two numbers in A is also in A.

Note that A can be any set of numbers. It may be the set of all numbers or just a subset of this set. There are sets of numbers that are not closed under addition. For A to be closed under addition it is necessary that the sum of *any* two numbers in A be in A. The word "any" in mathematics means not merely some particular one, but is used in the sense of "all" or "every." Thus A is not closed under addition if it contains even a single pair of numbers whose sum is not in A. The numbers comprising the sum do not even have to be distinct. If a is in A, then A must also contain $a + a$, or $2a$, if it is to be closed under addition.

When working with sets, one must note carefully the difference between such phrases as "*the* set of integers," which means the set of all integers, and "*a* set of integers," which means a set composed only of integers but not necessarily all of them. Our assertion that I is closed under addition applies specifically to the set of all integers. There are sets of integers that are not closed under addition. For example, $\{1, 3, 4, 7\}$ is not closed under addition, since the sum of 1 and 4 is not in the set, and neither is the sum of 3 and 3. The set of whole numbers is a set that also is closed under addition.

The definition of closure under multiplication is similar to that for addition. The words "addition" and "sum" are simply replaced by "multiplication" and "product," respectively. The set of integers is closed under multiplication, whereas the set of negative integers is closed under addition but not under multiplication.

PROBLEMS

1. Which of the following sets are closed under addition; under multiplication?
   $A = \{\cdots, -12, -8, -4, 0, 4, 8, 12, \cdots\}$,
   $B = \{2, 0, 4, 6\}$,
   $C = \{\cdots, -5, -3, -1, 1, 3, 5, 7, \cdots\}$.
2. Show that the set of whole numbers is closed under addition. Is it closed under multiplication?
3. Is the set $\{-1, 0, 1, 2, 3, \cdots\}$ closed under addition; under multiplication?
4. Is the set $\{-1, 0, 1\}$ closed under addition; under multiplication?
5. Is the set composed of all integers except the number 3 closed under addition?
6. Find a finite set of whole numbers that is not closed under addition. Do the same for an infinite set.
7. Give a definition of the closure of a set under subtraction, and show that the set of whole numbers is not closed under subtraction. Is the set of integers closed under subtraction?
8. Are the sets in Problems 3 and 4 closed under subtraction?
9. Is the set of integers closed under division?

1.3   Factors

Definition.   If a, b, and c are integers such that $a = bc$, b and c are *factors* or *divisors* of a, and a is a *multiple* of b (and c).

Thus 2 is a divisor of 12, since $12 = 2 \cdot 6$; so also are 6 and -3. Similarly, 12 is a multiple of 2 and 6.

An *even integer* is an integer that is a multiple of 2. We have just shown that 12 is an even integer. So also are 118 and -6, but 7 is not an even integer. An integer that is not even is called an *odd integer*. Thus every integer is either even or odd. It can be shown that every odd integer n can be expressed as $n = 2m + 1$ for some integer m (for example, if $n = 7$, $m = 3$, since $7 = 2 \cdot 3 + 1$).

Exercise A.   Show that 72 is a multiple of 9. Is it a multiple of 6; of -4; of 7?

Exercise B.   Show that 7 is a divisor of 105. Is 9 a factor of 105? Is -3 a divisor of 105?

Exercise C.   Show that 118 and -6 are even integers.

A positive integer p, other than 1, whose only positive divisors are p and 1 is called a *prime number*. Some prime numbers are 11, 13, 47, and 10,006,721. Because it has 5 as a divisor, 15 is not a prime number. The subject of prime numbers (prime integer would be a more appropriate name) is one of the oldest and yet most baffling in the history of mathematics. Much is known about primes, but most of our knowledge is fragmentary and a comprehensive theory still awaits discovery. Even their apparently random scattering among the integers is puzzling.

It is known that the number of primes is infinite; that is, there is no last or largest prime number. This was proved by Euclid. Many primes occur in pairs separated by just one integer, such as 5 and 7, 11 and 13, 29 and 31. Such primes, which are as close together as two primes can be, are called *twin primes*. It has been conjectured that the number of such twin prime pairs also is infinite. Indeed, if one examines tables of primes, some of which list primes up into the millions, such a conjecture seems reasonable. Twin prime pairs continue to be found as far as the tables go, though they become rather sparse in the higher reaches. However, no proof that they continue indefinitely has yet been found, and until one is we cannot be sure that somewhere beyond the extent of the present tables there is not a pair of numbers that is the last twin prime pair.

The integer 12 can be factored as $12 = 2 \cdot 6$. The factor 2, being prime, cannot be factored, but 6 can be factored, $6 = 2 \cdot 3$. Hence $12 = 2 \cdot 2 \cdot 3$, and 12 has been expressed as a product of factors each of which is prime. Starting afresh, we could have factored 12 as $12 = 3 \cdot 4$. The integer 4 can be factored again, $4 = 2 \cdot 2$, giving $12 = 3 \cdot 2 \cdot 2$, with the same factors we obtained before but in a different order. The reader has perhaps noticed that this situation is typical. If a positive integer is expressed as a product of prime factors, the same primes are always obtained no matter how the factoring is carried out, though naturally the order in which they appear in the product may be different. That this will always happen is not difficult to prove, but we shall not do so here.

PROBLEMS

1. Show that 136 is a multiple of 34. Of what other integers is it a multiple?
2. List all divisors of 24; of 48.
3. List all positive common multiples less than 100 of 6 and 8.
4. List all positive common divisors of 60 and 140.
5. By definition, every even integer n can be expressed as $n = 2m$ for some integer m. Find the corresponding m for each of the following even integers, thus proving that they are even: 8, 252, 2, 0, -18, -2.
6. Assuming that every odd integer n can be expressed as $n = 2m + 1$ for some integer m, find the corresponding m for the following odd integers: 13, 191, 3, 1, -5, -1.
7. Show that the square of an even integer is even and that of an odd integer is odd. (*Hint:* Use the definition of an even integer.)
*8†. Show that if a^2 is even, where a is an integer, then a is even.
9. Show that the set of even integers is closed under addition and multiplication.
10. (a) Show that the sum of two odd integers is even and their product odd. What does this imply about the closure under addition and multiplication of the set of odd integers?
    (b) Is the sum of an even number of odd integers even or odd?

†Problems marked with an asterisk develop theory used in later work.

11. Find a set of integers different from the set of all integers, the set of even integers, or the set of whole numbers that is closed under addition and multiplication.
12. List the primes between 1 and 200.
13. List the twin prime pairs less than 200.
14. Express each of the following as a product of prime factors: 49, 50, 73, 180.
15. Express each of the following as a product of prime factors: 990, 729, 9016, 4155.
16. Express 1800 as a product of two positive factors in three different ways. In each case express both of these factors as a product of prime factors.
17. Is the set of primes closed under addition?
18. The two sets of even and odd integers together divide the set of integers into two infinite subsets with no elements in common. Find a similar subdivision of the set of integers into three infinite subsets.
19. *Theorem.* Let a, b, and c be integers. If a divides b and c, then it divides $b + c$.
    (a) Verify this theorem in two instances by substituting specific numbers for a, b, and c.
    (b) Prove that the theorem is true for all integers a, b, and c.
20. Show that every prime greater than three is either one more or one less than a multiple of six.
21. Consider the expression $n^2 - n + 41$.
    (a) Find its value when $n = 1, 2$, and 5.
    (b) Show that it is a prime for $n = 9, 10, 14$, and 20.
    (c) Do you think that $n^2 - n + 41$ is prime for all positive integers n? Find additional evidence in support of your opinion.

1.4 Rational Numbers

We consider next the class of numbers consisting of what are commonly called fractions. Since the meaning of this word is somewhat ambiguous, we shall use instead the mathematical term *rational number* defined as follows:

Definition. A *rational number* is any number that can be expressed as a quotient of two integers, the denominator being different from zero.

For example, $\frac{2}{3}$, $\frac{7}{4}$, and $\frac{-1}{5}$ are rational numbers. So is $-\frac{2}{9}$, since this can be expressed in the form $\frac{-2}{9}$, a quotient of two integers. The number 5 in its usual form is not a quotient of two integers or even a quotient at all. This does not mean, however, that it is not a rational number; according to the definition, if there is any expression equal to 5 that is the quotient of two integers, then 5 is rational. Since $5 = \frac{10}{2}$, we see that it must be a rational number. We could equally well have used $\frac{5}{1}$ or $\frac{-100}{-20}$ to prove our point. It can be seen that a similar argument will work with any integer, for if a is an integer, then $a = a/1$ expresses a as a quotient of two integers. Thus the set of all rational numbers, which we shall denote hereafter by F, contains the set I of all integers, $I \subset F$.

The above discussion should show that it is not at all obvious whether or not $\sqrt{2}$ is rational. Just because the reader has never seen it expressed as a quotient of two integers does not mean that such a quotient does not exist.

The reader must not be misled by the frequently used equality $\sqrt{2} = 1.414$ (or equivalently, $\sqrt{2} = \frac{1414}{1000}$) into thinking that $\sqrt{2}$ is necessarily rational. $\sqrt{2}$ is defined to be that positive number whose square is 2. Now $1.414^2 = 1.999396$, which is close, but not exactly equal, to 2. Hence 1.414 is not equal to $\sqrt{2}$. Another rational number whose square is closer to 2 is 1.41421. In this sense, we say that 1.41421 is a better rational approximation to $\sqrt{2}$ than is 1.414. The equals sign in the expression $\sqrt{2} = 1.414$ is, strictly speaking, misused. The equation means and should be read as "$\sqrt{2}$ is approximately equal to 1.414."

Theorem 1. $\sqrt{2}$ is not a rational number.

A theorem is a statement of a mathematical truth. In view of the discussion above, the reader's first reaction should be, "How do you know this is true?" Most mathematical theorems are not obvious and require explanations. The formal explanation of why a theorem is true is called a *proof*. It consists of a series of statements starting from previously known results and proceeding logically, each step depending on earlier ones, until the conclusion is reached and the assertion of the theorem justified. Some proofs are short and some are long. The proof of this theorem that we are about to give ranks as one of the shorter ones, although if the reader has not seen many theorems and their proofs, he may disagree.†

If we are to prove that $\sqrt{2}$ is not rational, we must show that there are no integers a and b such that $a/b = \sqrt{2}$. Suppose there were two integers a and b such that $a/b = \sqrt{2}$. We can assume that a/b is in lowest terms; that is, all factors common to a and b have been cancelled. Multiplying both sides by b, we have $a = \sqrt{2}\,b$, and now squaring both sides, we obtain

$$(1) \qquad\qquad a^2 = 2b^2.$$

Since the square of an integer is an integer (closure of I under multiplication), we see that a^2 and b^2 are both integers, and (1) shows that a^2 is

---

†The word "proof" is used in mathematics in a different sense from that in a natural science such as biology.

The biologist says that a certain biological theory is proved if there is a substantial body of evidence supporting it and none contradicting it. In such circumstances, he feels reasonably certain that the theory is correct. However, the possibility that it may not be valid in some as yet undiscovered situation, while slight, cannot be definitely ruled out by the mere accumulation of evidence. Until it is, the theory cannot be said to be proved in the mathematical sense.

moreover an even integer. By Problem 8 of Section 1.3, a itself must then be an even integer and hence can be expressed as twice some integer c, $a = 2c$. Squaring both sides of this equation, we have $a^2 = 4c^2$, which when combined with (1) gives $4c^2 = 2b^2$, or $2c^2 = b^2$. This shows that b^2 is even and hence so is b. We have shown that a and b are both even; that is, they both have 2 as a factor. But this contradicts the assumption that all their common factors have been cancelled. Thus, starting from the supposition that there are two integers a and b such that $a/b = \sqrt{2}$, we arrive at a contradiction. The only way out of the difficulty is the inescapable conclusion that there cannot be two such integers. In other words, $\sqrt{2}$ is not rational.

The above theorem settles the question of rationality for $\sqrt{2}$. It says nothing about $\sqrt{3}$, $\log 7$, π, $\sqrt{\log 5}$, and all the other numbers. Many of these are known to be rational; for others the question is still undecided. The four numbers above are known to be not rational. Archimedes (287?–212 B.C.) was familiar with the number π and even found a remarkably good approximation of it, but it was not until 1761 that π was proved to be not rational, although this had been suspected for many years. The number $5^{\sqrt{3}}$ was shown to be not rational only as recently as 1934, and it is still not known whether 2^{π} is rational.

The sum of the rational numbers $\frac{1}{2}$ and $\frac{10}{7}$ can be expressed in the form $\frac{27}{14}$ and hence is again a rational number. The reader has probably noticed that this is typical for sums of rational numbers, as we shall now prove. To show this, it is not enough to observe that in every case encountered to date it is true. This may be a good reason for conjecturing that the theorem is true but does not give any guarantee that the next case tried will not fail. Neither can one offer as a proof the argument that it is difficult to imagine a situation in which it does not hold; all too often that which is hard to imagine becomes quite evident after it has been pointed out. In order to claim that the sum of any two rational numbers is rational, one must show it true for all cases. Fortunately, this is not so difficult as it sounds. We phrase the theorem in the equivalent form,

Theorem 2. The set F of rational numbers is closed under addition.

To prove this, let α and β be any two rational numbers.† We wish to show that $\alpha + \beta$ is rational. According to the definition of rationality we must show that $\alpha + \beta$ can be written as a quotient of two integers. To do this, one would rather expect to have to make use of the fact that α and β are themselves rational. Since α is rational, there are two integers a_1 and a_2 such that $\alpha = a_1/a_2$. Similarly, there are two integers b_1 and b_2

---

†α (alpha) and β (beta) are Greek letters corresponding to the English letters a and b.

such that $\beta = b_1/b_2$. Now by the theorem (Theorem 15) on the sum of two fractions, discussed in Section 2.16,

$$\alpha + \beta = \frac{a_1}{a_2} + \frac{b_1}{b_2} = \frac{a_1b_2 + a_2b_1}{a_2b_2},$$

and $\alpha + \beta$ is expressed as a quotient. If we can show that the numerator and denominator of this last fraction are integers, then we shall be done. Since a_1 and b_2 are integers, so is their product (closure of I under multiplication). Similarly, so is a_2b_1. With a_1b_2 and a_2b_1 now known to be integers, we can be sure that their sum $a_1b_2 + a_2b_1$ is an integer, since I is closed under addition. The denominator a_2b_2 is also an integer, because it is a product of the integers a_2 and b_2. Thus both numerator and denominator are integers, and $\alpha + \beta$ is rational.

It is also true that F is closed under subtraction, multiplication, and division.† The proofs are similar to the one for addition, and the reader who is familiar with the rules for handling fractions should have no trouble in constructing them. Because F is closed under division as well as under the other three operations, it is a more useful system than I. It is not perfect, however, for F would be still more useful if the square roots of all positive rational numbers were also rational. Our experience with $\sqrt{2}$ shows that this will not always be so, and hence F is not closed under the operation of taking roots. A larger number system is needed if all roots are to be in the system.

A decimal such as 5.74 represents a rational number, since it is just another way of writing $\frac{574}{100}$. So also do 2.7 and .045, for they can be written $\frac{27}{10}$ and $\frac{45}{1000}$, respectively. Similarly, every terminating decimal (that is, one that does not go on indefinitely) represents a rational number. There are rational numbers whose decimal representations are not terminating; for example, $\frac{4}{3} = 1.3333\cdots$, $\frac{37}{55} = .67272727\cdots$. Note, however, that a digit or block of digits repeats itself. Such decimals are called *repeating* or *periodic decimals*.

It can be shown that the decimal representation of every rational number is either terminating or repeating and, conversely, every such decimal represents a rational number. This implies that the decimal representation of $\sqrt{2}$ must be non-terminating and non-repeating. We shall discuss this further in the next section.

PROBLEMS

1. Show that 0 is a rational number.
2. Show that .3, .0057, and -1375.28 are rational numbers.
3. Show that $-4 + \frac{2}{7}$, $\frac{3}{5}/\frac{1}{2}$, and $(4 + \sqrt{3}) + (5 - \sqrt{3})$ are rational.

†For reasons that will be apparent after reading Chapter 2, division by zero is excluded and is so understood whenever a set is said to be closed under division.

4. Is $\dfrac{\sqrt{2}}{3\sqrt{2}}$ rational?

5. Show that 1.41421^2 is closer to 2 than is 1.414^2.

6. If $\sqrt{3}$ denotes the positive number whose square is 3, is $\sqrt{3} = 1.732$?

7. Find a rational number whose square is close to 7. Find another rational number whose square is closer to 7.

8. What is the relationship of the set of all terminating decimals to the set of all rational numbers?

Find the decimal representation of the following rational numbers. If non-terminating, find the repeating digit or block of digits.

9. $\dfrac{9}{6}$ 10. $\dfrac{13}{6}$ 11. $\dfrac{1}{9}$ 12. $\dfrac{5}{8}$ 13. $\dfrac{2}{7}$

14. $\dfrac{457}{12}$ 15. $\dfrac{4}{11}$ 16. $\dfrac{105}{32}$ 17. $\dfrac{10}{13}$

18. Assuming that $\sqrt{5}$ is not rational, show that $2 + \sqrt{5}$ is not rational. (*Hint:* Let $a = 2 + \sqrt{5}$. Suppose that a is rational and try to get a contradiction.)

*19. Show that $-\sqrt{2}$ is not rational.

20. Show that the set F of rational numbers is closed under (a) subtraction, (b) multiplication, (c) division.

21. Prove there is no rational number whose square is 7.

22. Prove there is no rational number whose cube is 2.

1.5   Real Numbers

All numbers that are not rational are called *irrational*. The set of irrational numbers is not closed under addition. We shall prove this by showing that there are two irrational numbers whose sum is not irrational. $\sqrt{2}$ is irrational and it is easy to prove that $-\sqrt{2}$ is also irrational (see Problem 19, Section 1.4). The sum of these is zero, a rational number. The failure of the irrationals to be closed under addition makes this set, when considered by itself, awkward to work with. Because of this, they are generally studied as part of the larger set of real numbers, which is closed under addition.

The rational and irrational numbers together constitute the set R of what are called *real numbers*. This is the technical mathematical term used to designate what we have been rather loosely referring to as numbers. Since mathematicians frequently refer to elements of still larger systems as numbers, the term real number should be used if there is any ambiguity. The set of real numbers includes in addition to the rationals such numbers as $\sqrt{2}$, π, $\log 7$, and $\sin 37°$. It does not include $\sqrt{-1}$ and the other imaginary numbers. To study these, we shall need the still larger set C of complex numbers, which includes the real numbers as well as the imaginary ones.

The set of real numbers, like that of the rational numbers, is closed under the four operations of addition, subtraction, multiplication, and division (for the last it being understood that division by zero is excluded). As the proofs of these are difficult and require careful analysis of the structure of the real number system, we shall assume this property of closure without proof. The positive real numbers are also closed under the operation of taking roots. Square, cube, and higher roots of positive real numbers are all real.

The line diagram in Figure 1.2 shows the relationship of the subsets of the real number system we have considered.

We have seen that every rational number has a terminating or repeating decimal representation and that such decimals represent only rational numbers. It can be proved that every irrational number also has a decimal representation, which therefore must be non-terminating and non-repeating.

The number formed by the first few digits of such a decimal is a rational number which approximates the irrational number. If one takes more digits, the corresponding rational number is a better approximation. It can be shown that by using a sufficient number of decimal places the irrational number can be approximated by a rational number to any desired degree of accuracy. It is this property of decimals that makes them so useful.

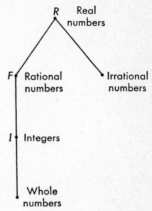

Figure 1.2

For example, the irrational number $\sqrt{5}$ is approximated by the rational number 2.24, but a better approximation is 2.2361, and a still better one is 2.236068. Since $\sqrt{5}$ is the symbol for the positive number whose square is 5, one can see by squaring these that none of them actually equals $\sqrt{5}$. There exist rational approximations of $\sqrt{5}$ to any desired degree of accuracy, although finding them may be laborious. While the theory assures the existence of rational approximations of an irrational number, it does not tell us how to find them. For some numbers this may be difficult.

PROBLEMS

1. Is the set of irrational numbers closed under multiplication?
2. What number represents the length of the side of a square whose area is 2? Is it rational or irrational?
3. What number represents the area of a square the length of whose side is 5? Is it rational or irrational?
4. What number represents the area of a circle with a diameter of 6? Is it rational or irrational?
5. For any real number a, let $[a]$ stand for the largest integer less than or equal to a. Determine which of the following are rational: $[1\frac{3}{4}]$, $[6]$, $[\sqrt{3}]$.

Chapter 2

The Algebra of Numbers

2.1 Axioms

Numbers as isolated entities are of little interest. They are interesting and useful only when considered with other numbers by means of two important properties possessed by the set of real numbers. The first of these enables us to combine numbers by addition and multiplication in order to form other numbers. For example, from 3 and 5 we obtain 8 by addition and 15 by multiplication. The second property ensures that given two distinct numbers one is larger than the other; that is, they can be compared. The reader is, of course, very familiar with these properties, so much so that he probably considers them hardly worth mentioning. But, however obvious they may be, they are by no means trivial. Without them our system of numbers, and indeed our daily lives, would be very different. In this chapter we consider the consequences of the first property of numbers and in Chapter 6, which discusses the ordering of real numbers, we shall study the second.

Although basically the usefulness of the real numbers stems from the closure of this set under addition and multiplication, this alone is not sufficient. Additional properties are needed if we are to have a useful arithmetic. It would be helpful if all properties needed could be proved. A little reflection, however, will show that this is impossible. Some things can be proved, but not all. Each proof will depend on results that, in order to be used in the proof, must have been proved previously. These in turn must have used facts established still earlier. This chain, reaching farther and farther back, cannot go on indefinitely. At some point there must be a beginning where we say, "This fact and that one and that one we shall assume true. Now, starting with these, we shall derive all the properties of the real numbers." Naturally, mathematicians try to push back this beginning point as far as possible and assume no more than what is absolutely necessary. What to assume is not always an easy matter to decide. It took much experimentation before the set of assumptions we shall use was known to be sufficient. Moreover, there is nothing unique about our set; it is possible to replace some of our assumptions by others and still achieve the same ends.

An assumption is called an *axiom* or *postulate*, just as in plane geometry. Many of them will undoubtedly seem obvious to the reader. Indeed, they should seem so, because axioms express some of the most fundamental properties of real numbers, properties that are essential to the proper functioning of the number system. For our purpose here it is better not to try to get along with the absolutely irreducible minimum of axioms. We shall list some axioms that actually can be proved from the others, as occasionally we shall challenge the reader in the exercises to show.

The first of our axioms says that the order in which two numbers are added is immaterial. That is, if a and b are any two real numbers, then $a + b = b + a$. For example, $3 + 7 = 10$ and $7 + 3 = 10$. This is a familiar property of numbers, and a little reflection on the complications that would be introduced into arithmetic if reversing the order of addition gave a different answer should convince one that it is a most useful and important axiom. This situation is described more succinctly by the statement "addition is *commutative* in the set R of real numbers," and the axiom is frequently referred to as the "commutative law for addition."† Multiplication is also commutative: for all a and b in R, $ab = ba$. For example, $3 \cdot 7 = 21$ and $7 \cdot 3 = 21$.

If the sum of three numbers, such as 2, 7, and 4, is desired, one can add 2 and 7 and then add 4 to this result, indicated by $(2 + 7) + 4 = 9 + 4 = 13$, or one can add 7 and 4 and then add this result to 2: $2 + (7 + 4) = 2 + 11 = 13$. That is, the manner of grouping of the terms in a sum, as indicated by parentheses, is immaterial. That this is true in general is asserted by the *associative* law for addition which says that for any a, b, and c in R, $(a + b) + c = a + (b + c)$. We emphasize that we are not proving this. It is an axiom, one of our basic assumptions about real numbers. There is similarly an associative law for multiplication: $a(bc) = (ab)c$.

Suppose one wants to multiply 3 by the sum of 8 and 5. Using parentheses, we indicate this by $3(8 + 5)$. One can proceed in either of two ways. The most natural way, perhaps, is first to add 8 and 5 and then multiply 3 by this sum, $3(8 + 5) = 3(13) = 39$. But one could also multiply 3 by 8 and 3 by 5 and then add these two products,

$$3(8 + 5) = 3 \cdot 8 + 3 \cdot 5 = 24 + 15 = 39.$$

---

†"Law" and "axiom" are used synonymously in this sense.

This is an illustration of the *distributive* law, which says that if a, b, and c are any three numbers in R, then $a(b + c) = ab + ac$.

In addition to the basic property of closure we now have six axioms for real numbers, fundamental laws which all numbers obey:

For all real numbers a, b, and c:

A. *Associative axioms*
  1. $(a + b) + c = a + (b + c)$
  2. $(ab)c = a(bc)$

C. *Commutative axioms*
  1. $a + b = b + a$
  2. $ab = ba$

D. *Distributive axioms*
  1. $a(b + c) = ab + ac$
  2. $(b + c)a = ba + ca.$

Since $(4 + 7) + \frac{3}{2} = 4 + (7 + \frac{3}{2})$ by axiom A1, it is customary to omit the parentheses and write $4 + 7 + \frac{3}{2}$, understanding by this either of the two above equal expressions. By extension, there is no ambiguity in the meaning of $a + b + c + d + e$ or similar expressions for the sum of any number of numbers. Similarly, we write abc for $(ab)c$, and $abcdef$ for the product of six numbers.

Note that the parentheses cannot be removed in the statement of D1. It is not true that $ab + c = ab + ac$ for all real numbers a, b, and c.

Let us review briefly the properties of the equals relation. The right and left sides of any equation can be interchanged. For example, if $x - 2 = a^2 + b^2$, then $a^2 + b^2 = x - 2$. If $3 + 4 = 7$ and $6 + 1 = 7$, then $3 + 4 = 6 + 1$. This illustrates the well known property that quantities equal to the same quantity are equal to each other. From this we see that if $a = b$, $b = c$, $c = d$, and $d = e$, then $a = e$, and we can write without ambiguity the continued equality $a = b = c = d = e$. If $a = b$, then $a + 2 = b + 2$; that is, if a number is added to each of two equal numbers, the sums will be equal. There are similar statements for differences, products, and quotients. Thus, if $a = b$, then $a - 2 = b - 2$, $2a = 2b$ and $a/2 = b/2$. Also if $a = b$ and $x = y$, then $a + x = b + y$ and analogously for subtraction, multiplication, and division. Finally, we shall assume that a quantity can be substituted for an equal quantity in any expression. If $x + 2 = \dfrac{3}{y} + 5$ and $y = (u - 1)^2$, then $(u - 1)^2$ can be substituted for y in the first equation: $x + 2 = \dfrac{3}{(u - 1)^2} + 5$.

These properties of the equals relation are really axioms, but since they are of a different nature from the others, we prefer to treat them somewhat informally. To sum up, we shall assume all the usual properties of the equals relation and use them henceforth, generally without specific comment.

If numbers are the bricks of our number system, axioms are the instructions for putting two or more bricks together. From these instructions walls, chimneys, and eventually whole buildings can be constructed. These are theorems. Just as one cannot have a building unless one has bricks and knows how to put two bricks together, so one cannot have a theorem unless there are numbers and axioms explaining how the numbers may be combined.

Exercise A.   Explain what is meant by $3(7 \cdot 5)$; that is, what products are indicated by this notation. Do the same for $(3 \cdot 7)5$. Which axiom does this illustrate?

Exercise B.   Explain what is meant by $(2 \cdot 5)(6 \cdot 3)$. Do the same for $(6 \cdot 3)(2 \cdot 5)$. Which axiom does this illustrate?

Exercise C.   Explain what is meant by $a(b + c)$, $ab + ac$, and $ab + c$. Give an illustration to show that the first and third may not be equal.

Note in the statements of the axioms that no restrictions are placed on the numbers a, b, and c. Some or all can be equal. For example, axiom A2 is true when $c = a$ and hence implies that $(ab)a = a(ba)$. From axiom C1 we have $0 + b = b + 0$. The importance of the word "all" in the statement "for all real numbers a, b, and c" before the listing of the axioms should not be overlooked. Because we know that C2 holds for all a and b in R, we can say at once that $(c + d)b = b(c + d)$ for all b, c, and d in R. To see this, we observe that since c and d are in R, so is $c + d$ (closure of R under addition). Let us denote $c + d$ by a. Then a is in R, and since C2 holds for all numbers in R, we have $(c + d)b = ab = ba = b(c + d)$. Similarly, the distributive law D1 ensures that $(ab)(c + d) = (ab)c + (ab)d$.

Much of the difficulty students have with mathematics is due to a basic misconception about the nature of numbers. When we write 2, the mark on the paper is not the number itself but a name or symbol for the number. Like all numbers, 2 is an abstraction. It is, however, none the less real. Honesty is also an abstract concept, but to most people it is just as real as the more concrete objects—a pencil or a clock. It is important not to confuse a number with the name or symbol for the number. The name and symbol are merely a means for talking about the number. When we write the word *house*, the word itself is not a house, but a symbol for a house, a means of talking about it.

Like other objects, a number has many different names. For example, a certain number has the name 6. Two other names for this number are $1 + 5$ and $3 \cdot 2$. When one is asked to find the sum of 1 and 5, one is really being asked to find, if possible, a shorter name for this number. In this sense 6 is said to be the answer. In particular, the plus sign in the expression $1 + 5$ should not be regarded as a signal to do something to 1 and 5. Other names for this number are $\frac{30}{5}$ and $10 - 4$. All the names for a number are perfectly legitimate; some are just more convenient than others.

To say that the set of real numbers is closed under addition means that to any two real numbers whose names are a and b corresponds another real number called their sum. To this number we give the name $a + b$. The closure property does not tell us whether there is a simpler name for this number, or if there is, how to find it. The numbers with names $\frac{2}{3}$ and $\frac{1}{7}$ have a sum. A common name for this sum is $\frac{2}{3} + \frac{1}{7}$. A shorter name is $\frac{17}{21}$. Similarly, $\sqrt{9}$ is a name for the positive number whose square is 9. Another and more convenient name for this number is 3. There is no simpler name than $\sqrt{2}$ for the positive number whose square is 2, nor is there a shorter one for $5 + \sqrt{2}$.

To simplify an expression such as $\dfrac{7 + 5}{2} + 8$ means to find another and simpler name for the corresponding number. One such name is 14. Another and not so simple is $\frac{42}{3}$. Much of the ordinary manipulation of expressions in algebra has as its objective the finding of more convenient names for numbers. Axioms A, C, and D tell us that certain operations on the symbols for numbers always lead to names for the same number. Thus, according to the commutative axiom, the number for which $b + a$ is a name is the same as the number whose name is $a + b$.

When we write $\frac{21}{7} = 5 - 2$, we mean that $\frac{21}{7}$ and $5 - 2$ are names for the same number. An equation is true only if the expressions on both sides of the equals sign are names for the same number. The equation $4 \cdot 6 = 3 + 7$ is not true. The statement $``\dfrac{11 + 2a}{2} = \dfrac{11}{2} + a\,"$ means that if a is the name of any number, then $\dfrac{11 + 2a}{2}$ and $\dfrac{11}{2} + a$ are names for the same number.

PROBLEMS

Each of the following is true by one of the axioms A, C, or D. In each case state which axiom applies, and illustrate the correctness of each by substituting the given numbers for the letters and computing both sides of the equality.

Example: $x + y + (u + 6) = y + x + (u + 6)$; $x = 1$, $y = -3$, $u = 0$. This is true because $x + y = y + x$ by C1, and hence we can substitute for $x + y$ the equal expression $y + x$. If $x = 1$, $y = -3$, and $u = 0$, the left side is $1 - 3 + (0 + 6) = -2 + 6 = 4$ and the right side is $-3 + 1 + (0 + 6) = -2 + 6 = 4$.

1. $x(ab) = (ab)x$; $x = 2$, $a = 6$, $b = \frac{1}{4}$.
2. $a + bc = bc + a$; $a = 1$, $b = 2$, $c = 1$.
3. $(4 + 10)3 = 12 + 30$.
4. $a[(b + c) + d] = a(b + c) + ad$; $a = 3$, $b = 0$, $c = 1$, $d = 1$.
5. $(2 + u)(5 + u) = 2(5 + u) + u(5 + u)$; $u = 3$.
6. $a3(cd)(u + 1) = a(3c)d(u + 1)$; $a = 2$, $c = 2$, $d = -1$, $u = 0$.

In each of the following, two axioms are needed to justify the assertion. Which ones are they and how are they used? As in Problem 1, illustrate with the given numbers.

Example: $x + 1 + ab = 1 + x + ba$; $x = 0$, $a = 2$, $b = 1$.

We have

$$x + 1 + ab = 1 + x + ab \text{ by axiom C1 } (x + 1 = 1 + x)$$
$$= 1 + x + ba \text{ by axiom C2 } (ab = ba).$$

The validity of the equation could also have been established by using C2 first and then C1. Substituting the numbers, the left side is $0 + 1 + 2 \cdot 1 = 3$ and the right is $1 + 0 + 1 \cdot 2 = 3$.

7. $4 + x + y + w = x + 4 + w + y$; $x = 0$, $y = 1$, $w = -1$.
8. $(a + 5) + c = a + (c + 5)$; $a = 2$, $c = 3$.
9. $3(x + y) + 7 = 7 + 3x + 3y$; $x = 1$, $y = 1$.
10. $5[(a + x)3] = (5a + 5x)3$; $a = 1$, $x = 4$.

In each of the following, one or more axioms are needed to justify the assertion. Which ones are they and how are they used? Illustrate with the given numbers.

11. $x(ab) = a(bx)$; $x = 2$, $a = 3$, $b = 4$.
12. $(x + 2) + 6c = c6 + (2 + x)$; $x = -4$, $c = 6$.
13. $(2 + u)(a + u) = 2a + 2u + u(a + u)$; $u = 1$, $a = 10$.
14. $(x + 6)(a + 5) = xa + x5 + 6a + 6 \cdot 5$; $x = 1$, $a = 2$.
15. Why is $2a + 5a = 7a$? That is, which axiom is used to justify this?
16. Show that $x + x = 2x$. (*Hint:* Replace x by $1 \cdot x$.)

Simplify:

17. $4xy + 3xy$.
18. $11c + c$.
19. $z(x + 1) + z(x + 2)$.
20. Find the values of the following when $x = 1$, $y = 3$, $a = 6$, $b = 2$.
   (a) $(x + y)(2a + b)$.
   (b) $x + y(2a + b)$.
   (c) $x \cdot 2a + yb$.
   (d) $x \cdot 2a + y \cdot 2a + xb + yb$.
21. Show that axiom D2 is redundant. That is, assuming only axioms A, C, and D1, *prove* the result stated as D2. Thus D2 could have been omitted from the list of axioms and proved as a theorem. We have assumed more than is necessary.

2.2 $(x + y)^2$

The well known equation

$$(1) \qquad\qquad (x + y)^2 = x^2 + 2xy + y^2$$

says that the square of the sum of two numbers is equal to the square of the first plus twice their product plus the square of the second. For example, $(3 + 4)^2 = 7^2 = 49$ and $3^2 + 2(3 \cdot 4) + 4^2 = 9 + 24 + 16 = 49$. Since no restrictions on the numbers are mentioned, it is understood according to convention that (1) is intended to be true for any numbers x and y. To see why this is so, we must show that (1) is true for *all* x and y. It is not enough to verify the theorem for certain x and y as we did for $x = 3$ and $y = 4$. Even if we did this for a large number of cases, we should not have established anything more than that it was true for those particular numbers. It would still be conceivable that there might be some pair for which it would not work, however unlikely one might feel this to be. The only way to remove all doubt is to proceed logically and deduce the result from our axioms.

To do this, we write $(x + y)^2$ in its other form $(x + y)(x + y)$ and use the distributive law D1, treating the first factor $x + y$ as a single number:

$$(x + y)(x + y) = (x + y)x + (x + y)y.$$

We now apply the other distributive law D2 to each of the terms in the sum on the right:

$$(x + y)x + (x + y)y = xx + yx + xy + yy.$$

By the commutative law for multiplication C2 we can replace yx by xy to obtain finally $x^2 + 2xy + y^2$. Thus $(x + y)^2 = x^2 + 2xy + y^2$. To establish the result, D1 was used once, D2 twice, and C2 once. It is quite permissible and indeed frequently necessary to use an axiom several times in the proof of a theorem.

PROBLEMS

1. Prove that $u + 2 + w(v + w) = u + vw + 2 + w^2$, showing which axioms are used at each step of the proof.
2. Prove that $(x + y)(a + 5) = xa + x5 + ya + y5$, showing which axioms are used at each step of the proof. Continuing the problem, show that this equals $xa + ya + 5x + 5y$.
3. Show that $(a + b)(c + d) = ac + b(c + d) + ad$.
4. Explain the difference between $(a + b)^2$ and $a^2 + b^2$. Substitute values for a and b to show that these are not always equal.

2.3   General Commutative and Distributive Laws

Like other specialized fields, mathematics uses many technical terms, some of which may have quite different everyday meanings. One is not expected to guess the meanings of these terms. A careful author will explain each new symbol or term as it is introduced. Such explanations are called *definitions* and are generally, though not always, stated rather formally. The reader should pay particular attention to definitions, for unless he knows the precise meanings of the terms he may have difficulty understanding the theorems in which they are used and following their proofs. Naturally, a definition should employ only terms that have previously been defined or whose meanings are generally known; otherwise, it would not be very enlightening. In a definition the term being defined is generally set in different type so that the reader will know just which word it is.

Our first definitions were given in Sections 1.1 and 1.2, when we defined *subset* and *closure*. Our next two will explain terminology connected with sums and products.

Definition. In a sum such as $x + 3 + y$, the numbers x, 3, and y are the *terms* of the sum.

Definition. In a product such as $4xy$, the numbers 4, x, and y are the *factors* of the product.

Note that here we are using the word "factor" in a slightly different sense from that in Section 1.3. This is not confusing. If the context does not make clear which is meant, the term "integral factor" can be used if the factors are to be integers.

In the sum $x + 5w + y$ there are three terms, x, $5w$, and y. The second term is a product with factors 5 and w. In the sum $x + (5w + y)$ there are only the two terms x and $(5w + y)$, since the parentheses indicate that $5w + y$ is to be considered as a single number. This illustrates the fact that whether a given quantity is a term of a sum depends on the form in which the sum is expressed. The expression $\left(\dfrac{x}{5} + 7\right)z$ is a product with factors $\left(\dfrac{x}{5} + 7\right)$ and z. The first factor is a sum with terms $x/5$ and 7. Being a quotient, $x/5$ is neither a sum nor a product. However, when written in the form $x \cdot \frac{1}{5}$ it is a product.

Since $x - y$ can be written as the sum $x + (-y)$, it is customary to call $x - y$ a sum even though it is, strictly speaking, a difference. The terms are x and $-y$, though some writers refer to y as the second term.

The commutative axiom for addition permits us to interchange the order of two adjacent terms in a sum. For example, $3 + x + y + z = 3 + y + x + z$. It does not directly guarantee that $3 + x + y + z = x + 3 + z + y$. By using C1 twice, however, we can establish this. First interchange x and 3, obtaining $x + 3 + y + z$; now use C1 again, this time interchanging z and y, to obtain $x + 3 + z + y$. For any other sum one could show in a similar fashion that the terms can be arbitrarily rearranged without affecting the value. A rigorous proof that this is true for all sums can be given, but it is too difficult to include here. Similarly, the value of a product is unaffected by any rearrangement of its factors.

The distributive law D1 can also be easily extended to show that $a(b + c + d) = ab + ac + ad$, as follows, where beside each step we have given the reason for its being equal to the expression immediately above:

$$a(b + c + d) = a([b + c] + d) \qquad \text{parenthesis convention} \\ \text{(see Section 2.1)}$$

$$= a[b + c] + ad \qquad \text{axiom D1}$$
$$= (ab + ac) + ad \qquad \text{axiom D1}$$
$$= ab + ac + ad. \qquad \text{parenthesis convention}$$

Analogous statements apply when the second factor contains more than three terms.

We shall assume these generalized commutative and distributive laws without proof and freely interchange terms or factors in any sum or product, as well as distribute a factor over any number of terms in a sum.

PROBLEMS

What are the terms of the following sums?

1. $-3 + 7$.

2. $\sqrt{2} + 13a + (bc)$.

3. $5 - 7u + a(x + y) + w$.
4. $5 + 7u + x + y + w$.
5. $(\frac{10}{8} + b) + (a - b)$.
6. $\frac{5}{4} + b$.

What are the factors of the following products?

7. $2(-8)$.
8. $\frac{1}{4}(xy)$.
9. $\frac{1}{4}xy$.

10. $(u - \sqrt{2})(7 + t)$.

11. $(-5)(-x + y + z)$.

12. $3 \cdot 5 \cdot \frac{1}{3}$.

13. Express the product $5(x + y + z)$ as a sum of three terms; as a sum of two terms. Which axioms are you using here?

14. Express $6x^2 + 3x$ as a product of two factors in two ways; as a product of three factors. Which axioms are you using here?

15. Express 12 as a product of two integral factors; as a product of three integral factors.

16. Express 7 as a product of two integral factors; as a product of two rational factors neither of which is an integer.

17. Express $\dfrac{x + h}{3}$ as a product of two factors; as a sum.

Determine whether the following are sums or products, and give their terms or factors as the case may be.

18. $(a + x)(b + y)$.

19. $a(b + y) + x(b + y)$.

20. $[a(b + y) + x(b + y)]r$.

21. $a(b + y) + x(b + y)r$.

24. $x^2 - 2xy + y^2$.

25. $(x + y)^2$.

26. $10x^2z$.

27. $2 \cdot 5x^2z$.

22. $a(-2 + t)\frac{1}{3}$.

28. $\dfrac{x + 7}{x^2 + 5x + 2} x + 3$.

23. $(-2a + al)\frac{1}{3}$.

29. $(4 + x)(5 - y)[(\frac{2}{3} + y)(2 + x) + 7] + 6$.

30. Show that $2wx6z = 6z2xw$, giving at each step the appropriate axiom used.

2.4 Exponents

By $(\frac{1}{5})^2$ we mean $\frac{1}{5} \cdot \frac{1}{5}$; $(\frac{1}{5})^3$ means $\frac{1}{5} \cdot \frac{1}{5} \cdot \frac{1}{5}$ and $(\frac{1}{5})^{14}$ means $\frac{1}{5} \cdot \frac{1}{5} \cdots \frac{1}{5}$ (14 factors), where the three dots stand for the missing eleven $\frac{1}{5}$'s. In the next definition we explain the meaning of a^n for any number a and positive integer n.

Definition.   For any number a and positive integer n, $a^n = a \cdot a \cdots a$ (n factors). a^n is said to be the nth *power* of a; a is the *base* and n the *exponent* of the power.

For example, $(\frac{1}{5})^3$ is the third power (or cube)of $\frac{1}{5}$, $\frac{1}{5}$ being the base and 3 the exponent. Note that the definition covers only the case in which n is a positive integer. It does not explain the meaning of $a^{1/2}$, a^{-3}, or a^0. Definitions of these will be given in Chapter 9.

Theorem 1.   If m and n are positive integers, then $a^m a^n = a^{m+n}$.

According to this theorem, $7^3 \cdot 7^5 = 7^{3+5} = 7^8$. The reason for this is easy to see. We have $7^3 = 7 \cdot 7 \cdot 7$ and $7^5 = 7 \cdot 7 \cdot 7 \cdot 7 \cdot 7$. Therefore $7^3 \cdot 7^5 = (7 \cdot 7 \cdot 7)(7 \cdot 7 \cdot 7 \cdot 7 \cdot 7)$. The right side is the product of eight 7's and hence is 7^8.

The proof of the theorem is almost as simple. By the definition of a power

$$a^m a^n = \overbrace{(a \cdot a \cdots a)}^{m \text{ factors}} \cdot \overbrace{(a \cdot a \cdots a)}^{n \text{ factors}}.$$

The right side is the product of $m + n$ a's and hence is equal to a^{m+n}.

PROBLEMS

Simplify:

1. $5^2 \cdot 5^4$.

2. $x^8 x^3$.

3. $6 \cdot 6^3 \cdot 6^2$.

4. $(3b)^3$.

5. $\left(\dfrac{2}{7}\right)\left(\dfrac{2}{7}\right)^4$.

6. $\left(\dfrac{1}{a}\right)^6 \left(\dfrac{1}{a}\right)^{10}$.

7. $a^3 b^2 a^4 b^5$.

8. $x^2 y\, 2y^3 x$.

9. $(a^3)^5$.

Simplify:

10. $x^2 y^2 + 5x^2 y^2$.

11. $2a^2 ba + 3aba^2$.

12. $y^5 + y^4 y$.

13. $y^4 + 2y^2 + y^3 y$.

14. $y^2(y^5 + y) + y^3$.

15. $x^2 3 + 2x(3x + 1)$.

16. $3a^3 x^2 + 7(ax)^2 a$.

17. $(x^2 y)^3 3y^2 x$.

18. Why cannot Theorem 1 be cited as justification of the assertions:

(a) $3^{1/2} \cdot 3^{7/2} = 3^4$;

(b) $\left(\dfrac{4}{5}\right)^{-2} \left(\dfrac{4}{5}\right)^{-1} = \left(\dfrac{4}{5}\right)^{-3}$?

19. (a) Explain the meanings of the notations $a^n b^n$ and $(ab)^n$, where n is a positive integer.

(b) Illustrate (a) with $a = -3$, $b = 2$, $n = 3$.

(c) Illustrate (a) with $a = \frac{1}{2}$, $b = 6$, $n = 4$.

*(d) Prove that $a^n b^n = (ab)^n$, where n is a positive integer.

20. (a) Explain the meanings of the notations $(a^m)^n$ and a^{mn}, where m and n are positive integers.

  (b) Illustrate (a) with $a = \frac{1}{2}$, $m = 2$, $n = 5$.

  (c) Illustrate (a) with $a = -3$, $m = 3$, $n = 2$.

  *(d) Prove that $(a^m)^n = a^{mn}$, where m and n are positive integers.

21. Simplify $[(x^4)^3 + x^5x] + x^5x^7 + 3(x^3)^2$.

22. Simplify $(a^2 + b^3)^2 + a(a^3 + 2ab^3)$. Check your answer by making the substitution $a = 1$, $b = 2$.

23. Simplify $3y(yx^2 + 2x) + 5(xy^2 + 2y + 3)x$.

24. Show that $a^l a^m a^n = a^{l+m+n}$, where l, m, and n are positive integers.

2.5 Addition of Polynomials

To simplify the sum of two expressions such as $3a + 2b + 5a^2 + 7$ and $2a + 6b + 2a^2 + 8c$, rearrange the terms in both expressions (commutative law) so that like terms are together:†

$$(3a + 2b + 5a^2 + 7) + (2a + 6b + 2a^2 + 8c)$$
$$= (3a + 2a) + (2b + 6b) + (5a^2 + 2a^2) + 7 + 8c$$
$$= 5a + 8b + 7a^2 + 7 + 8c.$$

If preferred, the work can be arranged as follows:

$$
\begin{array}{l}
3a + 2b + 5a^2 + 7 \\
2a + 6b + 2a^2 \qquad + 8c \\
\hline
5a + 8b + 7a^2 + 7 + 8c.
\end{array}
$$

Another example is

$$(3x^2y^2 + 2x^2y + 5xy + 7y^2 + y) + (x^2y + 2xy + 12y + 6x^2y^2 + y^2)$$
$$= (3x^2y^2 + 6x^2y^2) + (2x^2y + x^2y) + (5xy + 2xy) + (7y^2 + y^2) + (y + 12y)$$
$$= 9x^2y^2 + 3x^2y + 7xy + 8y^2 + 13y.$$

Using the other arrangement, the work looks like this:

$$
\begin{array}{l}
3x^2y^2 + 2x^2y + 5xy + 7y^2 + \quad y \\
6x^2y^2 + \quad x^2y + 2xy + \quad y^2 + 12y \\
\hline
9x^2y^2 + 3x^2y + 7xy + 8y^2 + 13y.
\end{array}
$$

PROBLEMS

Simplify the following sums:

1. $(x^2 + 3x + 4) + (6x^2 + x + 2)$.

2. $(y^3 + 2y^2 + 6) + (y^2 + 1)$.

3. $(x^2 + 2xy + 3y^2) + (xy + 5x^2 + y^2)$.

4. $2(x + y + w) + 3(x + y + w)$.

5. $3(x^2 + x) + 5(2x + 4x^3) + 8(x^2 + 5x + 4x^3)$.

6. $x(x + y) + (x^2 + x^3 + 2xy)$.

7. $(x^2 + a^2x + a^2) + (x^2 + 3a^2x + 11a^2) \cdot 3$.

†By like terms we mean those that differ only in the numerical coefficient; for example, $5a^2b$ and $2a^2b$.

2.6 Multiplication of Polynomials

Frequently one must express a product such as

$$(x^2 + 7y)(3x^3 + x^2y + y^2)$$

in the form of a sum. To do this, we proceed in much the same way as we did in proving the relation $(x + y)^2 = x^2 + 2xy + y^2$. Treating $3x^3 + x^2y + y^2$ as a single quantity, we can by the distributive law D2 multiply it in turn by x^2 and $7y$ and add:

$$(x^2 + 7y)(3x^3 + x^2y + y^2) = x^2(3x^3 + x^2y + y^2) + 7y(3x^3 + x^2y + y^2).$$

We now apply the other distributive law to both terms on the right and obtain

(1) $\qquad x^2 3x^3 + x^2 x^2 y + x^2 y^2 + 7y 3x^3 + 7yx^2y + 7yy^2.$

Each term in this sum can be simplified using Theorem 1 so that we have

(2) $\qquad 3x^5 + x^4y + x^2y^2 + 21x^3y + 7x^2y^2 + 7y^3.$

Rearranging and adding like terms, we have, finally,

(3) $\qquad 3x^5 + x^4y + 21x^3y + 8x^2y^2 + 7y^3.$

If we examine (1), we see that its terms are obtained by multiplying each term of $3x^3 + x^2y + y^2$ by each term of $x^2 + 7y$. If one keeps this in mind, much of the above work can be done mentally when one of the factors has but one or two terms, and (2) can be written down immediately.

Many people prefer to arrange the work as follows:

$$
\begin{array}{ll}
(4) & 3x^3 + x^2y + y^2 \\
& x^2 + 7y \\
\hline
(5) & 3x^5 + x^4y \qquad\qquad + \; x^2y^2 \\
(6) & \qquad\qquad\qquad 21x^3y + 7x^2y^2 + 7y^3 \\
\hline
(7) & 3x^5 + x^4y + 21x^3y + 8x^2y^2 + 7y^3.
\end{array}
$$

This is frequently used when both factors contain three or more terms.

Note that both factors of the product are arranged in descending powers of x. That is, in each factor the term with the highest power of x comes first, the term with the next highest power second, and so on, the term with no x coming last. This arrangement is a convenience but not necessary. Line (5) is obtained by multiplying each term of (4) by x^2 and line (6) by multiplying each term of (4) by $7y$, like terms being placed below each other. Of course, we are really applying the distributive and commutative laws just as before and again when we add these two rows to obtain the final result (7).

Illustration. To express the product $(8x + x^2 + 1 + 2x^4)$ $(3x + x^2 + 5)$ as a sum, we first rearrange both factors in descending powers of x and proceed as before:

$$
\begin{array}{l}
2x^4 +\; x^2 + 8x + 1 \\
x^2 + 3x\; + 5 \\
\hline
2x^6 \qquad\quad +\; x^4 + 8x^3 +\; x^2 \\
\quad 6x^5 \qquad\qquad + 3x^3 + 24x^2 +\; 3x \\
\qquad\quad 10x^4 \qquad\qquad + 5x^2 + 40x + 5 \\
\hline
2x^6 + 6x^5 + 11x^4 + 11x^3 + 30x^2 + 43x + 5.
\end{array}
$$

PROBLEMS

Express the following products as sums and simplify:

1. $(x + 6)(x + 10)$.
2. $(x + 2y)(x + y)$.
3. $(a + \frac{3}{2})(x + \frac{2}{5})$.
4. $(x + a)(x + b)$.
5. $x(x^2 + 3x + 1)$.
6. $(x^2 + 4y)^2$.
7. $(x + a)(x^2 + 4a + 7)$.
8. $(a + 3b)(a^2 + 6ab + b^2)$.
9. $(x^2 + 2x + 5)(3x^2 + x + 8)$.
10. $(x + y + z)^2$.
11. $(x + y)^3$.
12. $(x + 1)(x + 2)(x + 3)$.
13. $(x + a)(x^2 + ax + a^2)$.
14. Obtain expression (3) by using D1 instead of D2 at the beginning, treating $x^2 + 7y$ as a single quantity multiplied in turn by each term of $3x^3 + x^2y + y^2$.
15. Perform the multiplication in the illustration in the other order.

Simplify:

16. $(x + y)(x + 3y) + (2x + y)(x + 2y)$.
17. $6x(x^2 + x + 9) + (x + 2)(x + 11) + 3$.
18. $[(u + 4)(u + 1) + 2](u + 2)$.
19. $(y + 1)(y + 2y^2 + 5y + 6) + 3(y^3 + y + 1) + 18$.

2.7 Zero, Negative, and Identity Axioms

Axioms A, C, and D deal with operations on the symbols for numbers. Our remaining axioms have to do with properties of the numbers themselves and with certain particular numbers.

An important property of zero is that $a + 0 = a$ for any number a. The zero axiom below formalizes this and in effect assures us that there is a number with this property.

To each real number a corresponds the number $-a$. However, $-a$ is not necessarily negative. If a is positive, then $-a$ is negative, but if a is negative, $-a$ will be positive. For example, if $a = 5$, then $-a = -5$, which is a negative number; if $a = -3$, then $-a = -(-3) = 3$, a positive number. Whether a is positive or negative, it is true that $a + (-a) = 0$. It is also true when $a = 0$, since $-0 = 0$, as we shall show presently; and therefore is true for all real numbers a. Formally stated as an axiom

(axiom N), this property of numbers reads: To each number a there corresponds a number $-a$ such that $a + (-a) = 0$.

The parallel between addition and multiplication in axioms A and C is continued in the behavior of the numbers zero and one. The usefulness of 1 derives from the property that $a \cdot 1 = a$ for all numbers a. The identity axiom ensures that there is a number with this property. Comparing it with the zero axiom, we see that 1 does for multiplication what 0 does for addition.

We shall add to our list of axioms these last three.

Z. Zero axiom

There is a real number, called *zero* and denoted by 0, such that for any real number a, $a + 0 = a$ and $0 + a = a$.

N. Negative axiom

To each real number a, there corresponds a real number, denoted by $-a$, such that $a + (-a) = 0$ and $-a + a = 0$; $-a$ is called the *negative of a*.

I. Identity axiom

There is a real number, called *one* and denoted by 1, such that for any real number a, $a \cdot 1 = a$ and $1 \cdot a = a$; 1 is also called the *identity* or *unity* element. We shall assume that $0 \neq 1$.†

Note that 0 and 1 are fixed numbers. In the zero and identity axioms they are the same for all numbers a, but in the negative axiom the number $-a$ depends on a and will be different for different a's.

Except for one remaining axiom pertaining to division, which will be considered later, our set of axioms is complete. The reader may wonder why we have not listed as axioms such important properties of numbers as $2(-a) = -2a$ and $a \cdot 0 = 0$. These and all other results needed for arithmetic need not be assumed; they can be proved from our axioms, as we shall proceed to show. However, it would take too long for us to establish all the theorems used in arithmetic. We shall prove only the most important theorems, others we shall leave for the reader to work out, and still others whose proofs are like those already derived we shall assume can be similarly established and accept without formal proof.

Illustration.　Show that $-a + [b + (a + c)] = b + c$.

By repeated use of the associative and commutative laws $-a + [b + (a + c)] = (-a + a) + (b + c)$. By the negative axiom $-a + a = 0$, and we have $(-a + a) + (b + c) = 0 + (b + c)$. This last equals $b + c$ by the zero axiom. Hence $-a + [b + (a + c)] = b + c$.

†The symbol "$\neq$" means "not equal to".

PROBLEMS

Each of the following is true by one of the axioms Z, N, or I. In each case state which one applies.

1. $-5 + 0 = -5$.
2. $a \cdot 0 + 0 = a \cdot 0$.
3. $(xy) \cdot 1 = xy$.
4. $ab + [-(ab)] = 0$.
5. $\frac{1}{2}(y \cdot 1) = \frac{1}{2}y$.
6. $0 + 0 = 0$.
7. $1 \cdot 1 = 1$.
8. $(-u + 7 + t) + 0 = -u + 7 + t$.
9. $-w + [-(-w)] = 0$.
10. $[-a(y + z)] \cdot 1 = -a(y + z)$.

In each of the following one or more of the six axioms A, C, D, Z, N, and I is needed to justify the assertion. Which ones are they and how are they used?

11. $0 + 6 = 6$.
12. $-z + 1 \cdot z = 0$.
13. $-(ba) + ab = 0$.
14. $y \cdot 1 + z \cdot 1 = y + z$.
15. $(a + b) \cdot 1 + 0 = a + b$.
16. $-x + x + a + (-a) = 0$.
17. $x + y + [-(y + 0 + x)] = 0$.

Show the following:

18. $-a + (a + b) = b$.
19. $x(1 + 0) = x$.
20. $a + ab = a(b + 1)$.
21. $s + [-t + (-s + t)] = 0$.
22. $(xa + xb) + (ya + yb) = (x + y)(a + b)$.
23. $a + 1 \cdot (b + c + d) = (c + b) + (a + d)$.
24. Show that the second part of the negative axiom need not be assumed, by proving it from the first part of the axiom and the other axioms.

2.8 Additive Cancellation

Our first theorem derived from the new axioms will permit us to cancel the same term from both sides of an equation. For example, if $a + 5 = b + 5$, then $a = b$.

Theorem 2. If $a + c = b + c$, then $a = b$.

Before proving this, let us explain a convention regarding statements of theorems. Unless otherwise indicated, all letters in expressions will stand for numbers, and unless they are explicitly restricted, it will be understood that they may be any numbers for which the expression makes sense. Thus, since no restrictions are placed on a, b, and c, and since $a + c$ and $b + c$ exist for all a, b, and c, one is justified in assuming that the theorem above is intended to be true for all numbers. Theorem 1 is true for any number a, but m and n are explicitly restricted to positive integers. Whether $a^m \cdot a^n = a^{m+n}$ is true for negative m and n is an interesting question, but one that Theorem 1 does not attempt to answer. An expression that has no meaning for certain values of the letters occurs in Theorem 10. There a cannot be zero in b/a.

Returning to the proof of the theorem, we start with the hypothesis $a + c = b + c$. We are assuming that this is true. Adding $-c$ to both sides, we have

$$a + c + (-c) = b + c + (-c).$$

Since by the negative axiom $c + (-c) = 0$, we can replace $c + (-c)$ by 0 and obtain $a + 0 = b + 0$. By the zero axiom $a + 0 = a$ and $b + 0 = b$. Making these replacements, we have $a = b$. The essential idea of the proof is the addition of $-c$ to both sides of the equation. Indeed, when one cancels 5 from both sides of $a + 5 = b + 5$, one is really just adding -5 to both sides.

*Exercise A.   Show that cancellation on the "left" is possible: If $c + a = c + b$, then $a = b$.

The negative axiom ensures that for each number a there is a number, namely $-a$, such that $a + (-a) = 0$. It says nothing more. In particular, it does not say how many such numbers there are. It is quite possible that there is another number b such that $a + b = 0$. Our next theorem settles this question.

Theorem 3.   If $a + b = 0$, then $b = -a$.

That is, if b is any number such that $a + b = 0$, then b must be $-a$. In other words, $-a$ is the only number that when added to a gives zero. To see why this is so, suppose b is a number such that $a + b = 0$. But we already know by the negative axiom that there is a number $-a$ for which $a + (-a) = 0$ and hence $a + b = a + (-a)$. We now cancel the a's (Exercise A) obtaining $b = -a$. Of course, one can equally well conclude from $a + b = 0$ that $a = -b$.

PROBLEMS

1. If $a + b = 0$, show $a = -b$.
2. Use Theorem 3 to solve the equation $x + 3 = 0$.
*3. Show that if $a + b = a$, then $b = 0$. (*Hint:* Replace the right side of the equation by $a + 0$. Which axiom permits this?)
4. Show that if $-5 + x + 3 = -5 + y + 3$, then $x = y$.
5. Show that if $a + x + b = a + y + b$, then $x = y$.
6. If $a + c + b = u + c + v$, show that $a + b = u + v$.
7. If $-2 + x = 0$, show that $x = 2$ and $-(-2)$. Hence what conclusion can you draw about 2 and $-(-2)$?
*8. Show that if $a = b$, then $-a = -b$ by completing the following proof:

$$a = b \qquad \text{hypothesis}$$
$$a + (-b) = b + (-b) \qquad \text{add } -b \text{ to both sides}$$
$$= 0 \qquad \text{negative axiom, } b + (-b) = 0$$
$$= a + (-a) \qquad \text{negative axiom, } 0 = a + (-a)$$
$$\text{etc.}$$

*9. The negative axiom holds for all numbers a. It must then hold if a is itself the negative of some number b, $a = -b$. Therefore $-b + [-(-b)] = 0$. On the other hand, again by the negative axiom, $-b + b = 0$. Now use Theorem 2 to show that $-(-b) = b$.
10. Show that $-[-(-a)] = -a$.
*11. Show $-0 = 0$. (*Hint:* $0 + 0 = 0$—why?; $0 + (-0) = 0$—why?.)

2.9 Multiplication Theorems

Theorem 4. For every number a, $0 \cdot a = 0$.

This theorem is of a different character from the last two, which are of the form "if ..., then ...." Such theorems are called *implications* and assert that something is true if certain conditions are satisfied. Theorem 4 is a categorical statement about all numbers, and it is not surprising that the method of proof is somewhat different. We begin with the true statement $0 + 0 \cdot a = 0 \cdot a$. This is true because $0 \cdot a$ is a number and by the zero axiom $0 + 0 \cdot a = 0 \cdot a$. The reader may wonder why we start with this and how we happened to think of it. These are both good questions, but he must not let them divert him from the main issue, the truth of the statement. We now transform the right side of the equation.

$$\begin{aligned} 0 + 0 \cdot a &= 0 \cdot a, & \text{zero axiom} \\ &= (0 + 0)a & \text{zero axiom, } 0 = 0 + 0 \\ &= 0 \cdot a + 0 \cdot a. & \text{distributive law} \end{aligned}$$

We now have $0 + 0 \cdot a = 0 \cdot a + 0 \cdot a$ and by Theorem 2 can cancel $0 \cdot a$ from each side (or, equivalently, add $-(0 \cdot a)$ to each side), obtaining $0 = 0 \cdot a$, which is what we were to prove.

To return to the questions above, we point out that the motivation of a particular step in a proof often is not clear until later in the exposition. One should keep such questions until the end. Then in going back over the proof the answers to most of them will be apparent. Such questions, while irrelevant to the logical reasoning, do contribute to an understanding and appreciation of the proof.

Unfortunately, no satisfactory answer can be given to the second question. The construction of a proof is largely a creative art and, like all such, cannot be reduced to a set of rules. Some people are better at it than others, but anyone can improve with practice. It does help to study carefully the proofs of known theorems, noting the significance of major steps and trying to comprehend the proof as a whole.

*Exercise A. Show that $a \cdot 0 = 0$ for every number a.

The next two theorems concern the mysterious rules "minus times plus is minus" and "minus times minus is plus." Their proofs show why these must be true.

Theorem 5. $(-a)b = -(ab)$.

Proof. We begin with the statement $(-a)b + ab = (-a + a)b$, which is true by the distributive law, and proceed to transform the right side.

$$\begin{aligned} (-a)b + ab &= (-a + a)b & \text{axiom D2} \\ &= 0 \cdot b & \text{negative axiom, } -a + a = 0 \\ &= 0 & \text{Theorem 4} \\ &= -(ab) + ab. & \text{negative axiom} \end{aligned}$$

Therefore $(-a)b + ab = -(ab) + ab$. Now cancelling ab from each side, we have $(-a)b = -(ab)$.

According to this theorem, the product of -6 and 4 is equal to the negative of the product of 6 and 4: $(-6)4 = -(6 \cdot 4) = -24$. We shall frequently use $-ab$ to mean $-(ab)$ and by extension $-a^n$ to mean $-(a^n)$. With this notation, Theorem 5 reads $(-a)b = -ab$.

Theorem 6. $(-a)(-b) = ab$.

Proof.
$$
\begin{aligned}
(-a)(-b) + (-a)b &= (-a)(-b + b) &&\text{axiom D1}\\
&= (-a) \cdot 0 &&\text{negative axiom}\\
&= 0 &&\text{Exercise A}\\
&= ab + [-(ab)] &&\text{negative axiom}\\
&= ab + (-a)b. &&\text{Theorem 5}
\end{aligned}
$$

Cancelling $(-a)b$ gives us $(-a)(-b) = ab$.

This theorem shows that the product of -6 and -4 is equal to the product of 6 and 4: $(-6)(-4) = 6 \cdot 4 = 24$.

Corollary.† $(-1)(-1) = 1$.

PROBLEMS

*1. Show that $a(-b) = -(ab)$.

2. Prove the corollary to Theorem 6.

Simplify:

3. $7 \cdot 0$

4. $0 \cdot \pi$

5. $0 \cdot 1$

6. $(-43)(17)$

7. $(-10)(-\frac{1}{2})$

8. $8(-6)$

9. $(-5)^2$

10. -5^2

11. $(-\frac{5}{4})^2(-3)$

12. $(-3)^3$

13. $-(3)^3$

14. $-5(-4)^3$

*15. Show that $(-1)a = -a$.

*16. Show that $ab(-c) = -abc$.

17. Show that $-0 = 0$ by using Theorem 5 with a and b both 0.

Simplify if possible:

18. $(-a)^2$

19. $-(-10b^2)$

20. $-[a(-x)(x)]$

21. $[-(b + c)]^2$

22. $[-(b + c)^2]$

23. $(b + 11)[-a(b + 11)]$

24. $(-xb^2)^3x^2$

25. $-(xb^2)^3(-b^2)$

26. $-cy^4(-cy^2)$

27. $(-2bz^2)^4(-b^2z)$

28. $-(2bz^2)^4(-zb^2)(3b)$

29. $-(-a)(-b)(-15)(-d)$

30. $-(-7a)^2 + 16a^2$

31. $-(x + y)^2 + 4xy$

32. $[-(x + y)]^2 + (-x)^2 + (-y)^2$

33. $-(-a)b + (-c)(-d)$

2.10 Subtraction

In our work so far we have carefully avoided such expressions as $a - b$. Whenever the minus sign was used it was firmly attached to some quan-

---

†A corollary to a theorem is a result that follows almost immediately from the theorem or is a special case of it.

tity as in -4 or $7 + [-(w + z)]$ and denoted the negative of a number. It has not been used as a symbol connecting two numbers as in $x - y$ because we have not yet explained what is meant by subtraction. We shall define subtraction in terms of addition and negatives of numbers. For example, by $3 - 2$ we shall mean $3 + (-2)$ and $4 - 7$ will mean $4 + (-7)$.

Definition.　$a - b$ means $a + (-b)$.

The minus sign thus is used in two different senses. When we use $-b$ by itself or with brackets around it, we mean the negative of b. This is the sense in which it is used in $a + (-b)$. In $a - b$ the bar joins two numbers and means the difference of b from a. The definition shows how these are related.

The rules for subtraction are similar to those for addition. We shall prove one of them and leave the others to the reader.

Theorem 7.　$a(b - c) = ab - ac$.

This is the parallel of the distributive law D1. For addition this had to be assumed; for subtraction we are able to prove it. Note, however, that D1 is used in the proof.

Proof.

$$
\begin{aligned}
a(b - c) &= a[b + (-c)] &&\text{definition of subtraction} \\
&= ab + a(-c) &&\text{axiom D1} \\
&= ab + [-(ac)] &&\text{Problem 1, Section 2.9} \\
&= ab - ac. &&\text{definition of subtraction}
\end{aligned}
$$

The first step of the proof expressed $b - c$ in the more familiar form of a sum. This was necessary because we wanted to use axiom D1, which applies only to sums.

The procedures given in Sections 2.5 and 2.6 for simplifying sums and products of polynomials can be easily extended to cover polynomials containing negative signs.

Illustration 1.

$$
\begin{aligned}
&(a^2 - 5ab + 6b^2) + (7a^2 + 8ab - 10b^2) \\
&= (a^2 + 7a^2) + (-5ab + 8ab) + (6b^2 - 10b^2) \\
&= 8a^2 + 3ab + (-4b^2) = 8a^2 + 3ab - 4b^2
\end{aligned}
$$

Otherwise arranged, the work looks like this:

$$
\begin{array}{r}
a^2 - 5ab + 6b \\
7a^2 + 8ab - 10b^2 \\
\hline
8a^2 + 3ab - 4b^2.
\end{array}
$$

To subtract two such expressions, one can apply the definition of subtraction and Problem 5 of this section to transform the problem into one of addition and proceed as above.

Illustration 2.

$$(a^2 - 5ab + 6b^2) - (7a^2 + 8ab - 10b^2)$$
$$= (a^2 - 5ab + 6b^2) + (-7a^2 - 8ab + 10b^2)$$
$$= (a^2 - 7a^2) + (-5ab - 8ab) + (6b^2 + 10b^2)$$
$$= -6a^2 - 13ab + 16b^2.$$

Illustration 3.   Express $(2x - 5)(x - 2)$ as a sum.

$$(2x - 5)(x - 2) = (2x + (-5))(x + (-2))$$
$$= 2x^2 + (-5)x + 2x(-2) + (-5)(-2)$$
$$= 2x^2 - 5x - 4x + 10$$
$$= 2x^2 - 9x + 10.$$

A problem of frequent occurrence in mathematics is that of finding all numbers x such that $x + a = b$, where a and b are given numbers. Any number x for which $x + a = b$ is called a *solution* of the equation. One solution is $b - a$ because

$$(b - a) + a = b + (-a) + a = b + 0 = b.$$

We shall now show that $b - a$ is the only solution of the equation. If x is any number for which $x + a = b$, then

$$x + a + (-a) = b + (-a).$$

Now

$$x + a + (-a) = x + 0 = x \quad \text{and} \quad b + (-a) = b - a.$$

Hence $x = b - a$. That is, if x is a solution of the equation, then x must be $b - a$. The equation, then, has only the single solution $b - a$.

Illustration 4.   The only solution of $x + 6 = 4$ is $4 - 6 = -2$.

PROBLEMS

*1. Show that $(b - c)a = ba - ca$.
2. Is subtraction commutative? That is, is $a - b = b - a$ for all a and b?
3. Evaluate $2 - 2, 1 - 1$.
*4. Show that $a - a = 0$.
*5. Show that $-(a + b) = -a - b$. (*Hint:* $-(a + b) = (-1)(a + b)$ by Problem 15, Section 2.9.) Why is this not just a restatement of axiom D1?
*6. Show that $-(a - b) = -a + b$.
*7. Show that $0 - a = -a$.
*8. Show that $a - (-b) = a + b$.
9. By writing $2 = 1 + 1$ and $3 = 1 + 1 + 1$, show that $3 - 2 = 1$. Similarly, show that $2 - 4 = -2$.
*10. Show that if $a - b = c$, then $a = b + c$. This says that the difference $a - b$ is what must be added to b in order to obtain a. It is possible to adopt this as the definition of $a - b$, in which case our definition of $a - b$ as $a + (-b)$ would appear as a theorem.
11. Show that $a + b - c = a - c + b$.

12. Is $(a + b) - c = (a - c) + b$?

13. Is $a - (b + c) = a - b - c$?

14. Is subtraction associative? That is, is $a - (b - c) = (a - b) - c$?

Simplify the following sums and check by substituting the given values where shown.

15. $(x - 7y + x^2) + (4x + 6y + 3x^2); x = 1, y = -1.$

16. $(2x^3 + 6x^2 - x - 4) + (x^3 - x^2 - 7x - 2); x = 2.$

17. $-4x(x^2 - 7x + 1) - 3(x^3 - x^2 - x); x = 1.$

18. $16(y[y - x] + 3x^2) + 2(y^2 + [3y + x]x); x = 2, y = 3.$

19. $2(3x - x^2) + 7(x^2 + x) - \frac{1}{2}x; x = -2.$

20. $(2x^2 + \frac{1}{3}x - 1) - 7(x^2 - x^3 + \frac{4}{3}x + 6).$

21. $8\left(y - \frac{1}{y} + y^2\right) - \left(y + 2\left(\frac{1}{y}\right) + 3y^2\right); y = 2.$

22. $u^2(11u^2 - 3uv^2 + v^3) + v^2(2u^3 + u^2v - v^2).$

23. $xy(x^2 + y^2) + 2x^2(x^2 - y^2) - y^2(4x^2 + xy + 4y^2).$

Express the following products as sums and simplify. Check by making the substitutions where indicated.

24. $(x + 2)(x - 5); x = 2.$

25. $(3x - 7)(x - 4); x = 1.$

26. $(a - b)^2.$

27. $(x + y)(x - y).$

28. $(3 - x)(7 - x).$

29. $(2 + 3y)(-y + 2).$

30. $(2w + 6)(3w - 1).$

31. $(ax - b)(-cx + d).$

32. $(x^2 - 9y^2)(x^2 + 9y^2).$

33. $(2st - 5t^2)^2.$

34. $(-4 + x + a)^2; x = 0, a = 2.$

35. $(a + b + 1)(a - b + 1); a = 1, b = 1.$

36. $(3b - x + 5)(3b - x - 5).$

37. $(u + v - w)(u + v + w); u = 1, v = 0, w = -1.$

38. $(a^2 + x - y)(a^2 - x - y).$

39. $-6(x^2 + x)(-x)(2x - 5).$

40. $(x - a)(x^2 + ax + a^2).$

41. $(x + a)(x^2 - ax + a^2).$

42. $(a^2 - 3a + 2)(6a^2 - 2a - 3).$

43. $(x^2 - 2xy + y^2)(x^2 + 2xy + y^2); x = -1, y = 1.$

44. $(a - b)^3; a = 1, b = 2.$

Simplify:

45. $(2x - 3)(x + 5) - (6x - 7)(x + 1).$

46. $5(x + 6 - x^2) + (x^2 - 3)(x + 2) - x^3 - 4x.$

47. $x[(x + y) + 2(x - 3y)y] + (5x - 2y)(x - y).$

Simplify each of the following and check by substitution:

48. $x^2 \cdot 3 + 2x(3x - 1); x = \frac{1}{3}.$

49. $-(x - 3) - [5x + (x - 2)]; x = 2.$

50. $2a(a^2x^2 + 5) - 2(x^2 + 3a); a = 2, x = 1.$
51. $(7x + 4)^2 2x - x^2 \cdot 2(7x + 4) \cdot 7; x = 0.$
52. $ab(a^2 - b^2) + ab^2(b + a); a = -2, b = -2.$
53. $-\{x - [x + 3 + (2x - 6)]\}; x = 1.$
54. $6b^2(d^2 - y^2) + 2y^2(7y^2 - 3b^2); b = 3, d = -1, y = 1.$
55. $2x - 3z - [4 - (x + 5z)] - [z - 7x + \frac{1}{2}]; x = 1, z = -2.$
56. $a[x(x + y) + y(y - x) - x(x + a)]; a = 5, x = 1, y = 1.$
57. $b^6[(b^2)^3 + (-b^3)^3] + (b^5)^3 - (-a^3)^4; a = 1, b = -1.$
58. $x^2 \cdot 3(x - 1)^2 + 2x(x - 1)^3; x = -1.$
59. $(x + 1)[(x^2 - 3x)2(x - 5) + (2x - 3)(x - 5)^2] + (x^2 - 3x)(x - 5)^2; x = 1.$

Solve the following equations for the indicated letters:

60. $x - 3 = 6$; for x.   61. $x + 5 = 8$; for x.
62. $y + a = 2$; for y, for a.   63. $u + 2 = -7$; for u.
64. $x - \frac{1}{2} = 0$; for x.   65. $y + b = x - 3$; for y, for x.
                    66. $x + 3 = b + c$; for x, for c.

2.11   Factoring

The distributive law says that $a(b + c) = ab + ac$, and we have seen how indispensable it is in our work so far. Read backward, $ab + ac = a(b + c)$, it is equally useful, for now it is the familiar statement about factorization. For example, $2x + 2y = 2(x + y)$, and

$$(x + a)x + (x + a)(-5) = (x + a)[(x + (-5)]$$
$$= (x + a)(x - 5).$$

In this section we shall study the technique of factoring certain simple expressions; namely, those that contain only letters and rational numbers. To factor such a sum means here to express it as a product of factors containing only letters and rational numbers. Later, in Chapter 5 we shall use the term in a broader sense.

The simplest and most easily recognizable factor of a sum is one that is a factor of every term. Each term of $2x^5 - 2x^4 - 12x^3$ has $2x^3$ as a factor, and hence this sum can be written in the factored form $2x^3(x^2 - x - 6)$ by the general distributive law. Since $x + 3$ is a factor of each term of

$$x^3(x + 3) - 5x(x + 3) + (x + 3),$$

this can be written $(x^3 - 5x + 1)(x + 3)$. It is easier to detect the remaining factors if factors of this type are removed first, and generally this should be done as a preliminary to further factoring.

A frequently occurring expression is the quadratic $ax^2 + bx + c$. Such an expression does not always have factors in the above sense, but when it does, they can usually be found most quickly by trial and error. To factor $x^2 - x - 6$, we see that the factors must be of the form $(x + \alpha) \cdot (x + \beta)$, where α and β are numbers to be determined. Now $(x + \alpha)(x + \beta)$

$= x^2 + (\alpha + \beta)x + \alpha\beta$, and if this is to be identical with $x^2 - x - 6$, α and β must be chosen so that $\alpha\beta = -6$ and $\alpha + \beta = -1$. If α and β are two integers whose product is -6, then the only possibilities are either $\alpha = 1$, $\beta = -6$; $\alpha = -1$, $\beta = 6$; $\alpha = 2$, $\beta = -3$; or $\alpha = -2$, $\beta = 3$. (There is no need to consider $\alpha = -6$, $\beta = 1$, since this would give the same factors as the first possibility, but in reverse order.) Out of these four possibilities we now choose the one satisfying the second condition, $\alpha + \beta = -1$. Trying each in turn, we see that only the third fits. Hence $x^2 - x - 6 = (x + 2)(x - 3)$.

Illustration 1.   Factor $x^2 - 7x + 12$.

The factors of 12 are 1, 2, 3, 4, 6, 12, and their negatives. One quickly sees that the only possible pair of these whose product is 12 and sum is -7 is -3 and -4. Therefore $x^2 - 7x + 12 = (x - 3)(x - 4)$.

In a polynomial such as $2x^3 - 7x^2 + x + 3$ the quantity that is multiplied by each power of x is called the *coefficient* of that power. Thus 2 is the coefficient of x^3, -7 the coefficient of x^2, and 1 the coefficient of x. The number 3 is called the *constant term*.

When the coefficient of x^2 is other than 1, factoring is a little more troublesome, but the procedure is essentially the same.

Illustration 2.   Factor $6x^2 - 11x - 10$.

Now the coefficients of x in both factors must be such that their product is 6 and hence must be chosen from the numbers 1, 2, 3, 6, and their negatives. The constant terms, as before, must have a product -10 and hence are either 1, 2, 5, 10, or the negatives of these. By trying various combinations, we find that $6x^2 - 11x - 10 = (3x + 2)(2x - 5)$.

One might well ask why we tried only factors with integral coefficients and none with fractional ones. The answer is simple though not obvious. If a polynomial with integral coefficients has a factorization as a product of polynomials with rational coefficients, then it has a factorization as a product of polynomials with integral coefficients. Thus the polynomial $x^2 + 3x - 2$ must have factors with integral coefficients or have no rational factors at all. There is no point in trying a factor such as $\frac{1}{3}x + 7$. In this example the only possibilities are those for which $\alpha = 2$, $\beta = -1$, or $\alpha = -2$, $\beta = 1$. Since neither of these is suitable, we can conclude that $x^2 + 3x - 2$ has no factors with rational coefficients. We shall not prove this theorem.

The factorization of the expression $x^2 - a^2$ as the product $(x + a)(x - a)$ occurs so often that one should be constantly on the watch for it. For example,

$$x^2 - \tfrac{64}{25} = (x + \tfrac{8}{5})(x - \tfrac{8}{5}).$$

It frequently occurs even when the constant term a^2 does not have a rational square root, as in

$$x^2 - 13 = (x + \sqrt{13})(x - \sqrt{13})$$

and

$$x^2 - c = (x + \sqrt{c})(x - \sqrt{c}),$$

where $c \geq 0$.† In this important instance we violate our rule and admit factors with non-rational coefficients. Two common factorizations are

$$x^2 + 2ax + a^2 = (x + a)^2$$

and

$$x^2 - 2ax + a^2 = (x - a)^2.$$

Such expressions are called *perfect squares*. Two factorable forms, which occur occasionally, are $x^3 - a^3$ and $x^3 + a^3$. By multiplying the right sides, the reader can verify that their factorizations are

$$x^3 - a^3 = (x - a)(x^2 + ax + a^2),$$

(1) $$x^3 + a^3 = (x + a)(x^2 - ax + a^2).$$

Illustration 3. Factor $(a - 3c)^2 - (2c)^2$.

$$(a - 3c)^2 - (2c)^2 = [(a - 3c) + 2c] \, [(a - 3c) - 2c]$$
$$= (a - c) \, (a - 5c).$$

Although this is the quickest way to factor the expression, one could have proceeded by expanding the left side, obtaining $a^2 - 6ac + 5c^2$, and then factoring this expression.

Illustration 4. Factor $4x^4 + 20x^3b + 25x^2b^2$.

$$4x^4 + 20x^3b + 25x^2b^2 = x^2(4x^2 + 20xb + 25b^2)$$
$$= x^2(2x + 5b)^2.$$

Illustration 5. Factor $a^3 + 27b^3$.

By (1)

$$a^3 + 27b^3 = a^3 + (3b)^3$$
$$= (a + 3b) \, [a^2 - a(3b) + (3b)^2]$$
$$= (a + 3b) \, (a^2 - 3ab + 9b^2).$$

When the polynomial contains fractional coefficients, the reader may find it helpful first to find a common denominator for the coefficients and then factor the resulting polynomial, which will now have integral coefficients.

Illustration 6. Factor $x^2 - \dfrac{5}{6}x - \dfrac{2}{3}$.

$$x^2 - \frac{5}{6}x - \frac{2}{3} = \frac{6x^2}{6} - \frac{5x}{6} - \frac{4}{6} = \frac{1}{6}(6x^2 - 5x - 4)$$

$$= \frac{1}{6}(2x + 1) \, (3x - 4).$$

†The notation $a > b$ means that a is greater than b, and $a \geq b$ that a is greater than or equal to b.

The product can also be written in other forms:

$$\left(\frac{1}{3}x + \frac{1}{6}\right)(3x - 4), \quad \text{or} \quad (2x + 1)\left(\frac{1}{2}x - \frac{2}{3}\right), \quad \text{or} \quad \left(x + \frac{1}{2}\right)\left(x - \frac{4}{3}\right).$$

Illustration 7. Factor $2ax - 4ay + bx - 2by$.

$$2ax - 4ay + bx - 2by = 2a(x - 2y) + b(x - 2y)$$
$$= (2a + b)(x - 2y).$$

Illustration 8. Factor $3x^3 + x^2 - 3x - 1$.

$$3x^3 + x^2 - 3x - 1 = x^2(3x + 1) - (3x + 1)$$
$$= (x^2 - 1)(3x + 1)$$
$$= (x + 1)(x - 1)(3x + 1).$$

PROBLEMS

Factor if possible:

1. $y^2 + 3y$.
2. $20x^4 - 20x^3$.
3. $a^2b + b^2a$.
4. $25x^2 - 16$.
5. $a^2 + b^2$.
6. $a^3b - b^3a$.
7. $x^2 + 8x - 15$.
8. $\left(\frac{1}{x}\right)^2 - \frac{1}{25}$.
9. $\left(\frac{1}{a}\right)^2 - \left(\frac{1}{y}\right)^2$.
10. $9z^2 - 42z + 49$.
11. $x^2 - 5$.
12. $4x^2 + 9$.
13. $3x^3 - 5x^2 + 4x$.
14. $6ax^2 + 7ax - 10a$.
15. $-2x^2 + 15 + x$.
16. $6x^2 - 5xy - 4y^2$.
17. $2a - 11ab + 15ab^2$.
18. $15x^4 - 15x^2$.
19. $(a - 9)^2 - 16$.
20. $(a - 9)^2 + 16$.
21. $(a + 9)^2 - 16$.
22. $(a + 9)^2 + 16$.
23. $(x + 2y)^2 - z^2$.
24. $a^2 - b^4$.

25. $34t - 21 - 8t^2$.
26. $2y^2 + 10y - 48$.
27. $6a^2c - 5acb - cb^2$.
28. $x^{10} - 9x^8$.
29. $5u(x - y) - 2(x - y)$.
30. $12x^2 - 21xy - 9y^2$.
31. $a^2x^2 - 3ax - 28$.
32. $(x + y)^2 - (x - y)^2$.
33. $(x - 1)^4 + 4(x - 1)^3(x - 6)$.
34. $5(x - 1)^3 + 15(x - 1)^2(x - 5)$.
35. $2x^4 + 17x^2 + 30$.
36. $15(a + b)^2 + 11(a + b) + 2$.
37. $(y^3 + 4y^2) - (y + 4)$.
38. $x^3 + x^2 + x + 1$.
39. $x^5 + 3x^4 + x^3 + 3x^2$.
40. $ax + ay + bx + by$.
41. $7a - b - 7ax + bx$.
42. $8x^3 - 1$.
43. $8x^3 + 1$.
44. $x^4 - y^4$.
45. $x^3 - x + x^2 - 1$.
46. $ax + y^2 - yx - ay$.
47. $x^2 - a^2 + x + a$.
48. $xs - 6yt - 2xt + 3ys$.
49. $-3ax - bx + 6ay + 2yb$.
50. $3acd + 6bcd - dax - 2bdx$.

Express as a product:

51. $(cx + d)a - (ax + d)c$.
52. $(1 - x^2)2x - (1 + x^2)(-2x)$.
53. $(x^2 - 2x + 1)(-1) + (4 - x)(2x - 2)$.

54. $(x^2 + 4x)(2x - 8) + (2x + 4)(x^2 - 8x + 16)$.
55. $(x^2 + y^2)^2 - 4x^2y^2$.
56. $(x + 2)^2 4(x + 3)^3 + (x + 3)^4(x + 2)2$.
57. $3x^8(-14x^2 + 1)^2(-28x) + 8x^7(-14x^2 + 1)^3$.
58. $3nx^{n-1} - 3nx^2$, where n is an integer greater than 3.

2.12   Division of Polynomials

To divide an expression such as

$$(1) \qquad\qquad 2x^3 + 5x^4 + 2x^5 - 8 - 8x + 3x^2$$

by

$$(2) \qquad\qquad x^2 + 3x + 1,$$

first arrange both expressions in descending powers of x if they are not already in that form,

$$(1a) \qquad\qquad 2x^5 + 5x^4 + 2x^3 + 3x^2 - 8x - 8$$

and

$$(2a) \qquad\qquad x^2 + 3x + 1.$$

The first term of the quotient is obtained by dividing the first term, $2x^5$, of the dividend (1a) by the first term, x^2, of the divisor (2a). The result is $2x^3$. Next, multiply $2x^3$ by the divisor and subtract the product from the dividend, obtaining $-x^4 + 3x^2 - 8x - 8$. The work can be arranged as follows:

$$
\begin{array}{r}
2x^3 \qquad\qquad\qquad\qquad\qquad\quad \\
\hline
x^2 + 3x + 1 \,\overline{\smash{\big)}\, 2x^5 + 5x^4 + 2x^3 + 3x^2 - 8x - 8} \\
2x^5 + 6x^4 + 2x^3 \qquad\qquad\qquad \\
\hline
-x^4 \qquad + 3x^2 - 8x - 8 \ .
\end{array}
$$

The process is now repeated, this time using the first stage remainder, $-x^4 + 3x^2 - 8x - 8$, in place of the dividend. After four such stages the work looks like this:

$$
(3)\quad
\begin{array}{r}
2x^3 - \ x^2 + 3x\ - 5 \qquad\qquad\qquad\quad \\
\hline
x^2 + 3x + 1 \,\overline{\smash{\big)}\, 2x^5 + 5x^4 + 2x^3 + 3x^2 - \ 8x - 8} \\
2x^5 + 6x^4 + 2x^3 \qquad\qquad\qquad\qquad \\
\hline
-\ x^4 \qquad + 3x^2 - \ 8x - 8 \\
-\ x^4 - 3x^3 - \ x^2 \qquad\qquad\quad \\
\hline
3x^3 + 4x^2 - \ 8x - 8 \\
3x^3 + 9x^2 + \ 3x \qquad\quad \\
\hline
-\ 5x^2 - 11x - 8 \\
-\ 5x^2 - 15x - 5 \\
\hline
4x - 3 \ .
\end{array}
$$

Note that at each stage we subtracted a multiple of $x^2 + 3x + 1$ from the preceding remainder and hence, in effect, from (1a). First we subtracted $(x^2 + 3x + 1)2x^3$, then $(x^2 + 3x + 1)(-x^2)$, then $(x^2 + 3x + 1)3x$, and finally $(x^2 + 3x + 1)(-5)$. The total effect of these is the subtraction of

$$(x^2 + 3x + 1)(2x^3 - x^2 + 3x - 5)$$

from (1a). Since the last remainder is $4x - 3$, we have shown that

$$(2x^5 + 5x^4 + 2x^3 + 3x^2 - 8x - 8)$$
$$- (x^2 + 3x + 1)(2x^3 - x^2 + 3x - 5) = 4x - 3,$$

or

(4) $\qquad 2x^5 + 5x^4 + 2x^3 + 3x^2 - 8x - 8 =$
$$(x^2 + 3x + 1)(2x^3 - x^2 + 3x - 5) + (4x - 3).$$

That is,

(5) $\qquad$ dividend $=$ (divisor)$\cdot$(quotient) $+$ remainder.

If we rewrite (4) as

$$\frac{2x^5 + 5x^4 + 2x^3 + 3x^2 - 8x - 8}{x^2 + 3x + 1} = (2x^3 - x^2 + 3x - 5) + \frac{4x - 3}{x^2 + 3x + 1},$$

we have expressed the result of the division process in the form

$$\frac{\text{dividend}}{\text{divisor}} = \text{quotient} + \frac{\text{remainder}}{\text{divisor}}.$$

In (3) the division process could have been terminated at an earlier stage or continued beyond the point where we stopped. For most applications one needs a quotient that is a polynomial and a remainder of degree less than that of the divisor, as in (3).† If we had continued, terms involving $1/x$ would have appeared in the quotient. Of course, the remainder can, and often will, be zero.

If the dividend and divisor involve more than one letter, arrange them in descending powers of one of the letters.

Illustration. Perform the division

$$\frac{-6x^3y + 2x^2y^2 - 3xy^2 + 2x^4 + y^3 + x^2y}{2x^2 + y}.$$

We rearrange the dividend and divisor in descending powers of y (x would serve equally well),

$$
\begin{array}{r}
y^2 - 3xy + x^2 \\
y + 2x^2 \overline{\smash{\big)}\, y^3 + (2x^2 - 3x)y^2 + (-6x^3 + x^2)y + 2x^4} \\
\underline{y^3 + 2x^2y^2} \\
-3xy^2 + (-6x^3 + x^2)y + 2x^4 \\
\underline{-3xy^2 - 6x^3y} \\
x^2y + 2x^4 \\
\underline{x^2y + 2x^4}
\end{array}
$$

---

†The degree of a polynomial is the largest exponent. The degrees of the polynomials in (1) and (2) are 5 and 2.

The remainder is zero. Expressed in the form (5), the division is

$$y^3 + (2x^2 - 3x)y^2 + (-6x^3 + x^2)y + 2x^4 = (y + 2x^2)(y^2 - 3xy + x^2).$$

PROBLEMS

Perform the indicated divisions and express the result in the form

$$\text{dividend} = (\text{divisor}) \cdot (\text{quotient}) + \text{remainder},$$

where the remainder is either zero or of degree less than that of the divisor.

1. $\dfrac{x^2 + x + 1}{x + 3}.$

2. $\dfrac{x^3 - 2x^2 - 8x - 35}{x - 5}.$

3. $\dfrac{3x^4 + x^2}{x^2 + 1}.$

4. $\dfrac{x^3 + 5ax^2 + (4a^2 + 6)x + 6a}{x + a}.$

5. $\dfrac{x^4 + 5x^2 + 8x^3 - 39x + 10}{x + 6}.$

6. $\dfrac{2x^4 - 3x^3 + 6x^2 - 2x - 4}{2x^3 - x^2 + 5x + 3}.$

7. $\dfrac{x^4 + 3x^3y - 11x^2y^2 + 3xy^3 - 2y^4}{x - 2y}.$

8. $\dfrac{15x^4 - 3 + 3x - 20x^2 - 4x^3}{x + 3x^2 - 1}.$

9. $\dfrac{x^2 - 2xy - 3y^2 + 3x - 13y - 4}{x - 3y - 1}.$

10. $\dfrac{2x^5 - x^3 + 23x^2 - 19 + 3x^4 - 14x}{-3 + 2x + x^2}.$

11. Perform the division in the illustration after rearranging the numerator and denominator in descending powers of x.
12. Factor $x^5 - a^5$. (*Hint:* Divide $x^5 - a^5$ by $x - a$.)
13. Factor $x^n - a^n$, where n is a positive integer.

2.13   Reciprocal Axiom

The reader will recall that before we discussed subtraction we introduced the concept of the negative of a number and postulated the negative axiom in order to ensure that to each number a there would be a number $-a$ such that $a + (-a) = 0$. We shall develop division in a similar fashion, and it may help if one keeps in mind the parallel with subtraction.

We have already remarked on the analogy between addition and multiplication in the axioms and in the roles of zero and one. Continuing this, one might ask whether the concept of the negative of a number has a counterpart in multiplication. That is, given a number a, is there a number b such that $ab = 1$? It is our common experience that this is so, as for example, $7 \cdot \frac{1}{7} = 1$ or $\frac{3}{4} \cdot \frac{4}{3} = 1$. However, to be sure that this will always happen and to provide a firm basis for the theory of division, we need an axiom, just as we did for negatives.

R. Reciprocal axiom

To each real number a, with the exception of 0, there corresponds a real number, denoted by a^{-1}, such that $aa^{-1} = 1$ and $a^{-1}a = 1$.

We say that a^{-1} is the *inverse* or *reciprocal* of a. For the present it should be considered as a symbol for a number, just as a is, with no meaning other than that implied by the axiom. In particular, we have no indication as yet that the exponent -1 will obey any of the laws of exponents. Some other letter, such as b, could just as well have been used to indicate this number, but it is convenient to have a notation that suggests that the inverse is related to a. The situation is analogous to the use of $-a$ to indicate the negative of a. When first introduced, $-a$ was just a symbol for a number. Not until later were its properties and connection with subtraction developed.

The analogy between the reciprocal and negative axioms is not perfect, since 0 is excepted in the former. The reason for this is easy to see. If 0 had a reciprocal, say c, then by the reciprocal axiom we should have $0 \cdot c = 1$. But by Theorem 4, $0 \cdot c = 0$. Thus to postulate a reciprocal of 0 would lead to a contradiction.

Exercise A.   Find 1^{-1}, $(-1)^{-1}$, 13^{-1}, $(\frac{1}{4})^{-1}$, $(-\frac{6}{7})^{-1}$.

Exercise B.   Find 2^{-1}, 3^{-1}, $2^{-1} + 3^{-1}$, $(2 + 3)^{-1}$, $2^{-1} \cdot 3^{-1}$, $(2 \cdot 3)^{-1}$.

Exercise C.   Show that $a^{-1}(ab) = b$ if $a \neq 0$.

Exercise D.   Show that $ab^{-1}a^{-1}b = 1$, where $a \neq 0$ and $b \neq 0$.

Exercise E.   Find $(8^{-1})^{-1}$.

Corresponding to Theorem 2, we have a cancellation theorem for multiplication.

Theorem 8.   If $ac = bc$ and $c \neq 0$, then $a = b$.

That $c = 0$ must be excluded is apparent on testing the theorem with $a = 3$, $b = 2$, and $c = 0$. We have $3 \cdot 0 = 0$ and $2 \cdot 0 = 0$, and so $3 \cdot 0 = 2 \cdot 0$. Yet $3 \neq 2$.

To prove this theorem, multiply both sides of the equation $ac = bc$ by c^{-1}. Since $c \neq 0$, the reciprocal axiom guarantees that there will be such a number.
$$acc^{-1} = bcc^{-1}.$$
But $cc^{-1} = 1$, and therefore $a \cdot 1 = b \cdot 1$, or $a = b$.

Theorem 4 says that a product of two numbers is zero if one of its factors is zero. It is common experience that the converse is also true; a product is never zero unless at least one of its factors is zero. The proof of the next theorem shows why this is so.

Theorem 9. If $ab = 0$, then $a = 0$ or $b = 0$.†

Proof. If $a = 0$, there is nothing to prove. Suppose now $a \neq 0$. We shall show that in this event b must be zero. If $a \neq 0$, then a^{-1} exists by the reciprocal axiom and we have $a^{-1}ab = a^{-1} \cdot 0$. Hence $1 \cdot b = b = 0$.

Theorem 9 is basic in the solution of quadratic and higher degree equations. Although we shall not take up this topic until Chapter 3, we shall illustrate here with a simple example the role played by this theorem in the solution of such equations.

Illustration. Find all solutions of the equation $(x - 3)(x + 1) = 0$.

By direct substitution we see that 3 and -1 are solutions: $(3 - 3)(3 + 1) = 0 \cdot 4 = 0$, and $(-1 - 3)(-1 + 1) = -4 \cdot 0 = 0$. We shall now show that they are the only ones. If x is any number for which $(x - 3)(x + 1) = 0$, by Theorem 9 either $x - 3 = 0$ or $x + 1 = 0$ (or both). If $x - 3 = 0$, then $x = 3$. If $x + 1 = 0$, then $x = -1$. Thus 3 and -1 are the only solutions.

PROBLEMS

1. Show that if $x \neq 0$, then $x^{-1}(3x) - 3 = 0$.
2. Show that if $5x + c = (3 + a)x + c$ and $x \neq 0$, then $5 = 3 + a$.
*3. State and prove a companion theorem to Theorem 8 justifying cancellation on the left.
4. State and prove conditions under which $3bc = xby$ implies $3c = xy$.
5. Find all solutions of the following two equations, justifying each step:
   (a) $5x + 7 = 5 \cdot 2 + 7$.
   (b) $10(2x + 8) = 10(6 + 8)$.
6. If $x \neq 0$, show $x^2 \neq 0$.
*7. Show that if $a \neq 0$, then $a^{-1} \neq 0$.
8. Why is it not necessary in Theorem 2, as it is in Theorem 8, to restrict c to non-zero numbers?
9. For $a \neq 0$, we know that $aa^{-1} = 1$. Now prove that if b is any number for which $ab = 1$, then $b = a^{-1}$. Of which theorem is this an analogue?
10. Derive Theorem 9 directly from Theorem 8. (*Hint:* Write 0 as $a \cdot 0$.)
*11. Show that if $ab = a$ and $a \neq 0$, then $b = 1$. What can you say about b if $a = 0$?
*12. If $a = b \neq 0$, show that $a^{-1} = b^{-1}$. (*Hint:* Multiply both sides of the equation $a = b$ by a suitable quantity.)
*13. Show that $(a^{-1})^{-1} = a$ if $a \neq 0$. (*Hint:* Compare with Problem 9, Section 2.8.)

†The word "or" as used in mathematics does not preclude the possibility of both events occurring. It is equivalent to the phrase "and/or." The conclusion of the theorem means a, or b, or possibly both are zero.

Find all solutions of the following equations.

14. $5x = 0$.   16. $x(x - 2) = 0$.

15. $-2(x + 4) = 0$.   17. $x^2 = 0$.

          18. $(x - a)(x + \frac{2}{3}) = 0$.

*19. If $a \neq 0$ and $b \neq 0$, show that $(ab)^{-1} = a^{-1}b^{-1}$. (*Hint:* Show that $a^{-1}b^{-1}ab = 1$ and $ab(ab)^{-1} = 1$.) Illustrate this theorem with specific numbers.

20. Is $(a + b)^{-1} = a^{-1} + b^{-1}$ if $a \neq 0$ and $b \neq 0$?

*21. Show that if $abc = 0$, then $a = 0$, $b = 0$, or $c = 0$. (*Hint:* Write abc as $a(bc)$ and apply Theorem 9.)

Find all solutions of the following equations.

22. $3(x + 5)(x + 6) = 0$.   26. $(x - 8)(x + 11)(x - \frac{3}{4}) = 0$.

23. $x^2 - \frac{25}{9} = 0$.   27. $x^2 - c^2 = 0$.

24. $(x - \frac{1}{2})^2 = 0$.   28. $(x - c)^2 = 0$.

25. $(x - a)(x - b) = 0$.   29. $(x^2 - 1)(x + 17) = 0$.

30. Find the fallacy in the following argument:
    Let $a = 2$. Then $aa = 2a$ and $a^2 - 4 = 2a - 4$. Factoring, we have $(a + 2)(a - 2) = 2(a - 2)$. By Theorem 8 we may cancel $a - 2$, obtaining $a + 2 = 2$. Cancelling the 2's, we have $a = 0$. Therefore $2 = 0$!

*31. Show that if the product $a_1a_2 \cdots a_n = 0$, then at least one of the factors must be zero.

2.14   Division

Definition.   The number ba^{-1}, where $a \neq 0$, will be denoted by $\dfrac{b}{a}$ and is called the *quotient of b by a*.

Other notations for the quotient are b/a and $b \div a$, the latter rarely being used today except in elementary arithmetic and occasionally in print in order to save space.

It is obvious from the definition that since 0 has no inverse, there can be no number $b/0$. In other words, it is impossible to divide a number by zero. Even 0 itself is not exempt; $0/0$ has no meaning, and it is therefore ridiculous to claim that $0/0 = 1$.

Remark.   If $a \neq 0$, then $\dfrac{1}{a} = 1 \cdot a^{-1} = a^{-1}$, and $\dfrac{b}{a} = b\left(\dfrac{1}{a}\right)$.

Illustration 1.   Show that $a\left(\dfrac{b}{a}\right) = b$, $a \neq 0$.†

$$a\left(\frac{b}{a}\right) = a(ba^{-1}) = baa^{-1} = b \cdot 1 = b.$$

Illustration 2.   If $\dfrac{a}{b} = 1$, show that $a = b$.

We know $b \neq 0$, since otherwise the hypothesis $a/b = 1$ would be meaningless.

†This is a common mathematical notation. The part following the comma describes restrictions on the numbers involved. Here we are to show that $a(b/a) = b$ provided $a \neq 0$. The restriction is necessary because b/a is meaningless when $a = 0$.

Then b^{-1} exists, and the hypothesis can be rewritten as $ab^{-1} = 1$. If we multiply both sides by b, we have $ab^{-1}b = 1 \cdot b$. Hence $a \cdot 1 = b$ and $a = b$.

Theorem 10. If $ax = b$, $a \neq 0$, then $x = ba^{-1} = \dfrac{b}{a}$.

Proof. Multiplying both sides of $ax = b$ by a^{-1}, we have $a^{-1}ax = a^{-1}b$ and hence $x = ba^{-1}$.

It is easily seen by direct substitution that b/a is a solution of $ax = b$ (see Illustration 1). Theorem 10 asserts that it is the only solution by showing that if there is a number x for which $ax = b$, then that number must be b/a.

PROBLEMS

1. In the proof of Theorem 10 we multiplied by a^{-1}. Justify this step by showing that there is such a number.
2. By considering the equation $4x = 12$ show that $\frac{12}{4} = 3$.
3. Find a solution of the equation $2y = 16$. Why is this the only one?
4. Show that $\frac{5}{3}$ is the solution of $3x = 5$.

Solve the following equations for the indicated letters.

5. $2x = 6$; for x.   7. $3x = 9y$; for x, for y.
6. $7x = -15$; for x.   8. $5x = a - 3$; for x.

9. The statement is often made that "any number divided by itself is one." This is not always true. Rephrase the statement correctly and prove it.

10. Show that

   (a) $\left(\dfrac{4}{5}\right) 3 = \dfrac{12}{5}$;   (b) $-8\left(\dfrac{1}{10}\right) = \dfrac{-8}{10}$;   *(c) $a\left(\dfrac{b}{d}\right) = \dfrac{ab}{d}$, $d \neq 0$.

11. Show that

   (a) $\dfrac{0}{4} = 0$;   *(b) $\dfrac{0}{a} = 0$, $a \neq 0$.

12. Show that

   (a) $\dfrac{-6}{1} = -6$;   (b) $\dfrac{\frac{3}{5}}{1} = \dfrac{3}{5}$;   *(c) $\dfrac{b}{1} = b$.

*13. Show that $\dfrac{a}{a} = 1$, $a \neq 0$.

*14. Show that $a\left(\dfrac{b}{c}\right) = b\left(\dfrac{a}{c}\right)$, $c \neq 0$.

15. Find the values, if any, of

   (a) $\dfrac{0}{-5}$;   (b) $\dfrac{6}{0}$;   (c) $\dfrac{0}{0}$;   (d) $\dfrac{\frac{1}{3}}{\frac{1}{3}}$;   (e) $\dfrac{a}{0}$.

16. *(a) Is $b\left(\dfrac{1}{b}\right) = 1$? If not, find its value.

   (b) Find the values, if any, of

   (i) $-5\left(\dfrac{1}{-5}\right)$;   (ii) $0\left(\dfrac{1}{0}\right)$;   (iii) $1\left(\dfrac{0}{1}\right)$.

17. Show that if $b \neq 0$, then $\dfrac{1}{b} \neq 0$.

18. Show that a fraction is zero only if its numerator is zero; that is, if $b \neq 0$ and $\dfrac{a}{b} = 0$, then $a = 0$.

Find the solutions, if any, of the following equations.

19. $\dfrac{x}{10} = 0$.

20. $\dfrac{x-2}{3} = 0$.

21. $\dfrac{x+7}{x} = 0$.

22. $\dfrac{2x+3}{5} = 3$.

23. $\dfrac{x}{x} = 0$.

24. $\dfrac{x}{x} = 1$.

25. (a) Show that if $a = c$ and $b = d \neq 0$, then $\dfrac{a}{b} = \dfrac{c}{d}$.

   (b) If $\dfrac{a}{b} = \dfrac{c}{d}$, where $b \neq 0$ and $d \neq 0$, must it follow that $a = c$ and $b = d$?

26. Show that if $\dfrac{a}{b} = \dfrac{c}{b}$, $b \neq 0$, then $a = c$.

27. Show that if $\dfrac{a}{b} = \dfrac{c}{d}$, $b \neq 0$, $d \neq 0$, then $ad = bc$. (*Hint:* Multiply both sides by a suitable quantity.)

28. Is division commutative? That is, is $\dfrac{a}{b} = \dfrac{b}{a}$ for all non-zero a and b?

2.15   Multiplication of Fractions and Cancellation

The next theorem shows how the product of two fractions can be expressed as a fraction.

Theorem 11. $\dfrac{a}{b} \cdot \dfrac{c}{d} = \dfrac{ac}{bd}$, $b \neq 0$, $d \neq 0$.

This is the familiar rule for multiplying two fractions—one multiplies the two numerators to obtain the numerator of the product, and similarly for the denominator. For example,

$$\frac{2}{5} \cdot \frac{-4}{9} = \frac{2(-4)}{5 \cdot 9} = \frac{-8}{45}.$$

It is necessary that $b \neq 0$ and $d \neq 0$, for otherwise the fractions a/b and c/d would not exist.

Proof. $bd\left(\dfrac{a}{b} \cdot \dfrac{c}{d}\right) = bdab^{-1}cd^{-1} = ac$. Now apply Theorem 10 with bd in place of a in the statement of that theorem, $\dfrac{a}{b} \cdot \dfrac{c}{d}$ in place of x, and ac in place of b. Then $\dfrac{a}{b} \cdot \dfrac{c}{d} = \dfrac{ac}{bd}$.

We used Theorem 10 in this proof. Before using any theorem one must verify that its hypothesis is satisfied in every detail, for if it is not, the theorem cannot guarantee the conclusion. The hypothesis of Theorem 10 consists of two parts. The first, as used in the above proof, is $bd\left(\dfrac{a}{b}\cdot\dfrac{c}{d}\right)$ $= ac$, which we showed to be true. The second is that $bd \neq 0$, and this we did not verify. To settle this, we note that if bd were 0, then by Theorem 9, $b = 0$ or $d = 0$. Since both of these are specifically excluded, we can say $bd \neq 0$.

Illustration 1.

$$\frac{\frac{1}{2}}{5}\cdot\frac{3}{2} = \frac{(\frac{1}{2})3}{5\cdot 2} = \frac{\frac{3}{2}}{10}.$$

Illustration 2.

$$\frac{2}{7}\cdot\frac{a-x}{b} = \frac{2(a-x)}{7b}, \quad b \neq 0.$$

Theorem 12.   If $b \neq 0$ and $c \neq 0$, then $\dfrac{ac}{bc} = \dfrac{a}{b}$.

This theorem justifies the cancellation of like factors from the numerator and denominator, and when read backwards permits one to multiply the numerator and denominator by the same number. For example, $\dfrac{12}{30} = \dfrac{6\cdot 2}{15\cdot 2} = \dfrac{6}{15}$. Note the condition that c be different from zero. Overlooking this is a frequent source of error (see Illustrations 3 and 4).

Proof.   We have $\dfrac{c}{c} = c\cdot c^{-1} = 1$. Hence $\dfrac{a}{b} = \dfrac{a}{b}\cdot 1 = \dfrac{a}{b}\cdot\dfrac{c}{c} = \dfrac{ac}{bc}$ by Theorem 11.

Illustration 3.

$$\frac{3x^2}{5x} = \frac{3x\cdot x}{5\cdot x} = \frac{3x}{5} \quad \text{if } x \neq 0.$$

One frequently hears the following argument: $\dfrac{3x}{5} = 0$ if $x = 0$; since $\dfrac{3x}{5} = \dfrac{3x^2}{5x}, \dfrac{3x^2}{5x}$ must also be zero when $x = 0$. If $\dfrac{3x}{5}$ were equal to $\dfrac{3x^2}{5x}$ for all x, this reasoning would be correct, but this is not the case. The equality fails when $x = 0$, which unfortunately happens to be the value of x under consideration.

Illustration 4.

$$\frac{x^2 - y^2}{x - y} = \frac{(x+y)\,(x-y)}{1\cdot(x-y)} = \frac{x+y}{1} = x+y,$$

provided $x \neq y$. If x and y are the same number—say 5—the right side is 10 while the left is not a number at all, and of course the two are not equal. However, if $x = 6$ and $y = 2$, the left side is $\dfrac{36-4}{6-2} = \dfrac{32}{4} = \dfrac{8\cdot 4}{1\cdot 4} = \dfrac{8}{1} = 8$, which equals $x+y$.

Exercise A.　Find the values of $\dfrac{3x^2}{5x}$ and $\dfrac{3x}{5}$ when $x = 2, -6, 0$.

Exercise B.　Find the values of $\dfrac{x^2 - y^2}{x - y}$ and $x + y$ when $x = 3$ and $y = 7$; $x = 4$ and $y = -4$; $x = -1$ and $y = -1$.

Exercise C.　Where in the proof of Theorem 12 is the hypothesis $c \neq 0$ used?

Combining Theorems 11 and 12, we see that in a product of two or more fractions a factor appearing in any numerator can be cancelled against a like factor of any denominator. When simplifying a product of fractions this can be used to avoid some of the arithmetic.

Illustration 5.　Simplify $\dfrac{84}{78} \cdot \dfrac{143}{60}$.

$$\frac{84}{78} \cdot \frac{143}{60} = \frac{84 \cdot 143}{78 \cdot 60} \qquad\qquad \text{Theorem 11}$$

$$= \frac{7 \cdot 12 \cdot 11 \cdot 13}{6 \cdot 13 \cdot 5 \cdot 12}$$

$$= \frac{7 \cdot 11}{6 \cdot 5} \qquad\qquad \text{Theorem 12}$$

$$= \frac{77}{30}.$$

The direct procedure gives an answer that is equally correct, $\dfrac{84}{78} \cdot \dfrac{143}{60} = \dfrac{84 \cdot 143}{78 \cdot 60}$

$= \dfrac{12{,}012}{4{,}680}$, but entails more work. Also the reduction of the answer to lowest terms is not as easy.

Illustration 6.　Simplify $\dfrac{8x}{2x(a + x)}$.

$$\frac{8x}{2x(a + x)} = \frac{2 \cdot 4 \cdot x}{2x(a + x)} = \frac{4}{a + x}, \qquad x \neq 0, -a.$$

Since the original expression is meaningless if $x = 0$ or $-a$, we must exclude these values.

Illustration 7.　Simplify $\dfrac{x^2 + 2x - 3}{-2x^3 + 4x^2 + 30x}$.

$$\frac{x^2 + 2x - 3}{-2x^3 + 4x^2 + 30x} = \frac{(x + 3)(x - 1)}{-2x(x - 5)(x + 3)}$$

$$= \frac{x - 1}{-2x(x - 5)}, \qquad x \neq 0, 5, -3.$$

The numbers 0, 5, and -3 are the values of x that must be excluded.

Illustration 8.   Simplify $\dfrac{x}{2} \cdot \dfrac{6}{x^2(x-1)} \cdot \dfrac{7(x^2 + 4x - 5)}{3}$.

$$\frac{x}{2} \cdot \frac{6}{x^2(x-1)} \cdot \frac{7(x^2 + 4x - 5)}{3}$$

$$= \frac{x}{2} \cdot \frac{3 \cdot 2}{x \cdot x(x-1)} \cdot \frac{7(x-1)(x+5)}{3}$$

$$= \frac{7(x+5)}{x}, \qquad x \neq 0, 1.$$

One can cancel only if the quantity to be cancelled is a factor of both the numerator and denominator. Thus

$$\frac{ac}{(4+d)c} = \frac{a}{4+d},$$

since c is a factor of the numerator and denominator ($c = 0$ and $d = -4$ are, as usual, excluded). But most definitely

$$\frac{ac}{4+dc} \neq \frac{a}{4+d},$$

as can be verified by letting $a = 2$, $c = 3$, and $d = -1$. Here c is not a factor of the denominator.

The drift of the negative sign from the numerator to the denominator of a fraction, as in $-\dfrac{2}{5} = \dfrac{-2}{5} = \dfrac{2}{-5}$, is explained by the next theorem.

Theorem 13. $-\dfrac{a}{b} = \dfrac{-a}{b} = \dfrac{a}{-b}, \qquad b \neq 0.$

Proof.

$$-\frac{a}{b} = -(ab^{-1}) \qquad \text{definition of division}$$

$$= (-a)b^{-1} \qquad \text{Theorem 5}$$

$$= \frac{-a}{b}.$$

For the second part we have

$$\frac{-a}{b} = \frac{(-1)a}{(-1)(-b)} \qquad \text{Problem 15, Section 2.9}$$

$$= \frac{a}{-b}. \qquad \text{Theorem 12}$$

There are three places for plus and minus signs in a fraction: before the numerator, before the denominator, and in front of the fraction itself. Theorem 13 says that any two of these can be changed without affecting the value of the fraction.

Illustration 9.

(a)
$$- \frac{+(x-y)}{-7} = + \frac{-(x-y)}{-7}$$

by the first part of Theorem 13.

(b)
$$- \frac{+(x-y)}{-7} = + \frac{+(x-y)}{-(-7)} = + \frac{+(x-y)}{+7}$$

by the second part of Theorem 13.

Theorem 14. Let m and n be positive integers with m greater than n and $a \neq 0$. Then $\dfrac{a^m}{a^n} = a^{m-n}$ and $\dfrac{a^n}{a^m} = \dfrac{1}{a^{m-n}}$.

Proof. Since $m = n + (m - n)$, we have by Theorem 1 $a^m = a^n a^{m-n}$. (Why is $m - n$ a positive integer?) Hence

$$\frac{a^m}{a^n} = \frac{a^n a^{m-n}}{a^n \cdot 1} = \frac{a^{m-n}}{1} = a^{m-n}.$$

The second half of the theorem can be proved similarly.

Illustration 10.
$$\frac{6^5}{6^3} = \frac{6^3 \cdot 6^2}{6^3 \cdot 1} = \frac{6^2}{1} = 6^2 = 6^{5-3}.$$

Illustration 11.
$$\frac{a^6}{a^{17}} = \frac{1}{a^{11}}, \qquad a \neq 0.$$

Illustration 12. Simplify $\dfrac{-15x^6(x+2)^3}{9x^2(x^2-4)}$.

$$\frac{-15x^6(x+2)^3}{9x^2(x^2-4)} = \frac{3(-5)x^6(x+2)^3}{3^2 x^2(x+2)\,(x-2)}$$

$$= \frac{-5x^4(x+2)^2}{3(x-2)}, \qquad x \neq 0, \pm 2.$$

Exercise D. In the proof of Theorem 14 we cancelled a^n. This is permissible only if $a^n \neq 0$. Show that this is true.

PROBLEMS

1. Show that $\dfrac{1}{3} \cdot \dfrac{1}{4} = \dfrac{1}{12}$.

2. Show that $\dfrac{ax}{a} = x, \qquad a \neq 0.$

3. Write with a negative sign in the numerator

    (a) $-\dfrac{7}{2}$;   (b) $\dfrac{a+x}{5}$;   (c) $-\dfrac{1}{-4}$.

4. Show that $\dfrac{-a}{-b} = \dfrac{a}{b}$, $\quad b \neq 0$.

5. Show that $-\dfrac{a}{b+c} = \dfrac{a}{-b-c}$, $\quad b \neq -c$.

6. Reduce the number of minus signs to a minimum and simplify. Which values of the letters must be excluded?

   (a) $-\dfrac{5}{-a}$; $\quad$ (b) $\dfrac{-6(-x)}{-b-c}$; $\quad$ (c) $-\dfrac{-8}{2}$; $\quad$ (d) $\dfrac{(a+b)^2}{-3a-3b}$.

7. Carry out the details of the proof of the second half of Theorem 14 for $a = 5$, $m = 7$, $n = 4$.

*8. *Theorem.* If n is a positive integer and $b \neq 0$, $\left(\dfrac{a}{b}\right)^n = \dfrac{a^n}{b^n}$.

   (a) Illustrate this theorem for $a = 6$, $b = 3$, $n = 3$.
   (b) Prove the theorem.

9. Show that $\left(\dfrac{a}{b}\right)^{-1} = \dfrac{b}{a}$, $\quad a \neq 0$, $\quad b \neq 0$.

Simplify if possible:

10. $\dfrac{3 \cdot 4}{4 \cdot 2}$.

11. $\dfrac{2 \cdot 5}{5}$.

12. $\dfrac{64}{-96}$.

13. $\dfrac{79}{27}$.

14. $\dfrac{72}{108}$.

15. $\dfrac{3a}{2a+b}$.

16. $\dfrac{-20a}{55a^2b}$.

17. $\dfrac{35(-a^2)}{140(-a)^2}$.

18. $\dfrac{30(-a^3)}{6(-a)^3}$.

Supply the missing part of the fraction:

19. $\dfrac{4}{9} = \dfrac{}{45}$.

20. $\dfrac{2a}{5} = \dfrac{}{15a}$.

21. $\dfrac{-x-y}{7(a+c)} = \dfrac{(x+y)^2}{}$.

22. By substituting specific numbers show that

$$\dfrac{-ax + 2(x+y)}{5x} \neq \dfrac{-a + 2y}{5} \text{ for all } x \text{ and } y.$$

23. Is $\dfrac{(-a)c}{a(b+c)} = -\dfrac{c}{b+c}$?

24. Prove that $\dfrac{a}{b} \cdot \dfrac{c}{d} \cdot \dfrac{e}{f} = \dfrac{ace}{bdf}$. Which values of the letters must be excluded?

Simplify if possible, and show which values of the letters must be excluded:

25. $\dfrac{49}{35}$.

26. $\dfrac{24a}{60a}$.

27. $\dfrac{3a(a-b)}{2a(a-b)}$.

28. $\dfrac{a^{10}}{a^2}$.

29. $\dfrac{25x^5a^2}{15(-a)x^2}$.

30. $\dfrac{(x+y)^2}{x+y}$.

31. $\dfrac{x^2+y^2}{x+y}$.

32. $\dfrac{2x^4}{(2x)^4}$.

33. $\dfrac{ax^n}{(ax)^n}$, n a positive integer.

34. $\dfrac{x}{x^7+x^2}$.

35. $\dfrac{6a}{-7a+2a^2}$.

36. $\dfrac{(x+y)^3}{(x+y)^2}$.

37. $\dfrac{a(z-w)^5}{(z-w)^4a^4}$.

38. $\dfrac{4a^2-x^2}{2ay-xy}$.

39. $\dfrac{-3x^2-5x+2}{3x^2-x}$.

40. $\dfrac{cb+3bd+7b}{bd^2-bx^2}$.

41. $\dfrac{3x^2-5ax-2a^2}{3x^2+4ax+a^2}$.

42. $\dfrac{x^4-b^4}{x+b}$.

43. $\dfrac{x^2-4}{x^2+(a-2)x-2a}$.

44. $\dfrac{x^3-x}{-x^2y+xy}$.

45. $\dfrac{x}{x^7+c}$.

Simplify:

46. $\dfrac{(x+1)-(x-1)}{(x+1)^2}$.

47. $\dfrac{x^2\cdot 3x^2-(x^3+8)2x}{x^4}$.

48. $\dfrac{3x^3+6x(x+2)-12x}{(x^2-4)^2}$.

49. $\dfrac{(x+1)^2 2x-(x^2-1)2(x+1)}{(x+1)^4}$.

50. $\dfrac{(5x-3)7-(7x+2)5}{(5x-3)^2}$.

Express as a fraction and simplify. Which values of the letters must be excluded?

51. $6\left(\dfrac{13}{16}\right)$.

52. $\dfrac{4}{7}\cdot\dfrac{x}{3d}$.

53. $8^{-1}\cdot 4$.

54. $a^{-1}b$.

55. $\dfrac{3y}{8y}\cdot\dfrac{4ax}{6y}$.

56. $\dfrac{9xw}{16x^3}\cdot\dfrac{4x^5}{3xw}$.

57. $5xb^{-1}$.

58. $(5xb)^{-1}$.

59. $\dfrac{xy^2}{x^3(a^2 - b^2)} \, x(a^2 - b) \cdot \dfrac{1}{y}$.

60. $\dfrac{(x + y)^2}{(x + y)(x - 3)} \, (x^2 + 9)$.

61. $(d^2 - w^2) \dfrac{5a}{cd - wc}$.

62. $(x + y)^{-1}x$.

63. $(x + y)^{-1}(x + y)$.

64. $(x + 2a)^{-1}$.

65. $a(3y - 2x)^{-1}$.

66. $\dfrac{1}{3ab} \cdot \dfrac{x}{x - 5} \cdot \dfrac{-9(x^2 - 25)a^2b^3}{x}$.

67. $\dfrac{25x^2 - 1}{16 - a^2} \cdot \dfrac{a^2 + 4a}{6x - 2}$.

68. $\dfrac{2x^2 - x - 10}{2x^2 + 5x + 3} \cdot \dfrac{2x^2 - 5x - 12}{12x - 30}$.

69. $\dfrac{(2a - c)ac}{a^2 + ac - 2c^2} \, (c^2 - a^2)$.

70. $\dfrac{1}{a^2} \cdot \dfrac{x^2 + (a^2 - x^2)}{x^2}$.

71. $\dfrac{4x - 4}{x^2 - 1} \cdot \dfrac{-3x - 3}{x + 4} \cdot \dfrac{9x^2 - 1}{x^2 + 2x + 1}$.

72. $\dfrac{x^2 + ax - 6a^2}{-5a} \cdot \dfrac{5(a^2x^2 + 6a^3x - 7a^4)}{x^2 - 3ax + 2a^2}$.

73. $\dfrac{x}{a^2 - b^2} \cdot \dfrac{a^2 + ab}{6(x - 7)} \cdot \dfrac{10x^2 - 40x - 210}{2x^4 + 3x^3}$.

Factor:

74. $\dfrac{1}{x^2} - \dfrac{1}{25}$.   75. $\dfrac{1}{a^2} + \dfrac{2}{ay} + \dfrac{1}{y^2}$.   76. $\dfrac{1}{a^2x} + \dfrac{1}{xb^2} - \dfrac{1}{x^2ab}$.

77. Prove Theorem 11 by using Problem 19, Section 2.13.

78. Show that the set F of all rational numbers is closed under multiplication.

2.16 Addition of Fractions

The sum of two fractions can also be expressed as a fraction, but the result is not so simple as it is for products.

Theorem 15. $\dfrac{a}{b} + \dfrac{c}{d} = \dfrac{ad + bc}{bd}$, $b \neq 0, \, d \neq 0$.

Proof.

$$\frac{a}{b} + \frac{c}{d} = \frac{ad}{bd} + \frac{bc}{bd} \qquad\qquad \text{Theorem 12}$$

$$= ad\left(\frac{1}{bd}\right) + bc\left(\frac{1}{bd}\right) \qquad \begin{array}{l}\text{Remark following the} \\ \text{definition of division}\end{array}$$

$$= (ad + bc)\frac{1}{bd}$$

$$= \frac{ad + bc}{bd}.$$

Illustration 1. Express $\dfrac{7}{12} + \dfrac{5}{18}$ as a fraction.

$$\frac{7}{12} + \frac{5}{18} = \frac{7 \cdot 18}{12 \cdot 18} + \frac{12 \cdot 5}{12 \cdot 18} = 126\left(\frac{1}{216}\right) + 60\left(\frac{1}{216}\right)$$

$$= (126 + 60)\frac{1}{216} = \frac{126 + 60}{216} = \frac{186}{216}.$$

Since 186 and 216 have common factors, the answer can be simplified:

$$\frac{186}{216} = \frac{31 \cdot 6}{36 \cdot 6} = \frac{31}{36}.$$

Illustration 2. Express $\dfrac{3}{ab^2} + \dfrac{2}{a^2b}$ as a fraction.

$$\frac{3}{ab^2} + \frac{2}{a^2b} = \frac{3(a^2b)}{ab^2(a^2b)} + \frac{(ab^2)2}{(ab^2)a^2b}, \qquad a \neq 0,\, b \neq 0,$$

$$= 3a^2b\left(\frac{1}{a^3b^3}\right) + 2ab^2\left(\frac{1}{a^3b^3}\right)$$

$$= (3a^2b + 2ab^2)\frac{1}{a^3b^3}$$

$$= \frac{3a^2b + 2ab^2}{a^3b^3}.$$

Again, the numerator and denominator have non-zero common factors, which can be cancelled to simplify the answer:

$$\frac{3a^2b + 2ab^2}{a^3b^3} = \frac{(3a + 2b)ab}{a^2b^2 \cdot ab} = \frac{3a + 2b}{a^2b^2}.$$

The crux of the proof of Theorem 15 is the replacement of the original fractions by equivalent ones with equal denominators. Although bd can always be used as such a common denominator, frequently a simpler one can be found, and when this is possible the arithmetic is easier. In Illustration 1, 36 is a possible denominator. Using this, we have

$$\frac{7}{12} + \frac{5}{18} = \frac{7 \cdot 3}{12 \cdot 3} + \frac{5 \cdot 2}{18 \cdot 2} = 21\left(\frac{1}{36}\right) + 10\left(\frac{1}{36}\right)$$

$$= (21 + 10)\frac{1}{36} = \frac{31}{36}.$$

In Illustration 2, a^2b^2 is a simpler common denominator then a^3b^3. Using this, the work is as follows:

$$\frac{3}{ab^2} + \frac{2}{a^2b} = \frac{3a}{a^2b^2} + \frac{2b}{a^2b^2} = 3a\left(\frac{1}{a^2b^2}\right) + 2b\left(\frac{1}{a^2b^2}\right)$$

$$= (3a + 2b)\frac{1}{a^2b^2} = \frac{3a + 2b}{a^2b^2}.$$

To find a simple common denominator, one looks for the simplest quantity that is a multiple of both denominators.

Exercise A.   Show that $\dfrac{a}{u} + \dfrac{b}{u} + \dfrac{c}{u} = \dfrac{a+b+c}{u}$, $u \neq 0$.

Illustration 3.   Express

$$\frac{1}{2(y-2a)} + \frac{5}{a} + \frac{y}{y^2 - 4a^2}$$

as a fraction and simplify the result.

A common denominator is $2(y-2a)a(y^2 - 4a^2)$, but since $y^2 - 4a^2 = (y-2a)(y+2a)$, we see that a simpler one is $2a(y^2 - 4a^2)$. Replacing each fraction by an equivalent one with this as a denominator, we have

$$\frac{1}{2(y-2a)} + \frac{5}{a} + \frac{y}{y^2 - 4a^2}$$

$$= \frac{a(y+2a)}{2a(y^2 - 4a^2)} + \frac{5 \cdot 2(y^2 - 4a^2)}{2a(y^2 - 4a^2)} + \frac{y \cdot 2a}{2a(y^2 - 4a^2)},   \quad a \neq 0,\ y \neq \pm 2a,$$

$$= \frac{a(y+2a) + 10(y^2 - 4a^2) + 2ay}{2a(y^2 - 4a^2)}$$

$$= \frac{10y^2 + 3ay - 38a^2}{2a(y^2 - 4a^2)}.$$

Subtraction is just as easily performed by the simple device of writing $\dfrac{a}{b} - \dfrac{c}{d}$ as $\dfrac{a}{b} + \dfrac{-c}{d}$ and proceeding as before.

Illustration 4.   Express $\dfrac{1}{x^2} - \dfrac{2}{5x(x-1)}$ as a fraction.

$$\frac{1}{x^2} - \frac{2}{5x(x-1)} = \frac{5(x-1)}{x^2 \cdot 5(x-1)} + \frac{-2x}{5x^2(x-1)},   \quad x \neq 0,\ 1,$$

$$= \frac{5(x-1) - 2x}{5x^2(x-1)} = \frac{3x - 5}{5x^2(x-1)}.$$

Illustration 5.   Express $4(x+2) + \dfrac{x}{3(x-1)}$ as a fraction.

$$4(x+2) + \frac{x}{3(x-1)} = \frac{4(x+2)3(x-1)}{3(x-1)} + \frac{x}{3(x-1)},   \quad x \neq 1,$$

$$= \frac{12(x^2 + x - 2) + x}{3(x-1)}$$

$$= \frac{12x^2 + 13x - 24}{3(x-1)}.$$

When simplifying an expression that is a sum or product, it generally is best first to simplify each term or factor before combining them.

Illustration 6. Simplify $\left(x + \dfrac{2ax}{x - 2a}\right)\left(x - \dfrac{4a^2}{x}\right)$.

$$\left(x + \frac{2ax}{x - 2a}\right)\left(x - \frac{4a^2}{x}\right) = \frac{x(x - 2a) + 2ax}{x - 2a} \cdot \frac{x^2 - 4a^2}{x}, \qquad x \neq 0, 2a,$$

$$= \frac{x^2}{x - 2a} \cdot \frac{(x + 2a)\,(x - 2a)}{x}.$$

Up to this point we have worked with the factors separately, simplifying each and factoring the numerator of the second factor preparatory to cancelling $x - 2a$. Now we combine them, obtaining

$$\frac{x^2}{x - 2a} \cdot \frac{(x + 2a)\,(x - 2a)}{x} = x(x + 2a).$$

In the original expression x cannot equal 0 or $2a$. For all other x's the expression is equal to $x(x + 2a)$.

The removal of any common factors of the terms of a sum will usually make the addition easier, as in the next illustration.

Illustration 7. Simplify

$$\frac{x}{3x - 1}\,2(x + 2) + (x + 2)^3\frac{3x - 1 - 3x}{(3x - 1)^2}.$$

Since $x + 2$ and $\dfrac{1}{3x - 1}$ are factors of both terms, we remove these and obtain

$$\frac{x}{3x - 1}\,2(x + 2) + (x + 2)^3\frac{3x - 1 - 3x}{(3x - 1)^2}$$

$$= \frac{x + 2}{3x - 1}\left(2x + (x + 2)^2\frac{-1}{3x - 1}\right), \qquad x \neq \frac{1}{3},$$

$$= \frac{x + 2}{3x - 1} \cdot \frac{2x(3x - 1) - (x + 2)^2}{3x - 1}$$

$$= \frac{(x + 2)\,(5x^2 - 6x - 4)}{(3x - 1)^2}.$$

It is often difficult to decide on the form in which to leave an answer. Algebra is a tool for solving certain mathematical problems, and algebraic manipulations are not ends in themselves, but merely means of solving these problems. The form in which an expression is left is dictated by the uses intended for it. For some applications fractions are best left in a form in which the numerator is factored; for others it is better to leave the numerator as a sum. Since many of the problems in this book are exercises intended to develop manipulative skill, they can contain no inherent indication of the best form in which to leave the answer. For our purposes let us agree that in the absence of specific directions answers are to be left in the form that looks best. This, of course, makes it a matter of individual taste, but usually opinions on this point differ only in minor details. Generally it will be the form that is most compact. Thus there is little to choose between

$$\frac{3x + 3}{(x - 2)(x - 4)}$$

and

$$\frac{3(x + 1)}{(x - 2)(x - 4)},$$

but everyone would agree that

$$\frac{1}{5}(x^2 + 7)$$

is better than

$$\frac{1}{10}(2x^2 + 14).$$

Since it is important to know which values of the letters make the denominators of fractions zero, denominators are often left in factored form so that it will be easier to find these critical values.

PROBLEMS

Find two common multiples and the least or simplest common multiple of each of the following:

1. 6, 8.
2. 5, 7.
3. 8, 10, 12.

4. $8x, 12x^2$.
5. $a(x + 2), x^2 + 5x + 6$.
6. $x^2 - 3x - 4, 2x^3 - 4x^2 - 16x$.

7. Show by an example that $\dfrac{a}{b} + \dfrac{c}{d} \neq \dfrac{a + c}{b + d}$.

8. Express as fractions with a common denominator. Which values of the letters must be excluded?

(a) $\dfrac{7}{4}, \dfrac{-1}{8}$;

(b) $\dfrac{2}{6}, \dfrac{1}{9}$;

(c) $\dfrac{2}{5}, \dfrac{4}{7}$;

(d) $\dfrac{7}{4}, 3$;

(e) $\dfrac{2}{8}, \dfrac{3}{-12}$;

(f) $\dfrac{1}{a}, \dfrac{1}{2a}$;

(g) $\dfrac{3}{280}, \dfrac{5}{490}$;

(h) $\dfrac{2}{5}, \dfrac{5}{12}, \dfrac{4}{15}$;

(i) $\dfrac{1}{x + 2}, \dfrac{1}{x}$;

(j) $\dfrac{5x + 1}{(x + 2)(x - 7)}, \dfrac{1}{(x - 7)(x - 1)}$;

(k) $\dfrac{b}{y^2 - b^2}, \dfrac{y}{(y - b)^2}$;

(l) $\dfrac{x - 6}{2x^2 + 5x - 3}, \dfrac{x - 3}{x^2 - 9}$;

(m) $\dfrac{2x^2 - 7x}{x^2 + 10x + 25}, \dfrac{3x + 10}{2x^2 + 15x + 25}$.

9. Express the sum of each pair of fractions in Problem 8 as a fraction and simplify.

10. Express the product of each pair of fractions in Problem 8 as a fraction and simplify.

Express as a fraction and simplify. Check by making the substitutions where indicated.

11. $\dfrac{5}{2} - \dfrac{3}{7} + \dfrac{1}{3}.$

12. $-16 + \dfrac{3}{4}.$

13. $\dfrac{3}{4} + \dfrac{1}{6} - \dfrac{2}{9}.$

14. $3^{-1} + 7.$

15. $5^{-1} - 2^{-1}.$

16. $\dfrac{x}{y} + \dfrac{2x}{5y};\ x = -5,\ y = 10.$

17. $-\dfrac{2}{x^2} + \dfrac{6}{x^3};\ x = -2.$

18. $x + \dfrac{2a}{x^2};\ a = 16,\ x = 2.$

19. $\dfrac{8}{a^2} - \dfrac{c}{ab};\ a = 2,\ b = 1,\ c = 3.$

20. $-\dfrac{u}{v} + \dfrac{v}{u};\ u = 7,\ v = 3.$

21. $x^{-1} + y.$

22. $a^{-1} - 2b^{-1}.$

23. $a^{-1} - (2b)^{-1}.$

24. $\dfrac{x-4}{x-2} + \dfrac{3-4x}{2-x};\ x = 5.$

25. $-x - 1 + \dfrac{x^2}{x-1}.$

26. $\dfrac{4}{3a^2y^3} - \dfrac{a-y}{2ay};\ a = -1,\ y = 2.$

27. $x(b + x^2)^{-1}.$

28. $(x + a)^{-1}x + a.$

29. $\dfrac{1}{3(x+3)x} + \dfrac{9-x^2}{x(x+3)^2}.$

30. $\dfrac{1}{x+y} - \dfrac{1}{x-y} + \dfrac{2x}{x^2-y^2};\ x = 2,\ y = 0.$

31. $\dfrac{x}{x-1} + x.$

32. $-\dfrac{2y-5}{y+3} + \dfrac{3y}{4y+1}.$

33. $\dfrac{1}{b-1} - \dfrac{b+8}{b^2+3b-4}.$

34. $x^2(x+y)^{-1} - (x+y).$

35. $1 - x + x^2 - \dfrac{x^3}{1+x}.$

36. $2z + \dfrac{az}{z-a} + \dfrac{z^2}{a-z}.$

37. $\dfrac{x^2}{x^2+3x+1} - \dfrac{7x-3}{x-1}.$

38. $\dfrac{3}{x} + 2 - \dfrac{x-1}{x^2+3x}.$

39. $\dfrac{x}{x^2+2x} + 3x + 6.$

40. $\dfrac{y^2}{x^2-2xy+y^2} + \dfrac{x+y}{x-y}.$

41. $\dfrac{x}{x^2-3x-10} + \dfrac{7}{x^2-6x+5} \cdot \dfrac{1}{2}.$

42. $\dfrac{3x-1}{3x^2+5x-2} + \dfrac{5x-10}{x^2-4}.$

43. $\dfrac{1}{x^3+9x^2} - \dfrac{1}{x^3-9x}.$

44. $\dfrac{y-3}{y^2-y-6} - \dfrac{3y+2}{2y^2-y-15} + \dfrac{2y-1}{2y^2+9y+10}.$

45. $\dfrac{3a+2b}{6a^2-ab-b^2} + \dfrac{ab}{2a^2-9ab+4b^2} - \dfrac{a+b}{3a^2-11ab-4b^2}.$

46. $\left(\dfrac{x}{9a} - \dfrac{a}{x}\right)\dfrac{6a^2x^4}{x+3a}.$

48. $\left(y + \dfrac{1}{y} - 2\right)\dfrac{y^3}{y^2-1}.$

47. $\dfrac{a-x}{a^2+x^2}\left(\dfrac{x}{x-a} - \dfrac{a}{x+a}\right).$

49. $\left(1 - \dfrac{2xy}{x^2+y^2}\right)\dfrac{(x^2+y^2)^2}{x^2-y^2}.$

Simplify:

50. $\dfrac{9-x^2}{x+3} + 3 - x + a.$

51. $-x + 4 + \dfrac{x^2+3x-10}{x+5}.$

52. $-\dfrac{2}{x^3} + \dfrac{1}{5}\left[x \cdot 2(x+1) + (x+1)^2\right].$

53. $\dfrac{2x-1}{x+3}\, 2(7x+4)7 + (7x+4)^2\dfrac{(x+3)2 - (2x-1)}{(x+3)^2}.$

54. $\dfrac{(-4x+3)(2x+5) - (x^2+5x)(-4)}{(-4x+3)^2} + 12x.$

55. $\dfrac{(x+1)^2\, 2(x-1) - (x-1)^2\, 2(x+1)}{(x+1)^4}.$

56. $\dfrac{y^4\, 4(y^2+1)^3\, 2y - (y^2+1)^4\, 4y^3}{y^8}.$

Find numbers a and b, not involving x, such that

57. $\dfrac{3x-6}{x^2-3x} = \dfrac{a}{x} + \dfrac{b}{x-3}.$

58. $\dfrac{3}{x^2-2x-8} = \dfrac{a}{x-4} + \dfrac{b}{x+2}.$

59. Express $\dfrac{2}{x^2-25}$ as a sum of two fractions.

2.17 Division of Fractions

In elementary arithmetic one learns that fractions whose numerators and denominators are themselves fractions can be simplified by multiplying the numerator by the inverted denominator, as in

$$\frac{\dfrac{10}{3}}{\dfrac{25}{7}} = \frac{10}{3}\cdot\frac{7}{25} = \frac{2}{3}\cdot\frac{7}{5} = \frac{14}{15}.$$

That the same procedure can be used to simplify algebraic fractions should not be surprising, when one remembers that the letters in an algebraic expression stand for numbers. For example,

$$\frac{\dfrac{a}{x^2 - a^2}}{\dfrac{2}{b(x + a)}} = \frac{a}{x^2 - a^2} \cdot \frac{b(x + a)}{2}$$

$$= \frac{ab}{2(x - a)}, \qquad x \neq \pm a, \ b \neq 0.$$

The proof of the next theorem shows the correctness of this rule.

Theorem 16. $\quad \dfrac{\dfrac{a}{b}}{\dfrac{c}{d}} = \dfrac{a}{b} \cdot \dfrac{d}{c}, \qquad b \neq 0, \ c \neq 0, \ d \neq 0.$

Proof. $\quad \dfrac{\dfrac{a}{b}}{\dfrac{c}{d}} = \dfrac{\dfrac{a}{b} \cdot \dfrac{d}{c}}{\dfrac{c}{d} \cdot \dfrac{d}{c}} = \dfrac{\dfrac{a}{b} \cdot \dfrac{d}{c}}{1} = \dfrac{a}{b} \cdot \dfrac{d}{c}, \qquad b \neq 0, \ c \neq 0, \ d \neq 0.$

Corollary. $\quad \dfrac{\dfrac{a}{b}}{c} = \dfrac{a}{bc}, \text{ and } \dfrac{a}{\dfrac{b}{c}} = \dfrac{ac}{b}, \qquad b \neq 0, \ c \neq 0.$

Proof. In the fraction $\dfrac{\dfrac{a}{b}}{c}$ replace c by $\dfrac{c}{1}$ and use the theorem. The second part is similarly proved.

Exercise A. Carry out the details of the proof of Theorem 16 with (a) $a = 2$, $b = 3$, $c = 8$, $d = 7$; (b) $a = -3$, $b = x + 5$, $c = c$, $d = x^2 + x - 20$.

Exercise B. Compute $\dfrac{\dfrac{60}{5}}{\dfrac{28}{-7}}$ in two ways.

Theorem 16 can be used only with fractions whose numerators and denominators are quotients. Thus

$$\frac{\dfrac{a}{y}}{x + \dfrac{3}{y}} \neq \frac{a}{y} \cdot \frac{y}{x + 3} = \frac{a}{x + 3}.$$

Here the denominator is a sum, and Theorem 16 does not apply. If the denominator is first expressed as a quotient, however, the theorem can be used:

$$\frac{\dfrac{a}{y}}{x+\dfrac{3}{y}} = \frac{\dfrac{a}{y}}{\dfrac{(xy+3)}{y}} = \frac{a}{y}\cdot\frac{y}{xy+3}$$

$$= \frac{a}{xy+3}, \qquad y \neq 0,\ x \neq -\frac{3}{y}.$$

In general, when simplifying a fraction the best procedure is to simplify the numerator and denominator separately. Then, if it applies, use Theorem 16 or its corollary to simplify the resulting quotient.

Illustration. Simplify

$$\frac{\dfrac{1}{1+y}+\dfrac{1}{1-y}}{\dfrac{1}{1-y}-\dfrac{1}{1+y}}.$$

We first simplify the numerator and denominator, which are sums:

(1)
$$\frac{\dfrac{1}{1+y}+\dfrac{1}{1-y}}{\dfrac{1}{1-y}-\dfrac{1}{1+y}} = \frac{\dfrac{(1-y)+(1+y)}{(1+y)(1-y)}}{\dfrac{(1+y)-(1-y)}{(1-y)(1+y)}} = \frac{\dfrac{2}{(1+y)(1-y)}}{\dfrac{2y}{(1-y)(1+y)}}.$$

With the numerator and denominator now in the form of quotients, we can apply Theorem 16 to obtain

(2)
$$\frac{2}{(1+y)(1-y)}\cdot\frac{(1-y)(1+y)}{2y} = \frac{1}{y}.$$

It is obvious that y cannot equal ± 1 in the original fraction. What is not so obvious is that y also cannot equal zero. This would have been noticed, however, by the time the last fraction in (1) was reached and again in the final result $1/y$.

PROBLEMS

1. Prove the second part of the corollary.

2. Is division associative? That is, is $\dfrac{\left(\dfrac{a}{b}\right)}{c} = \dfrac{a}{\left(\dfrac{b}{c}\right)}$?

Simplify and check by substituting the values where given:

3. $\dfrac{\dfrac{8}{13}}{\dfrac{2}{5}}.$ 4. $\dfrac{\dfrac{4}{-5}}{\dfrac{-1}{2}}.$ 5. $\dfrac{7}{\dfrac{2}{5}}.$ 6. $\dfrac{\dfrac{7}{2}}{5}.$ 7. $\dfrac{1}{\dfrac{1}{x+y}}.$

8. $\dfrac{\dfrac{d}{1}}{1}.$

9. $\dfrac{2 + \dfrac{2}{6}}{1 + \dfrac{3}{4}}.$

10. $\dfrac{8^{-1} + 3}{2}.$

11. $\dfrac{2a^{-1} + a}{7b}.$

12. $\dfrac{2}{\dfrac{1}{z + 3}}.$

13. $\dfrac{\dfrac{a}{b}}{\dfrac{2a}{b + c}}; a = 1, b = 2, c = 3.$

14. $\dfrac{x^{-1}}{y^{-1}}.$

15. $\dfrac{x^2 - y^2}{\dfrac{x - y}{x + y}}; x = 5, y = 3.$

16. $\dfrac{\dfrac{x^2 - y^2}{x - y}}{x + y}; x = 5, y = 3.$

17. $\dfrac{\dfrac{1}{a} + \dfrac{1}{b}}{\dfrac{1}{a} - \dfrac{1}{b}}; a = 3, b = 5.$

18. $\frac{1}{2}(a^{-1} - b^{-1}).$

19. $\dfrac{\dfrac{c}{2} - \dfrac{1}{2c}}{\dfrac{c}{4} - \dfrac{1}{4c}}; c = -3.$

20. $\dfrac{\dfrac{2x}{x + a} - 1}{\dfrac{x}{x + a} - 1}; a = 2, x = 4.$

21. $\dfrac{9x^2 - 4}{1 + \dfrac{2}{3x}}; x = -1.$

22. $\dfrac{\dfrac{6}{b^2} - \dfrac{13}{ab} - \dfrac{5}{a^2}}{2a - 5b}; a = 1, b = -1.$

23. $\dfrac{z + \dfrac{z}{y}}{1 + \dfrac{1}{y}}.$

24. $\dfrac{1 + \dfrac{x}{x^2 - 4}}{x + 2}.$

25. $\dfrac{1 - \dfrac{8x}{x^2 - 9}}{\dfrac{x - 9}{x - 3}}.$

26. $\dfrac{2 + \dfrac{1}{x}}{x} + 5x^2 + 2x - 1.$

27. $1 + \dfrac{1}{2 + \dfrac{1}{3 + x}}.$

28. $\dfrac{(x + 3)^2 - x \cdot 2(x + 3)}{(x + 3)^4} + 2(x + 3).$

29. $\dfrac{\dfrac{u}{u + 6} - \dfrac{u}{u - 3}}{\dfrac{u + 6}{u - 6} - \dfrac{u - 6}{u + 6}}.$

30. $\dfrac{\dfrac{1}{x - 1} + \dfrac{1}{x^2 - 1}}{x + 2} - \dfrac{6}{x}.$

31. Simplify $\dfrac{\dfrac{x - 7}{x + 7} - \dfrac{x + 7}{x - 7}}{\dfrac{x^2 + 49}{x^2 - 49} + 1}.$ Which values of x must be excluded?

32. Show that $\dfrac{\dfrac{x+y}{x-y}+\dfrac{x-y}{x+y}}{\dfrac{x+y}{x-y}-\dfrac{x-y}{x+y}} = \dfrac{x^2+y^2}{2xy}.$ Which values of x and y must be ex-

cluded?

33. Show that the set of all rational numbers except zero is closed under division.
34. Let S be the set of all rational numbers expressible in the form $a/2^n$, where a is an integer and n is a positive integer. Show that S is closed under addition, subtraction, and multiplication, but not under division.

2.18 Fields

The set F of all rational numbers is closed under addition and multiplication, and the associative, commutative, and distributive axioms hold for all numbers in F. Zero and one are in F. A rational number $-a$ exists for each rational a, and if a is in F and not equal to 0, so is a^{-1}. Therefore, the zero, negative, identity, and reciprocal axioms hold in F. Hence all the theorems about the real numbers derived in this chapter would be equally true if we had limited ourselves to the set of all rational numbers.

The rational numbers are not unique in this respect. There are other sets of numbers closed under addition and multiplication and satisfying the above axioms. Indeed, one can go further. There are sets whose elements are not numbers, but which can be combined in a way resembling addition and multiplication so that the sum and product is again in the set and all the axioms hold. Such systems are called fields.

Definition. A *field* is a set K of elements in which two operations, called addition and multiplication, are defined such that the following axioms hold:

Closure axiom.   For all a and b in K, $a + b$ and ab are in K.

Associative axioms. For all a, b, and c in K,
1. $(a + b) + c = a + (b + c)$
2. $(ab)c = a(bc)$

Commutative axioms. For all a and b in K,
1. $a + b = b + a$
2. $ab = ba$

Distributive axioms.   For a, b, and c in K,
1. $a(b + c) = ab + ac$
2. $(b + c)a = ba + ca$

Zero axiom.   There is an element of K, called *zero* and denoted by 0, such that for any element a of K, $a + 0 = a$ and $0 + a = a$.

Negative axiom.   To each element a of K there corresponds an element of K, denoted by $-a$, such that $a + (-a) = 0$ and $-a + a = 0$.

Identity axiom. There is an element of K, called the *identity* element and denoted by 1, such that for any element a of K, $a \cdot 1 = a$ and $1 \cdot a = a$.

Reciprocal axiom. To each element a of K, $a \neq 0$, there corresponds an element of K, denoted by a^{-1}, such that $aa^{-1} = 1$ and $a^{-1}a = 1$.

Loosely speaking, a field is a system in which one can add, subtract, multiply, and divide and whose elements behave like real numbers with respect to such operations. The axioms for a field say nothing about the magnitudes of its elements nor do they guarantee that an element has, for example, a cube root. Many fields, in particular the real field, have such properties, but others do not. In any case, additional axioms are necessary to derive them.

All the theorems in this chapter about the real numbers were derived using only the above axioms. Nowhere did we use any intrinsic properties of the real numbers. Therefore, using these axioms and following the same proofs, one could prove that the same theorems are valid in any field. For example, we would know that for any field if $ab = 0$, then $a = 0$ or $b = 0$. It is economical, then, to study abstract fields, since any theorem about them is true not only for the real and rational fields, but for all other fields as well. In Chapter 4 we shall discuss complex numbers from this point of view.

The set of axioms for a field that we have given is by no means unique, and many others are possible. Our development of the algebraic properties of the real numbers is a standard one first presented by E. V. Huntington in the *Transactions of the American Mathematical Society*, Vol. 4 (1903).

PROBLEMS

1. Is it true that every positive rational number has a rational square root?

2. Let S be the set of all real numbers expressible in the form $a + b\sqrt{2}$, where a and b are rational. For example, $2 + 5\sqrt{2}$ and $\frac{11}{4} - 7\sqrt{2}$ are in S, but $\pi + \frac{2}{9}\sqrt{2}$ is not. If $\alpha = a + b\sqrt{2}$ and $\beta = c + d\sqrt{2}$, where a, b, c, d are rational, are any two elements of S, then their sum $\alpha + \beta$ can be expressed as $(a + c) + (b + d)\sqrt{2}$. Since $a + c$ and $b + d$ are rational, $\alpha + \beta$ is in S and S is closed under addition.

   (a) Show that S is closed under subtraction and multiplication.
   (b) Show that 0 and 1 are in S.
   (c) If α is in S and $-\alpha$ is the number for which $\alpha + (-\alpha) = 0$, is $-\alpha$ in S?
   (d) If α is in S and $\alpha \neq 0$, show that α^{-1} is in S by writing it in the form $c + d\sqrt{2}$, where c and d are rational.
   (e) Is S a field?
   (f) Show that $F \subset S$, where F is the rational field.

3. Did any particular properties of the number 2 enter into Problem 2? For each

positive integer m let S_m be the set of all real numbers expressible in the form $a + b\sqrt{m}$, where a and b are rational. For which m do you conjecture that S_m will be a field different from the rational field?

4. Let V be the set of three elements a, b, and c and let two operations called addition ($+$) and multiplication ($\cdot$) be defined in V according to the following tables (to be read like an ordinary multiplication table):

$+$	a	b	c
a	a	b	c
b	b	c	a
c	c	a	b

$\cdot$	a	b	c
a	a	a	a
b	a	b	c
c	a	c	b

For example, $b + c = a$, and $b \cdot c = c$.

(a) Find $c + b$, $c + c$, $a \cdot c$, and $c \cdot b$.

(b) Is V closed under addition and multiplication?

(c) Is there an element z in V such that $x + z = x$ for all x in V?

(d) Verify that $(c + c) + a = c + (c + a)$ and $(b \cdot c) \cdot b = b \cdot (c \cdot b)$.

(e) Is V commutative under addition and multiplication?

(f) Verify the distributive law in three instances.

(g) Assuming that V is associative under addition and multiplication and that the distributive law holds, show that V is a field.

(h) Find $c - b$, $\dfrac{c}{b}$, $\dfrac{a}{b}$, $\dfrac{b}{a}$.

(i) Solve the equation $\dfrac{b + a}{c} \cdot x = c$ for x.

5. Is the set S in Problem 34, Section 2.17, a field?

2.19 Roots

The symbol a^n, n a positive integer, has been defined as the number $a \cdot a \cdots a$ (n factors). This suggests the problem; Given a real number b, and positive integer n, is there a real number a for which $a^n = b$? For some b's this can be easily answered in the affirmative by exhibiting an a. For example, if $b = -\frac{343}{27}$ and $n = 3$, then such an a is $-\frac{7}{3}$, since $(-\frac{7}{3})^3 = -\frac{343}{27}$. For other b's and n's an a is not always so easily found and in some cases may not even exist. If n had been 2 in the above example, there would be no real a for which $a^2 = -\frac{343}{27}$, since the square of any real number is always positive or zero.†

The question of the existence of a's has been completely settled, though we shall not be able to do more than state the results:

Theorem 17. Let b be a real number and n a positive integer.

(1) If n is odd, there is a real number a such that $a^n = b$.

†This property of real numbers, which agrees with experience, will be proved in Chapter 6.

(2) If n is even, there is a real number a such that $a^n = b$ if and only if b is positive or zero.

We call a an nth *root* of b. However, second and third roots ($n = 2$ and 3) are commonly called *square* and *cube roots*.

It can be shown that in the first case, when n is odd, there is only one real a, and this is positive, negative, or zero according as b is. We use the symbol $b^{1/n}$ or $\sqrt[n]{b}$ to indicate this real number.

In the second case, when n is even, there are two possibilities for a, one positive and the other negative (unless b is zero, in which event a is zero). In this case we shall agree that $b^{1/n}$ (or $\sqrt[n]{b}$), $b > 0$, is to stand for the *positive* root, so that there will be no ambiguity as to which is meant.†
Thus the symbol $\sqrt{36}$ or $36^{1/2}$ stands for 6 and not -6, since 6 is positive and $6^2 = 36$. Of course, -6 being a number whose square is 36 is also a square root of 36. It can be indicated by $-\sqrt{36}$. We define $\sqrt[n]{0}$ and $0^{1/n}$ to be 0.

We have then
$$a^n = (b^{1/n})^n = (\sqrt[n]{b})^n = b.$$

As with the notation b^{-1} indicating the reciprocal of b, no meaning should be attached to $b^{1/n}$ other than that given by the definition. In particular, it cannot yet be considered as a power obeying the laws of exponents. That will have to wait until we have extended the concept of exponents to the rational numbers.

The notation $-b^{1/n}$ will always mean $-(b^{1/n})$.

Illustrations.

$$\sqrt{\frac{1}{49}} = \left(\frac{1}{49}\right)^{1/2} = \frac{1}{7}; \qquad -16^{1/2} = -\sqrt{16} = -4;$$

$$(-16)^{1/2} \text{ or } \sqrt{-16} \text{ does not exist};$$

$$8^{1/3} = \sqrt[3]{8} = 2; \qquad (-27)^{1/3} = \sqrt[3]{-27} = -3.$$

PROBLEMS

Which of the following are symbols for real numbers? If possible, simplify those that are.

1. $\sqrt{400}$.

2. $-\sqrt{\frac{1}{4}}$.

3. $\sqrt{17}$.

4. $\sqrt{-17}$.

5. $\sqrt[3]{216}$.

6. $81^{1/4}$.

7. $\sqrt{\frac{25}{36}}$.

8. $(-1)^{1/15}$.

9. $\sqrt{-81}$.

10. $(-64)^{1/4}$.

†When $n = 2$ it is customary to write $\sqrt{b}$ for $\sqrt[2]{b}$.

11. $2 + 7\sqrt{5}$.

12. $9^{1/2} + 16^{1/2}$.

13. $\sqrt{9} - \sqrt{16}$.

14. $(-32)^{1/5}$.

15. $-16^{1/4}$.

16. $\sqrt[3]{343}$.

17. $(.001)^{1/3}$.

18. $(\sqrt{25})^{-1}$.

19. $(25^{-1})^{1/2}$.

20. $(-1)^{1/14}$.

21. $(\sqrt{19})^2$.

22. $(2^8)^{1/8}$.

23. $((-3)^2)^{1/2}$.

24. $\sqrt{(-4)^2}$; $\sqrt{-4^2}$; $-\sqrt{4^2}$.

25. $\sqrt{-a^2}$.

26. $\sqrt[3]{-a^3}$.

27. $[(-243)^{1/5}]^2$.

28. $\sqrt{36a^4}$.

29. $\left(-\dfrac{27b^3}{x^6}\right)^{1/3}$.

30. $(.09x^8)^{1/2}$.

31. $(\sqrt[3]{7ax^2})^3$.

32. Is $\sqrt{4^2} = (\sqrt{4})^2$?

33. Is $(8^3)^{1/3} = (8^{1/3})^3$?

34. Explain the difference between $(a^{1/n})^m$ and $(a^m)^{1/n}$, where m and n are positive integers.

35. Is $[(-8)^2]^{1/3} = [(-8)^{1/3}]^2$?

36. Find all real numbers whose squares are $\frac{64}{121}$.

37. Find all real numbers y for which $y^4 = 10{,}000$. Which one can be represented by the symbol $10{,}000^{1/4}$?

38. Find all real numbers whose cubes are $\frac{64}{27}$; $-\frac{64}{27}$.

39. Write the symbols for the real numbers whose squares are 15.

40. Write the symbols for the real numbers whose fifth powers are $\frac{1}{30}$. How many such numbers are there?

41. Explain the difference between $(-10)^{1/3}$ and $-10^{1/3}$.

42. Show that $\sqrt{\dfrac{1}{a}} = \dfrac{1}{\sqrt{a}}$, $a > 0$.

*43. If a and b are real numbers for which $a^2 = b^2$, does it necessarily follow that $a = b$? When will $a = b$?

*44. Show by an example that the equation $\sqrt{a^2} = a$, is not always correct. For which a's is $\sqrt{a^2} = a$? What is $\sqrt{a^2}$ for the other a's?

45. If a and b are real numbers for which $a^3 = b^3$, does it necessarily follow that $a = b$?

46. Show that $x - y = (\sqrt{x} + \sqrt{y})(\sqrt{x} - \sqrt{y})$, $x, y \geq 0$. Illustrate with $x = 4$, $y = 25$.

*47. Show that $\sqrt{a}\sqrt{b} = \sqrt{ab}$ if $a \geq 0$ and $b \geq 0$. (*Hint:* Square both sides and use Problem 43.)

*48. Show that $\dfrac{\sqrt{a}}{\sqrt{b}} = \sqrt{\dfrac{a}{b}}$, $a \geq 0, b > 0$.

Simplify:

49. $\dfrac{2^{-1} + 4^{1/2}}{1 + \sqrt[3]{-27}}.$

50. $\dfrac{(\frac{1}{125})^{1/3}}{(-\frac{1}{2})^2}.$

51. $(\frac{1}{8})^{-1} \cdot 8^{1/3}.$

52. $\sqrt{48}.$

53. $\sqrt{2}\sqrt{18}.$

54. $\sqrt{3}\sqrt{21}.$

55. $\sqrt{y}\sqrt{5y^3}, \quad y \geqq 0.$

56. $(3\sqrt{3})(7\sqrt{6}).$

57. $\dfrac{\sqrt{3}}{\sqrt{12}}.$

58. $\dfrac{\sqrt{30}}{\sqrt{6}}.$

59. $\dfrac{\sqrt{a^3}}{\sqrt{a}}, \quad a > 0.$

60. $\dfrac{x^2}{\sqrt{x^5}}, \quad x > 0.$

61. $\frac{1}{3}(15 + \sqrt{45}).$

62. $-\frac{1}{2}(10 - \sqrt{68}).$

63. $\sqrt{7}(\sqrt{14} + 3\sqrt{7}).$

Chapter 3

Equations

3.1 Equations

In this chapter we shall examine critically the subject of equations and their solution. To deal confidently with this subject, one must understand what an equation is, the problem posed when asked to solve one, and the reasoning employed in obtaining the solution.

The reader should keep in mind the distinction between a number and a symbol for the number. Every number has many different names or symbols. An *equation* is a statement that asserts that two symbols are names for the same number. For example, 12 is a symbol for a number and so is 4 · 3. Therefore the statement, "12 = 4 · 3," is an equation. So also is "$\frac{4.5}{4}$ = 15." Such statements are really English sentences written in a convenient shorthand. In the first "12" is the subject, the equals sign is the verb, and "4 · 3" the object. Some people believe everything they hear, or think that whatever appears in print must be true. Most of us, however, have learned that many statements are not true. "New York City has over one million inhabitants," is a true statement, but, "the earth is flat," and, "five is greater than 8," are not. Equations are no exception, and the mere placing of an equals sign between two numbers, thus creating a statement, does not in itself imply that this assertion is necessarily true. The first equation above happens to be true, but "$\frac{4.5}{4}$ = 15" is not.

If x denotes a number, then the statement

$$(1) \qquad\qquad 3x^2 + 2x + 5 = (3x - 1)(x + 2)$$

is also an equation, since the left and right sides are symbols for numbers. Whether it is true depends on the value of x. If x is 1, the left side is the number $3 + 2 + 5$, or 10, and the right is $(3 - 1)(1 + 2)$, or 6; thus the equation is not true if x is 1. If x is $\frac{7}{3}$, we have on the left $3(\frac{7}{3})^2 + 2(\frac{7}{3}) + 5$, or 26, and on the right $[3(\frac{7}{3}) - 1][\frac{7}{3} + 2]$, or 26; hence the equation is true if x is $\frac{7}{3}$. How we discovered this value for x and whether there are others for which the statement is true is one of the things we shall learn in this chapter.

If an equation contains letters, it is understood that the writer is saying that the equation is true for all values of the letters for which the expressions are meaningful unless the contrary is indicated or implied. Thus when one sees the simple statement

$$(x - 3)^2 = x^2 - 6x + 9,$$

one may assume the writer is asserting that it is true for all x, since nothing is said to the contrary. He may, of course, have made a mistake, and the equation may be true for only some x's. Nevertheless, this is what he is saying. (In this example he was right.)

The equation

(2)
$$\frac{x^2 - a^2}{x - a} = x + a$$

means that for any numbers x and a the two sides are expressions for the same number provided that $x \neq a$. Although the restriction $x \neq a$ is not explicitly mentioned, it is implied, since the left side of (2) has no meaning when $x = a$. In order to be sure that the reader will not overlook this point, a careful writer will usually note this restriction explicitly the first time $x - a$ appears in a denominator in a piece of exposition. Almost certainly, however, he will not mention it every time, so it behooves the reader to watch for this. In an equation involving $\sqrt{x}$ it would be understood that x could be only zero or positive unless non-real numbers were to be allowed.

The sentence, "Find all numbers x for which $4x - 13 = 17$," indicates that the equation $4x - 13 = 17$ is not to be considered necessarily true for all x. The extent to which it is true has not yet been determined. Indeed, that is just the problem posed.

Illustration 1. The equation $x(x - 1) = 0$ is false. The statement asserts, since no restriction is placed on x, that the equation is true for all x, which is not so.

Illustration 2. The statement, "If $x = 1$, then $x(x - 1) = 0$," is true, as is the statement, "If $x = 1$ or $x = 0$, then $x(x - 1) = 0$."

Illustration 3. The statement, "There exists an x such that $x(x - 1) = 0$," is true.

Illustration 4. The equation $x^2 - 7x + 12 = (x - 4)(x - 3)$, $x \neq 1$, is true. It would also be true without the restriction on x.

PROBLEMS

Which of the following statements are true?

1. If $x = -7$, $3x + 13 = -8$.

2. If $x = 2$, $\dfrac{x - 2}{10} = 0$.

3. $x(x - 2) = 0$, if $x = 0$.

4. $x + 4 = 2x - 3$.

5. If $x = 1$, $x + 4 = 2x - 3$.

6. $x^2 - 1 = (x + 1)(x - 1)$.

7. $\dfrac{x^2 - 4x}{x - 4} = x$, $\quad x \neq 4$.

8. $x^2 - 5x - 24 = (x - 8)(x + 3)$, $\quad x \neq 1$.

9. $x^2 - 5x - 24 = (x - 8)(x + 3)$, $\quad x \neq -3$.

10. If $x = \dfrac{1}{5}(b - 6)$, $\dfrac{5x + b}{2} = b - 3$.

11. If $y = \dfrac{3}{6 - c}$, $c \neq 6$, then $cy + 1 = 6y + 4$.

12. $\dfrac{x^2 + 8x - 9}{x + 9} = x - 1$, $\quad x \neq -9$.

13. $\dfrac{x(x + 3)}{x} = x + 3$, $\quad x \neq 0, 7$.

14. $\dfrac{x(x + 3)}{x} = x + 3$ if $x = -3$.

15. $\dfrac{x(x + 3)}{x} = x + 3$ if $x = 0$.

16. There exists an x such that $(x + 3)^2 = x^2 + 8x + 9$.

17. For some x, $\dfrac{x^2 - 49}{x - 7} = x + 7$.

18. If $x = 4/a$, where a is any non-zero number, then $ax = 4$.

Each of the following statements is false. Explain why and rephrase each so that it will be true.

19. If $x = 0$, $x + 1 = 6$.

20. If $x = 2$, $x - 3 = 2x + 7$.

21. If $x = 0$, $\dfrac{x}{x(x + 1)} = \dfrac{1}{x + 1}$.

22. $2x + 3 = x - 1$.

23. For all x, $\dfrac{x^2 - 25}{x + 5} = x - 5$.

24. $\dfrac{x^2 - 81}{x - 9} = x - 9$, $\quad x \neq 9$.

25. $x^2 + 5x + 4 = (x + 2)^2$.

26. For all $x \neq 0$, $\dfrac{x^2 - 36}{x(x + 6)} = \dfrac{x - 6}{x}$.

27. $3x + 7 = \dfrac{4x + 3}{2} + x$.

3.2   Solutions

If an equation contains a letter, any value of that letter for which the equation is true is called a *solution* or *root* of the equation and is said to *satisfy* the equation. Thus 5 is a solution of $4x - 13 = 7$, since $4 \cdot 5 - 13 = 7$. The solution is often written $x = 5$ with the understanding that when x is 5 then $4x - 13 = 7$.

An equation may have one, two, or many solutions. We shall presently be able to show that 5 is the only solution of $4x - 13 = 7$. The equation $2x^2 - 3x - 5 = 0$ has -1 and $\frac{5}{2}$ as roots and no others. An equation may have no solution, as in $2x + 3 = 2x - 5$, or it may be true for all x, as in

$$(1) \qquad\qquad (x - 3)^2 = x^2 - 6x + 9.$$

Any number except 6 is a solution of

$$(2) \qquad\qquad \frac{x^2 - 36}{x - 6} = x + 6.$$

The set of all solutions of an equation forms a subset (possibly empty) of the set of all numbers. To *solve* an equation means to find this subset, that is, all solutions.

Exercise A. Show that 3, $\frac{4}{3}$, 0, and -7 are solutions of (1).

Exercise B. Show that 0, -2, -6, and $\frac{2}{3}$ are solutions of (2). Why is 6 not a solution?

An equation may contain more than one letter, as in $2x + a = 5$, and in such a case one may be asked to "solve for x in terms of a." This means that a is to be considered as some definite but unspecified number and the equation solved for x. As one would expect, the solution generally will involve the letter a, but not always. A solution of the above equation is $\frac{1}{2}(5 - a)$, since if this number is substituted for x,

$$2[\tfrac{1}{2}(5 - a)] + a = 5,$$

the resulting equation is true for every a. The letter for which one is solving is often called the *unknown*.

If one is asked to solve an equation that contains a letter from near the end of the alphabet and one or more from near the beginning, it is a convention in mathematics texts that unless directed otherwise one is to solve for the letter near the end of the alphabet in terms of the others.

Given a particular number, it usually is relatively easy to determine whether this is a solution of a certain equation; one has only to substitute the number for the unknown and simplify both sides of the equation. For most equations, however, one does not have advance information as to possible solutions, and even if one does, there may be no assurance that there are not others. Obviously, one cannot test all numbers in order to find the solutions. What is needed is a systematic procedure.

Unfortunately, systematic procedures are known for only a few relatively simple types of equations. For the majority of equations it is difficult, if not impossible, to find even one solution, let alone the others if they exist. For some equations for which a solution cannot be found, it can be established that at least there is a solution. Even such meager information as this can at times be useful.

In this chapter we shall learn how to solve certain simple yet important equations, and in later chapters we shall consider more difficult ones. In Chapter 5, which deals with polynomials, we shall see that for an important

class of equations much information about the roots can be obtained even
if they are not known. Finally, in Chapter 11 we shall give a method for
approximating roots that are not known exactly.

PROBLEMS

Show that the numbers are solutions of the corresponding equations:

1. $2x + 5 = 0; x = -\frac{5}{2}$.

2. $a + 4 = 2a - 1; a = 5$.

3. $x^2 - 3x = 10; x = 5, -2$.

4. $\dfrac{x + 25}{7x} = 3; x = \dfrac{5}{4}$.

5. $3x^2 - 22x + 7 = 0; x = \frac{1}{3}, 7$.

6. $2x^2 - 6ax + 3a = x; x = \frac{1}{2}, 3a$.

7. $\dfrac{(x - 1)(x - b)}{x + 5} = 0; x = 1, b$.

8. $2(3 - 2x^2) = x^3 + x; x = 1, -2, -3$.

9. $4y^2 - (5x + 12)y + x^2 + 3x = 0; y = \dfrac{x}{4}, x + 3$.

From each set of numbers select those that are solutions of the corresponding
equation.

10. $x + 3 = 7; x = -3, 7, 4$.

11. $2x + 1 = \dfrac{x}{2} - 5; x = -4, 2, 0, 10$.

12. $x + 1 = 4x + 13; x = 3, 0, 4, -\frac{7}{2}$.

13. $x(x + 1) = 0; x = 1, 0, -1, 2$.

14. $x^2(x + a) = 0; x = 5, a, -a, 0, 1$.

15. $x^2 - b^2 = 0; x = 2, b, 1, 0, -b$.

16. $(x - b)^2 = 0; x = 2, b, 1, 0, -b$.

17. $\dfrac{x}{2} + a = 6; x = 6 + a, 0, 12 - 2a, 12 - a$.

18. $\dfrac{(x - 1)(x - 4)}{ax} = 0, a \neq 0; x = 1, 4$.

19. $\dfrac{x(x - a^2)}{x + 2} = 0; x = 0, -a^2, a^2, -a, a, -2$.

20. $\dfrac{2x^2 + 21x + 40}{x(2x + 5)} = 0; x = 0, -2, \dfrac{1}{2}, -\dfrac{5}{2}$.

21. $\dfrac{(2x + 1)(x + 1)}{x - 2} = x + 1; x = -3, 2, -\dfrac{1}{2}, -1, 0$.

22. $\dfrac{x^2 + x - 30}{x + 6} = 0; x = 6, -6, 5, 7$.

23. $7\dfrac{(x + 3)^2(4x + 5)}{x + 3} = 0; x = \dfrac{5}{4}, -3, -\dfrac{4}{5}, -\dfrac{5}{4}, 0, 7$.

3.3   Solving Equations

The equations $x^2 + x = 2$ and $2x^2 - 2 = x(x - 1)$ have the same set of solutions, 1 and -2. Such equations are called equivalent.

Definition.   Two equations are *equivalent* if each has the same set of solutions.

The equations $2(x + 1) = x$ and $2(x^2 - 1) = x(x - 1)$ are not equivalent; the solution set of the first is -2 and of the second -2 and 1. The next theorem is fundamental in the solution of equations.

Theorem 1.   If the same number is added to both sides of an equation or if both sides are multiplied by the same non-zero number, the resulting equation is equivalent to the first.

For example, $2(x + 4) - 3 = 8$ and $2(x + 4) = 11$ are equivalent, since the second is obtained by adding 3 to both sides of the first. By multiplying both sides of $2(x + 4) = 11$ by $\frac{1}{2}$, we obtain the equivalent equation $x + 4 = \frac{11}{2}$. However, $2(x + 4) \cdot 0 = 11 \cdot 0$ is not equivalent to $2(x + 4) = 11$, since 5 is a solution of the first but not of the second.

To prove the theorem, let us write the original equation symbolically as $P = Q$, where P is everything, including the unknown number x, to the left of the equals sign and Q is everything to the right. The equation derived from this by adding the number a to both sides is $P + a = Q + a$. If s is a solution of $P = Q$, then the number obtained from P by replacing x by s will be equal to that obtained from Q. If we add a to each of these numbers, the resulting numbers are also equal. But since these are the numbers obtained by replacing x by s in $P + a$ and $Q + a$, s is a solution of the second equation. This shows that every solution of the equation $P = Q$ is a solution of $P + a = Q + a$. We must now show that the second equation does not have any more solutions than the first. By beginning with $P + a = Q + a$ and going through an almost identical argument, but this time adding $-a$, we can show that every solution of this equation is a solution of $P = Q$. Thus both equations have the same solution set. The second half of the theorem concerning multiplication is proved similarly.

Exercise A.   Prove the second half of Theorem 1. Where does the condition that the multiplier be non-zero come in?

Exercise B.   Show directly that if s is not a solution of $P = Q$, then it is not a solution of $P + a = Q + a$.

*Exercise C.   Explain how the statement of Theorem 1 tacitly includes subtraction or division of both sides of the equation by the same number.

*Exercise D.   Show that if one equation is equivalent to another and this in turn is equivalent to a third, the first equation is equivalent to the third. If this chain is extended to include more than three equations, each equivalent to its successor, will the first equation be equivalent to the last?

A basic method for solving many equations consists of constructing by Theorem 1 a sequence of equations, beginning with the given equation, such that each is equivalent to the preceding but simpler, the last being so simple that its solution set is obvious. The set of solutions of this last equation must then be the same as that of the original equation.

Let us illustrate with the equation $2(x + 4) - 3 = 8$. Note that each equation in the sequence below is equivalent to its immediate predecessor for the indicated reason.

$$
\begin{aligned}
(1) \qquad 2(x + 4) - 3 &= 8 \\
2(x + 4) &= 11 \qquad &\text{add 3 to both sides} \\
x + 4 &= \tfrac{11}{2} \qquad &\text{multiply both sides by } \tfrac{1}{2} \\
(2) \qquad x &= \tfrac{3}{2}. \qquad &\text{add } -4 \text{ to both sides}
\end{aligned}
$$

The last equation has $\tfrac{3}{2}$ as its only solution. Hence this must be the only solution of the original equation.

There are other paths by which one can go from (1) to (2). For example,

$$
\begin{aligned}
2(x + 4) - 3 &= 8 \\
x + 4 - \tfrac{3}{2} &= 4 \qquad &\text{multiply by } \tfrac{1}{2} \\
x + \tfrac{5}{2} &= 4 \\
x &= \tfrac{3}{2}. \qquad &\text{add } -\tfrac{5}{2}
\end{aligned}
$$

Again, by Theorem 1 each equation is equivalent to the one just above.

In Section 1 we showed that $\tfrac{7}{3}$ was a solution of the equation

$$3x^2 + 2x + 5 = (3x - 1)(x + 2).$$

We can now see how this was found and why it is the only solution:

$$
\begin{aligned}
3x^2 + 2x + 5 &= (3x - 1)(x + 2) \\
3x^2 + 2x + 5 &= 3x^2 + 5x - 2 \qquad &\text{distributive law} \\
2x + 5 &= 5x - 2 \qquad &\text{add } -3x^2 \\
-3x &= -7 \qquad &\text{add } -5x - 5 \\
x &= \tfrac{7}{3}. \qquad &\text{multiply by } -\tfrac{1}{3}
\end{aligned}
$$

In both examples our objective was the isolation of the unknown x on one side of the equation. The more efficiently one can do this, the fewer will be the steps required.

Illustration 1.   Solve the equation

$$(3) \qquad 2(x + 1)(x - 3) = 2x(x - 2) + 1.$$

Expanding both sides of the equation, we have

$$(4) \qquad 2x^2 - 4x - 6 = 2x^2 - 4x + 1,$$

and adding $-2x^2 + 4x$ to both sides of this, we obtain the equivalent equation

$$(5) \qquad -6 = 1.$$

Since no number x will make this last equation true, the original equation has no solution. Its solution set is empty. Looking at it somewhat differently, one can see that if there were a value of x for which (3) is true, then (4) and hence (5) would be true. Since this last is not true, no value of x can satisfy (3).

Illustration 2.   Solve the equation

(6) $$(x + 4)(x - 5) + 14 = (x + 2)(x - 3).$$

Proceeding as before, we have

$$x^2 - x - 20 + 14 = x^2 - x - 6$$

or

(7) $$-6 = -6.$$

This is true for all values of x. Hence so is (6). The set of solutions of (6) consists of all real numbers.

An equation such as (6) that is true for all values of the letters for which it is meaningful is called an *identity*. The equation

$$\frac{x^2 - a^2}{x - a} = x + a$$

is an identity, because it is meaningful for all $x \neq a$ and is true for each such x.

Illustration 3.   Solve the equation

(8) $$x(3 + a) + 5 = 6a - x.$$

Here it is understood that we are to solve for x in terms of a. Adding $x - 5$ to both sides and simplifying, we have

$$x(4 + a) = 6a - 5.$$

The next step is to divide by $4 + a$, which is possible only if $a \neq -4$,

(9) $$x = \frac{6a - 5}{4 + a}, \qquad a \neq -4.$$

Hence for $a \neq -4$ there is only one solution of (8), namely, that given by (9).†

If $a = -4$, equation (8) becomes

$$-x + 5 = -24 - x$$

or, equivalently,

$$5 = -24,$$

which has no solution. Thus (8) has no solution when $a = -4$.

Illustration 4.   Solve the equation

(10) $$3xy + 7 = 15y + 7$$

for y.

---

†Although there are actually many solutions, one for each value of a, it is customary, since they are all generated by the expression $\dfrac{6a - 5}{4 + a}$, to consider this as a single solution.

An equation equivalent to (10) is

(11) $(3x - 15)y = 0.$

If $x \neq 5$, then, on dividing by $3x - 15$, we see that $y = 0$ is the only solution. If $x = 5$, (11) becomes $0 \cdot y = 0$, and any y is a solution. Therefore the solutions of (10) are

$$y = 0 \text{ if } x \neq 5,$$
$$y = \text{any number if } x = 5.$$

Exercise E.   Show by direct substitution in the original equations that the answers obtained in Illustrations 3 and 4 are solutions.

Exercise F.   Show by direct substitution that 7, 0, −3 are not solutions of equation (3). Show that they are solutions of equation (6).

PROBLEMS

1. Show that -5 and 3 are roots of $x(x + 4) = 2x + 15$.
2. Prove that -1 is a root of $(x + 6)(x - 1) = x + x(x + 2) - 8$, and show that the equation has no other root.
3. Show that 0 is a solution of $x^2 = 3x$. If x is a number for which $x^2 = 3x$, must x be zero?
4. Show that $2x - 1 = 5(x + 1) - 3(x + 2)$ is true for all x.
5. Show there is no number x for which $2x - 5 = 3(x + 4) - x$.

Solve the following equations:

6. $x + 4 = 7.$
7. $5x - 7 = 13.$
8. $x + 6x = -14.$
9. $2x - 1 = 5 + 2x.$
10. $2 + 3x - 5 = x - 3 + 2x.$

11. $2x + 4 = 6a + 14.$
12. $2(4 - y) = 8 - 3y.$
13. $\frac{2}{3} + 4u = -u + \frac{7}{4}.$
14. $\frac{1}{5}w + \frac{13}{16} - w = -1.$
15. $7 - 8z = 7 + 3z.$

16. $12y - 5 = 4(y + \frac{3}{2}).$

17. $x^2 + 6x - 4 = (x + 3)^2 - 13.$
18. $(x - 2)^2 + 4(x - 2) + 9 = x(x + 2) - 11.$
19. $(x + 2)(x - 6) + \frac{1}{2} = x^2 + 3x - 11.$
20. $y^2 + (2y + 5)(y + 2) = 3y^2 + 15y.$
21. $\frac{9}{4}(2 - x) = -\frac{5}{3}x + \frac{1}{2}(x + 3).$

Which of the following equations are identities?

22. $(x - 2)(4 + x) = x^2 + 2x - 8.$
23. $x - 8(3a - x) = 3(3x - 8a).$
24. $2(x - 16) = 2(x - 7) + 2.$

25. $\dfrac{x^2 - 4x - 5}{x + 1} + 5 = x.$

26. $(x^2 + 3)(x - 3) = x^2(x - 3) + 3(2x - 7).$
27. $(x + a)^2 = x^2 + 2ax + a^2.$

28. $\dfrac{x - 7}{x - 7} = 1.$ 29. $A = \pi r^2.$

Solve the following equations:

30. $2x + 5 = a$.

31. $(z + 3)\frac{6}{7} - u = 0$; for z.

32. $2x + 3y + 1 = 0$; for x, for y.

33. $\frac{x}{2} + \frac{y}{-6} = 1$; for x, for y.

34. $y = 3x + 5$; for x.

35. $y = mx + b$; for x, for m.

36. $\frac{x}{7} - \frac{y}{3(b + 2)} = 0$; for x.

37. $y^2 = 8x$; for x.

38. $bw + 8 = 2w - 1$.

39. $2mx + 3m = 6x - m + 12$; for x.

40. $\frac{y + 3}{10} + 2y = 8$.

41. $5ay - a^2 = 5y - 1$.

42. $\frac{x^2}{4} + \frac{y^2}{1} = 1$; for y^2, for x^2.

43. $3x^2 - \frac{2}{9}y^2 = 1$; for x^2.

44. $\frac{x^2}{a^2} + \frac{y^2}{b^2} = 1$; for y^2, for x^2.

45. $b^2x^2 - a^2y^2 = -a^2b^2$; for y^2.

46. $2xy + 3x - 2y + 4 = 0$; for x, for y.

47. $(b + 2)y - 6 = 3b + 2by$.

48. $\dfrac{2x + 1}{c} - \dfrac{x}{5} = \dfrac{8}{3}$.

49. Solve the equation $y^2 = 4px$ for p, given that $x = 2$ and $y = -6$.

50. Solve $x - x_1 = x_2 - x$ for x.

51. Solve $\dfrac{x}{a} - \dfrac{y}{b} = 0$ for y.

52. Solve $\dfrac{y - y_1}{x - x_1} = m$ for y.

53. If $y = -\frac{7}{2}x + b$, determine b so that the equation will be true when $x = -5$ and $y = 10$.

54. Find a number k, if any, so that the equation $(x - 2y + 1) + k(3x + y + 4) = 0$ is true when: (a) $x = 1$, $y = 0$; (b) $x = -2$, $y = 2$.

55. Solve $f = ma$ for a.

56. Solve $s = \frac{1}{2}gt^2$ for g, for t^2.

57. Solve $t^2 = 4\pi^2 \, l/g$ for l.

58. If $F = k\dfrac{mM}{r^2}$, find k when $F = \dfrac{1}{13}$, $m = 3$, $M = \dfrac{9}{2}$, $r = 2$.

59. Solve $2x + 2yy' = 0$ for y' in terms of x and y. Find y' if $x = 3$, $y = -4$. Find y' if $x = 5$, $y = 0$. Now, if necessary, restate correctly your solution for y' in terms of x and y.

60. Solve $xy' + y + 2x = 0$ for y' in terms of x and y. Find y' if $x = 2$, $y = -2$. Find y' if $x = 0$, $y = 5$.

61. Solve $x^2y' + 2xy + 6y^2y' + 1 = 0$ for y'.

62. Solve $\dfrac{y - xy'}{y^2} + 2yy' = 2x$ for y'.

63. If $3x_1x + 4y_1y = 5$ and $x_1 = -2$ and $y_1 = 2$, find the value of x for which the equation is true when $y = 0$.

64. For what values of k will the equation $3x - 1 = k$ have the same solution for x as the equation $-2x + 5 = 8$?

65. If $2x + y = 6$ and $x - y = -1$, solve the second equation for y, and substitute this value for y in the first equation. Solve the resulting equation for x.

66. For what value of y will both of the equations $x - 2y + 10 = 0$ and $3x + y + 2 = 0$ have the same solution for x? What is x in this case?

67. For what value of x will both of the equations $5x + y = 3$ and $x - 4y = -12$ have the same solution for y? What is y in this case?

68. If $A = xy$ and $x + 2y = 1,000$, solve the second equation for y and substitute this value for y in the first equation.

69. If $V = \pi r^2 h$ and $\pi r^2 + 2\pi r h = 10$, solve the second equation for h, and substitute this value for h in the first equation.

70. Show that if a and b are rational, $a \neq 0$, the equation $ax = b$ has a rational root.

3.4 Polynomial Equations

Most of the equations in the last section were either of the first degree or could be reduced to equivalent equations of the first degree. Equations that are not of this simple type can be considerably harder to solve. In this and the next section we shall demonstrate methods for solving some of the commoner ones.

Let us consider the problem of solving the equation

$$(1) \qquad 2x^2 + 5(x - 2) = x^2 + 7x + 5.$$

An equivalent equation is

$$x^2 - 2x - 15 = 0$$

or

$$(2) \qquad (x - 5)(x + 3) = 0.$$

It is easily seen that 5 and -3 are roots of (2) and hence of (1). They are also the only solutions of (2). For this equation says that the product of the two numbers $x - 5$ and $x + 3$ is zero, and by Theorem 9 in Section 2.13 this can happen only if one factor or the other (or both) is zero. Hence any solution x of (2) must be such that either $x - 5 = 0$ or $x + 3 = 0$. Therefore x can be only 5 or -3. Since (1) and (2) are equivalent, we know that these are the only solutions of (1).

Theorem 9 in Section 2.13 is the key theorem here. It is essential when solving equations with its aid that the left side of the equation be expressed in factored form and that the right side be zero.

Illustration. Solve the equation

$$(3) \qquad 2x^3 + (1 - 2a)x^2 - ax = 0.$$

The left side of the equation can be factored:

$$(4) \qquad x(x - a)\,(2x + 1) = 0.$$

Equating in turn each factor to zero, we find that 0, a, and $-\frac{1}{2}$ are roots of (4). Again, Theorem 9, or rather its extension in Problem 21 in Section 2.13, shows that the product in (4) can be zero only if at least one of the factors is zero. Hence 0, a, and $-\frac{1}{2}$ are the only roots of (4) and (3).

This method is useful only if one is able to find the factors of the given expression, which is by no means always possible. In Chapter 4 we shall consider this problem with respect to polynomials and show how one can always find the factors of a quadratic polynomial and so solve any quadratic equation. If a is positive, however, the quadratic equation $x^2 - a = 0$ is immediately solvable, since it can be written as $(x - \sqrt{a})$ $(x + \sqrt{a}) = 0$. The roots are $\sqrt{a}$ and $-\sqrt{a}$.

Exercise A. Show that 5 and -3 are solutions of (1) by substituting directly in the equation. Do the same for the equation in the illustration.

Exercise B. Students, not understanding what is involved, frequently try to solve an equation such as $x^2 - x - 2 = 18$ in the following manner:

$$x^2 - x - 2 = 18$$
$$(x - 2)(x + 1) = 18$$

$x - 2 = 18$	$x + 1 = 18$
$x = 20$	$x = 17.$

Show that neither 20 nor 17 is a root, find the flaw in the argument, and solve the equation correctly.

A common, yet incorrect, method of solving the equation

$$(5) \qquad\qquad x^2 = 4x$$

is to cancel x from each side, obtaining $x = 4$. Since 4 satisfies (5), there is no doubt it is a root. But so also is 0, and this method did not produce it. The explanation is that the equation $x = 4$ is not equivalent to (5), since they do not have the same roots. It was obtained by multiplying (5) by $1/x$, which is possible only when $x \neq 0$. The correct procedure is to write (5) as $x(x - 4) = 0$ and argue as we did before.

Care must be taken whenever an equation is multiplied or divided by any expression containing the unknown that roots are not inadvertently lost or spurious roots obtained, as may happen if the resulting equation is not equivalent to the original.

PROBLEMS

Solve the equations:

1. $(x + 7)(x - 2) = 0$.
2. $x^2 + 6x - 27 = 0$.
3. $2x^2 + 3x = 0$.
4. $2x^2 + x = 3$.
5. $x^2 - 9 = 0$.
6. $x^2 + 6x + 10 = 1$.
7. $x^2 - (a + b)x + ab = 0$.
8. $8x^2 + 18x = 5$.

9. $x^2 - 4^2 = 0.$

10. $(x - 4)^2 = 0.$

11. $x^2 = 5.$

12. $6x^3 + 8x^2 = 0.$

13. $x^4 + x^3 = 6x^2.$

14. $ax^2 + (2a - 3)x - 6 = 0.$

15. $(x + 1)^2 - 17 = 0.$

16. $z^2 - 2(1 + b)z + 4b = 0.$

17. $2y^2 + cy - 3c^2 = 0.$

18. $8x^2(x - 1)^2 + 12x(x - 1)^2$
$$= -x^3(x - 1)^2.$$

19. Solve the equation $x^4 - 13x^2 + 36 = 0$ by regarding it as an equation in x^2.

20. Solve the equation $x^4 - 39x^2 + 108 = 0.$

3.5   Algebraic Equations

When the unknown appears in a denominator we must proceed carefully. Consider, for example, the solution of the equation

$$(1) \qquad \frac{2x(x - 5)}{x - 5} = x + 2.$$

If there is a solution, it cannot be 5, since the left side of the equation is not a number for this value of x. For $x \neq 5$, we can cancel $x - 5$ in (1) and obtain the equivalent equation

$$(2) \qquad 2x = x + 2, \quad x \neq 5.$$

The solution of this is 2, which is therefore the only solution of (1).

A common, but incorrect, method of solving (1) is to multiply both sides of that equation by $x - 5$, obtaining

$$(3) \qquad 2x(x - 5) = (x + 2)(x - 5),$$

which simplifies to

$$x^2 - 7x + 10 = 0$$

or

$$(4) \qquad (x - 5)(x - 2) = 0.$$

The solutions of (4) are 2 and 5—and hence, so the argument goes, of (1)—giving two answers where before there was but one. The fallacy lies not in the formal algebra, which is correct, but in the implied claim that (3) is equivalent to (1). Theorem 1 asserts they are equivalent for those x's for which $x - 5 \neq 0$. With this restriction we can now proceed to the solution of equation (4), remembering that only those roots of (4) that are different from 5 will necessarily be roots of (1). Whether 5 itself is a root will have to be settled by direct substitution in (1).

The foregoing discussion shows that equations derived from other equations by algebraic processes do not necessarily have the same solutions. The equation $x + 1 = 4$ has 3 as its only root, but the equation $x^2 + 6x + 5 = 4x + 20$, obtained from this by multiplying both sides by $x + 5$, has -5 as well as 3 as a root. Theorem 1 describes two algebraic processes that do lead to equations having the same set of solutions.

Illustration.   Solve the equation

(5)
$$\frac{3}{x-4} - \frac{1}{x+8} = \frac{2x}{x^2 - 3x - 4}.$$

Neither 4 nor -8 can be a solution, and since $x^2 - 3x - 4 = (x-4)(x+1)$, neither can -1. By multiplying both sides of (5) by $(x-4)(x+8)(x+1)$, we obtain the equation

$$3(x+8)(x+1) - (x-4)(x+1) = 2x(x+8),$$

which will be equivalent to (5) provided $x \neq 4$, -8, or -1. Solving this, we see that its only solution, and hence the only solution of (5), is -2.

To solve equations containing square roots of the unknown, one can proceed as in the solution of the equation

(6)
$$3\sqrt{x^2 + 16} - 5x = 0.$$

First, we remind the reader that if a and b are numbers such that $a = b$, then $a^2 = b^2$, but that the converse does not necessarily hold. That is, a^2 and b^2 may be equal even though $a \neq b$; for example, $7^2 = (-7)^2$. Now any solution of (6) is a number x for which

(7)
$$3\sqrt{x^2 + 16} = 5x,$$

and hence, squaring both sides, a number for which

$$9(x^2 + 16) = 25x^2,$$

or equivalently,

(8)
$$x^2 - 9 = 0.$$

Equation (8) was not derived from (7) by the equivalence operations of Theorem 1 and so may not be equivalent to it. Therefore, although every solution of (7) is a solution of (8), we cannot be sure that every solution of (8) is a solution of (7). If we find all the solutions of (8), however, then among them will be all the solutions of (7), though there may well be in addition some that are not. We can separate the sheep from the goats by testing each possibility in turn in (7) or (6). The solutions of (8) are 3 and -3. On substituting 3 in (6), we see that

$$3\sqrt{25} - 5 \cdot 3 = 3 \cdot 5 - 15 = 0,$$

but on substituting -3,

$$3\sqrt{25} - 5(-3) = 3 \cdot 5 + 15 \neq 0.\dagger$$

Hence 3 is the only solution of (6).

$\dagger$It is essential to remember here that by definition the symbol $\sqrt{25}$ stands for the positive number whose square is 25 and thus is 5, not -5. See the discussion in Section 2.19.

PROBLEMS

Solve the equations:

1. $\dfrac{8}{x} = 4.$

2. $\dfrac{7}{x-1} = 2.$

3. $ax + by + c = 0, b \neq 0;$ for $y.$

4. $\dfrac{5}{3x} - \dfrac{10}{7x} = \dfrac{1}{21}.$

5. Show that $\dfrac{10 - 3x^2}{x} = \dfrac{5 - 12x}{4}$ if $x = 8$ and for no other value.

6. For which values of x is $\dfrac{2x}{x-3} + 5 = 0$?

7. Show that if $w = \dfrac{1}{5}$, then $\dfrac{w^2 - w}{3w - 1} = \dfrac{2(w+1)}{6}$. Are there other values of w for which these two expressions are equal?

8. Show that the equation $-\dfrac{2}{x} + \dfrac{x+6}{x^2 - 2x} = \dfrac{4}{x-2}$ has no solution.

Solve the equations:

9. $2 + \dfrac{5}{2y} = \dfrac{2y}{y-1}.$

10. $\dfrac{7}{u-1} + \dfrac{3}{u+2} = \dfrac{10}{u-1}.$

11. $\dfrac{3x}{4} - \dfrac{x}{12} = \dfrac{12}{x} - \dfrac{4}{x}.$

12. $\dfrac{3}{2x+5} + x - 7 = -4 + x.$

13. $\dfrac{2z-1}{3} + \dfrac{3z+10}{z} = 8.$

14. $\dfrac{x}{a-1} + \dfrac{x}{a+1} = \dfrac{8}{3}.$

15. $\dfrac{a}{x-1} + \dfrac{a}{x+1} = 0.$

16. $\dfrac{x+10}{(x-2)(x+1)} = \dfrac{2x}{x-2}.$

17. $\dfrac{x}{x} = 1.$

18. $\dfrac{x}{x} = 2.$

19. $\dfrac{x}{x} = 0.$

20. $\dfrac{2(2-y)}{3} - 10 = \dfrac{(y-6)y}{y+1} - \dfrac{7}{y+1}.$

21. $\dfrac{2x-3}{2x} = 1 - \dfrac{5-x}{2-x}.$

22. $\dfrac{x^2(x+5) + 3(x+5)(4x+9)}{x+3} = 0.$

23. $x + 4 = \sqrt{5(x+14)}.$

24. $\sqrt{16x+7} = 4\sqrt{x+5}.$

25. $y + \sqrt{4y+5} + 2 = 0.$

26. $\sqrt{2x-3} - \sqrt{x+2} = 1.$

27. $\dfrac{z+6}{z-6} = \sqrt{\dfrac{z+41}{z-7}}.$

28. $-\sqrt{\dfrac{x}{x-1}} = \dfrac{x-2}{x-1}.$

29. $\sqrt{\frac{1}{2} - \frac{7}{4}x} + \sqrt{13 + 2x} = 5.$

30. $\sqrt{1-x^2} - \dfrac{x^2}{\sqrt{1-x^2}} = 0.$

31. $2x\sqrt{1-x^2} - \dfrac{x^3}{\sqrt{1-x^2}} = 0.$

32. Solve $t^2 = 4\pi^2 \dfrac{l}{g}$ for g.

33. Solve $F = \dfrac{mM}{r^2}$ for r^2, for M.

34. Solve the equation $bx + a = 0$ for all choices of a and b.

35. Solve $\dfrac{a^2}{x - a} = b$ for all choices of a and b.

36. Solve $\dfrac{\frac{2}{5} - \frac{1}{z}}{\frac{2}{5} + \frac{1}{z}} = 1$.

37. For which values of c does the equation $\dfrac{u + 3}{c + 2} + \dfrac{2u}{c} = 4$ have a solution for u? Find all of these solutions.

38. Solve $\dfrac{\frac{1}{x} - \frac{1}{a}}{\frac{1}{x} + \frac{1}{a}} = 1$.

39. Solve $\dfrac{x - x_1}{x_2 - x} = \dfrac{4}{5}$ for x.

40. Solve $bx - ax = \frac{1}{2}b^2 - \frac{1}{2}a^2$.

41. For which values of y does the equation $\dfrac{(y + 1)x}{y^2 - 1} + \dfrac{x + 5}{y - 1} = \dfrac{1}{2}$ have a solution for x? Find all of these solutions.

42. For which values of y is
$$\dfrac{\dfrac{a}{a + y} + \dfrac{y}{a - y}}{\dfrac{y}{a + y} - \dfrac{a}{a - y}} = -1?$$

43. Which values of the letters must be excluded in Problems 13, 20, 21, 22, 23, 24, 26, and 29 in Section 2.17?

44. Which values of the letters will make the expressions zero in Problems 13, 17, 20, 23, 29, and 31 in Section 2.17?

45. Find two consecutive even integers whose product is 288.

46. Find two integers whose sum is 22 and the sum of whose squares is 274.

Chapter 4

Complex Numbers

4.1 The Complex Field

If our number world were limited to the whole numbers, as it is for some primitive societies, we would quickly realize its inadequacies when we tried to solve even so simple an equation as $x + 9 = 5$. For a solution of this, one must go outside the set of whole numbers to the larger set of integers.

Provided a and b are integers, there is always an integral solution of the equation $x + a = b$. This is a consequence of the closure of the set of integers under addition and subtraction. But as soon as we consider equations of the form $ax = b$, the integers no longer suffice. There is no integer satisfying the equation $2x = 13$. To provide a solution, we must have access to the set of rational numbers. True, some equations of the form $ax = b$, $a \neq 0$, where a and b are integers, will have integral solutions—for example, $5x = 40$—but if we are to be sure that all such equations have solutions, we shall need the rationals.

Once rational numbers are admitted we can do more, for now even when a and b are rational, the equation $ax = b$ will have a rational solution provided $a \neq 0$. For example, $\frac{3}{7}x = \frac{12}{5}$ has the solution $\frac{28}{5}$. However, as soon as we consider more general equations with rational coefficients—for instance, $9x^2 = 2$—we must look beyond the set of rationals for a solution. Here it is the irrational $\dfrac{\sqrt{2}}{3}$.

We see that each of the important subsets of the real numbers is able to provide solutions for some equations, but none is sufficient for all types. The set of real numbers itself is no exception to this. For many equations there is a real number that is a solution; for others there is none. For example, there can be no real number x for which $x^2 = -25$, since the square of any non-zero real number must be positive. This chapter is concerned with the attempt to find solutions of such equations and the resulting consequences.

To search for a solution in a larger field containing the reals might seem fruitless, since it is difficult to imagine the existence of such a field. Actually, there are many fields containing the field of real numbers. If the reader has not been aware of this, it may be because until now he has had no need for them. One of these fields contains the solution to our equation $x^2 = -25$ and to many others as well. This field shall be denoted by C.

The major properties of C are:

    I. C is a field containing the real field R.

    II. C contains an element i such that $i^2 = -1$.

    III. For each element α of C, there are real numbers a and b such that $\alpha = a + bi$.

The field C is called the *complex field* and its elements *complex numbers*. As with most unfamiliar objects, complex numbers may seem peculiar at first.

To say that C is a field implies that its elements can be added, subtracted, multiplied, and divided by each other, and the resulting numbers are still in C. In brief, C is closed under these four operations. To say that C is a field implies that the axioms for a field discussed in Section 2.18 apply to C. As a consequence, all the theorems derived in Chapter 2 for real numbers must be valid for complex numbers as well. For example, if α and β are complex numbers, then $(-\alpha)(-\beta) = \alpha\beta$. Because C contains R, every real number must also be a complex number. In Chapter 6 we shall prove that the square of every real number is positive or zero. Therefore, since $i^2 = -1$, i cannot be in R, and C must be larger than R. We shall see presently that C contains many other complex numbers that are not in R. Figure 1.2 in Section 1.5, which shows the interrelationship of the subsets of the real number field, can be extended to include C (Figure 4.1).

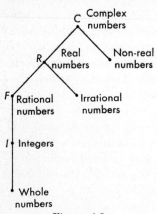

Figure 4.1

Let us see what some complex numbers look like. Since 3 and i are in C, so is $3 + i$, for C, being a field, is closed under addition. Similarly, $i(3 + i)$ must be in C. Applying the distributive law, we have

$$i(3 + i) = i3 + i^2.$$

By property II $i^2 = -1$, and therefore, using both commutative axioms,

$$i(3 + i) = -1 + 3i.$$

This illustrates property III. By closure we know that $i(3 + i)$ is a complex number and have found real numbers -1 and 3 such that $i(3 + i)$ $= -1 + 3i$. The expression $a + bi$ can be considered as a kind of standard form for complex numbers. Property III says that every complex number has such a standard form, and in Section 4.2 we shall show that it has only one.

From the three complex numbers 5, 3, and i can be formed the complex number $5 - 3i$. Therefore $(3 + i) + (5 - 3i)$ is a complex number. Using the field axioms, this can be rewritten as

$$
\begin{aligned}
(3 + i) + (5 - 3i) &= 3 + 5 + i - 3i \\
&= 8 + (1 - 3)i \\
&= 8 + (-2)i \\
&= 8 - 2i.
\end{aligned}
$$

The next to the last expression is in the form described in III. Here $a = 8$ and $b = -2$.

Note that property III does not explain how to find a and b; it merely says that there are such numbers. Finding them in any particular instance may be difficult.

The product of $3 + i$ and $5 - 3i$ can be expressed in the form $a + bi$ as follows:

$$
\begin{aligned}
(3 + i)(5 - 3i) &= (3 + i)5 + (3 + i)(-3i) \\
&= 15 + 5i - 9i - 3i^2 \\
&= 15 + (5 - 9)i - 3(-1) \\
&= 18 + (-4)i.
\end{aligned}
$$

These examples show that when dealing with complex numbers, i is to be treated no differently from any other letter except that i^2 may at any time be replaced by -1.

It is a little harder to express the quotient of two complex numbers in the form $a + bi$. We illustrate the procedure with $\dfrac{1 + 2i}{2 + 3i}$.

$$
\begin{aligned}
\frac{1 + 2i}{2 + 3i} &= \frac{(1 + 2i)(2 - 3i)}{(2 + 3i)(2 - 3i)} \\[2mm]
&= \frac{2 + 4i - 3i - 6i^2}{4 - 9i^2} \\[2mm]
&= \frac{8 + i}{13} \\[2mm]
&= \frac{8}{13} + \frac{1}{13}i.
\end{aligned}
$$

Our objective here was the replacement of the original fraction by an equivalent one with a real denominator. To do this, we multiplied the numerator and denominator by $2 - 3i$. The reader should examine the expression $(2 + 3i)(2 - 3i)$ carefully and understand why the choice of $2 - 3i$ as a factor makes this product real.

Returning to the equation $x^2 = -25$, which provoked this discussion, we see that the complex number $5i$ is a solution, since

$$(5i)^2 = 5^2 i^2 = -25.$$

Another solution is $-5i$. In Section 4.3 we shall show that there can be no others. In a similar fashion one can verify that $i\sqrt{7}$ and $-i\sqrt{7}$ are solutions of $x^2 + 7 = 0$. The equation

$$x^2 - 10x + 26 = 0$$

has $5 - i$ as a solution, since

$$(5 - i)^2 - 10(5 - i) + 26 = 25 - 10i + i^2 - 50 + 10i + 26$$
$$= 1 + i^2 = 0.$$

The symbol $\sqrt{-1}$ is often used instead of the letter i. Though suggestive, its use is not recommended because the square root symbol when representing a non-real number does not obey the usual rules; for example, it is not true that $\sqrt{a}\sqrt{b} = \sqrt{ab}$ if $a = b = -1$.

If d is a positive real number, we define $\sqrt{-d}$ to mean $i\sqrt{d}$, but as before, the latter notation is safer. Thus $i\sqrt{5}$ is preferable to $\sqrt{-5}$. In the course of formal algebraic manipulations, however, the symbol $\sqrt{-d}$ will occasionally creep into the calculation. When this happens, it is best to change it to the form $i\sqrt{d}$.

PROBLEMS

Simplify each of the following expressions for a complex number:

1. $2 - i + (-1 + \frac{1}{2}i)$.
2. $(1 + 3i)(1 - i)$.
3. $(7i - 2)^2$.
4. $(-1 - \frac{4}{5}i)(-1 + \frac{4}{5}i)$.
5. $(-i)^2$.
6. i^3.
7. i^4.
8. i^5.
9. $(6 - 7i)[(-1 - i) + 3 + 2i]$.
10. $(-7 + 2i)(5 - i) - (-2 - \sqrt{3}i)$.
11. $(1 + i)(2 - i)(3 + 5i)$.
12. $i(2i + 1)^3$.
13. $i^3 - i^7$.
14. i^{95}.

15. $\dfrac{1}{i}$.

Express in the form $a + bi$, where a and b are real:

16. $(1 + 3i) + (4 - \frac{3}{4}i) - (i - 6)$.
17. $7(\frac{1}{14} + i\sqrt{2})$.
18. $(2 - i)(1 + 3i)$.
19. $(1 + i)^2$.

20. $\dfrac{3 - 2i}{5}$.
21. 16.

22. $18 + 6\sqrt{2}$.

23. $\sqrt{3} + i - 2$.

24. $-4(5 - xi)$, x real.

25. $(a + i) + (6i - 5a)$, a real.

26. $(x_1 + y_1i) + (x_2 + y_2i)$, x_1, x_2, y_1, y_2 real.

27. $\dfrac{5}{i + 4}$.

28. $\dfrac{1 - i}{1 + 2i}$.

29. $\dfrac{\frac{1}{2} + 3i}{5 + \frac{1}{3}i}$.

30. $\dfrac{1}{i^3}$.

31. $\dfrac{4 + 7i}{(3 + i)(-1 - \frac{1}{2}i)}$.

32. $(1 + i)(3 - i)^{-1}$.

33. $\left(\dfrac{2}{i} + 1\right)\left(\dfrac{-i + 1}{i}\right)$.

34. $\dfrac{-6}{(1 + i)^2} \cdot \dfrac{5 - i^3}{i}$.

35. $\dfrac{2}{i^3} - \dfrac{5}{i^2} + \dfrac{3}{4i}$.

36. Verify the associative law $(\alpha\beta)\gamma = \alpha(\beta\gamma)$ for $\alpha = 3 + i$, $\beta = 1 - 2i$, $\gamma = 2 + 2i$.†

37. Express the product of the complex numbers $a_1 + b_1i$ and $a_2 + b_2i$, where a_1, a_2, b_1, b_2 are real, in the form $x + yi$ with real x and y.

38. Show that the quotient $\dfrac{a + bi}{c + di}$, where a, b, c, d are real, can usually be expressed in the form $x + yi$, where x and y are real. What restrictions must be placed on c and d?

39. For which positive integers n is $i^n = -1$?

40. If for the positive integers n and m, $i^n = i^m$, what can you say about $n - m$?

41. Show that the set $\{1, -1, i, -i\}$ is closed under multiplication.

Find a complex number in standard form whose square is:

42. -9.

43. -17.

44. 12.

45. -12.

46. Show that $(-1 + \sqrt{3}i)^3 = 8$.

47. Show that $\left(\dfrac{\sqrt{3}}{2} - \dfrac{1}{2}i\right)^3 = -i$.

Show that each of the following equations has the corresponding complex numbers as roots:

48. $x^2 + 64 = 0$; $8i$, $-8i$.

49. $x^2 = -21$; $-i\sqrt{21}$.

50. $x^2 + 14x + 50 = 0$; $-7 + i$.

51. $x^2 - 4x + 7 = 0$; $2 - \sqrt{3}i$, $2 + \sqrt{3}i$.

† γ is the Greek letter gamma and corresponds to c.

52. $y^2 + 2y - 4 = 0$; $-1 - \sqrt{5}$, $-1 + \sqrt{5}$.

53. $w^2 - 2\sqrt{3}w = -7$; $\sqrt{3} + 2i$.

54. $x^3 - 13x^2 + 52x - 40 = 0$; 1, $6 + 2i$, $6 - 2i$.

Find a complex number satisfying each equation:

55. $x^2 + 36 = 0$.

56. $x^2 + 6 = 0$.

57. $x^2 - 36 = 0$.

58. $x^2 = -13$.

59. $x^2 + 7 = 3$.

60. $5x^2 - 3 = -21$.

Express each of the following as a sum:

61. $(3x + 2i)(3x - 2i)$.

62. $(x + 5 + 4i)(x + 5 - 4i)$.

63. $(x + \sqrt{2} - 6i)(x + \sqrt{2} + 6i)$.

64. $(-x + i)(2x + 7)$.

65. $(x^2 + 2ix + 6)(2x - 3i)$.

66. $(2ix^2 + 1)[(3 + i)x - 2i]$.

Express each as a product of first degree polynomials with complex coefficients. For example, $2x^2 + 9 = (\sqrt{2}x + 3i)(\sqrt{2}x - 3i)$.

67. $x^2 + 1$.

68. $4x^2 - 25$.

69. $4x^2 + 25$.

70. $x^2 + 7$.

71. $(x + \frac{1}{2})^2 - 12$.

72. $(x - \frac{2}{5})^2 + 9$.

73. $-3x^2 - 8$.

4.2 Properties of Complex Numbers

Zero is a complex number, and hence by property III there are real numbers a and b such that $0 = a + bi$. Obviously, $a = 0$ and $b = 0$ are possible choices. It is easy to show that they are the only ones. For let $a + bi = 0$, where a and b are real. If $b \neq 0$, we would have $i = -a/b$, which would imply that i, being expressible as a quotient of real numbers, is real. Therefore b must be zero, and now from $0 = a + 0 \cdot i$ we see that also $a = 0$.

It is an immediate consequence that there is only one way in which a complex number α can be expressed in standard form as $\alpha = a + bi$ with real a and b. Otherwise expressed, if

$$(1) \qquad\qquad a + bi = a_1 + b_1 i,$$

then $a = a_1$ and $b = b_1$. For (1) implies that

$$(a - a_1) + (b - b_1)i = 0,$$

and hence $a - a_1 = 0$ and $b - b_1 = 0$. Thus a and a_1 are simply different symbols for the same number, and similarly for b and b_1. Sometimes we say that the standard form for α is *unique*, meaning it in this sense.

The unique real numbers a and b for which $\alpha = a + bi$ are called the *real* and *imaginary components* of α, respectively. The real and imaginary components of $\frac{1}{2} - 5i$ are $\frac{1}{2}$ and -5. Note that despite its name the imaginary component is real.

The complex number $a + bi$, where a and b are real, is certainly real if $b = 0$. Conversely, if $a + bi$ is real—say $a + bi = d$—then, since d can be written as $d = d + 0 \cdot i$, we must have $b = 0$ by the uniqueness of the imaginary component. A complex number is therefore real if and only if its imaginary component is zero.

Non-real complex numbers—that is, those for which $b \neq 0$—are frequently called *imaginary numbers*. This is a misnomer. Two hundred years ago they did seem mysterious and unreal, but today we understand our number system better and imaginary numbers are accepted as having just as much objective reality as real numbers. There was also a time when negative numbers seemed unreal and were regarded with suspicion.

Definition. If $\alpha = a + bi$ is a complex number in standard form so that a and b are real, the *conjugate* of α is the complex number $a - bi$.

The conjugate of α will be denoted by $\bar{\alpha}$; that is, $\bar{\alpha} = \overline{a + bi} = a - bi$. For example, if $\alpha = -3 + 2i$, then $\bar{\alpha} = -3 - 2i$. Likewise, $\overline{5 - i} = 5 + i$.

PROBLEMS

Find the real and imaginary components of the complex numbers:

1. $-3 + \frac{3}{5}i$.

2. $2i + 7 - 8i$.

3. $\dfrac{i - 6}{-5}$.

4. $1 + 2i^2$.

5. $(1 + i)^2$.

6. $(\frac{1}{3} + 4i)(i + 4)$.

7. $\dfrac{4}{2 - 7i}$.

8. $\dfrac{\frac{3}{5} - 3i}{(3i + 5)^2 - 1}$.

Find real numbers x and y for which the following equations are true. Why is there only one answer in each case?

9. $x + yi = 5 + 7i$.

10. $x - 3 + (y - 6)i = 0$.

11. $-4i = x - yi$.

12. $2x + 5yi = 9i^2$.

13. $x + \dfrac{8 - i}{4 + 2i}iy = 3x$.

Find the conjugate of:

14. $1 + \frac{1}{2}i$.

15. $-7i + \frac{1}{10}$.

16. 9.

17. $5i$.

18. i^3,

19. $\dfrac{4}{1 + i}$.

20. 0.

21. $(a + bi)^2$, a and b real.

22. $2 - \sqrt{6}$.

23. $\dfrac{3 + 2i}{2 - i}$.

24. For Problems 49, 50, 52, 53 in Section 4.1, show that the conjugate of each solution is also a solution.

25. If $\alpha = 2 + 3i$, show that $\alpha + \bar{\alpha}$ and $\alpha\bar{\alpha}$ are real.

*26. If α is any complex number, prove that $\alpha + \bar{\alpha}$ and $\alpha\bar{\alpha}$ are real.

*27. Let α be any complex number. Show that:
   (a) if α is real, $\alpha = \bar{\alpha}$;
   (b) if $\alpha = \bar{\alpha}$, α is real.
   (*Hint:* Express α in standard form.)

28. If α is any complex number, what is the relationship of $\bar{\bar{\alpha}}$ to α?

29. Let $\alpha = 2 + 3i$ and $\beta = 1 - i$.

   (a) Find $\bar{\alpha}$, $\bar{\beta}$, and $\overline{\alpha + \beta}$.

   (b) Show that $\overline{\alpha + \beta} = \bar{\alpha} + \bar{\beta}$.

   (c) Show that $\overline{\alpha\beta} = \bar{\alpha}\,\bar{\beta}$.

*30. If α and β are complex numbers, show that

   (a) $\overline{\alpha + \beta} = \bar{\alpha} + \bar{\beta}$,

   (b) $\overline{\alpha\beta} = \bar{\alpha}\,\bar{\beta}$.

   (*Hint:* Express α and β in standard form.)

*31. (a) Show that $\overline{\alpha + \beta + \gamma} = \bar{\alpha} + \bar{\beta} + \bar{\gamma}$ and state an analogous result for sums of more than three terms. Illustrate with $\alpha = 1 - i$, $\beta = 2 + i$ and $\gamma = 3 - 2i$.
   (b) State and prove a similar theorem for products, and illustrate.

32. If $\alpha = 1 + 2i$, find $\overline{(\alpha^2)}$ and $(\bar{\alpha})^2$. Show that $\overline{(\alpha^3)} = (\bar{\alpha})^3$.

*33. Show that $\overline{(\alpha^n)} = (\bar{\alpha})^n$, where n is a positive integer. (*Hint:* Use Problem 30(b).)

34. Show that the set of all non-real complex numbers is not closed under addition. Is it closed under multiplication?

4.3 Quadratic Equations

In Section 3.4 we saw that certain quadratic equations could be solved by factoring. At that time we were limited to those quadratic polynomials whose factors could be found by guessing, since we had no general method for determining the factors. Actually, it is a relatively simple matter to factor any quadratic polynomial with real coefficients, where now we use "factoring" in the broader sense of expressing the quadratic polynomial as a product of two first degree polynomials with complex coefficients. For example,

$$x^2 + 2x - 4 = (x + 1 + \sqrt{5})(x + 1 - \sqrt{5})$$

and

$$4x^2 + 9 = (2x + 3i)(2x - 3i).$$

Let us solve the equation

(1) $$x^2 + 2x - 17 = 0.$$

In order to factor the left side, we rewrite it as

$$x^2 + 2x - 17 = x^2 + 2x + 1 - 18.$$

The first three terms form a perfect square, giving us

(2) $$x^2 + 2x - 17 = (x + 1)^2 - 18$$
$$= [(x + 1) + \sqrt{18}][(x + 1) - \sqrt{18}]$$
(3) $$= (x + 1 + \sqrt{18})(x + 1 - \sqrt{18}).$$

Now, as before, we can argue that if x is a complex number for which either $x + 1 + \sqrt{18} = 0$ or $x + 1 - \sqrt{18} = 0$, then this x will satisfy (1). Two such numbers are $-1 - \sqrt{18}$ and $-1 + \sqrt{18}$. These are the only solutions. For if x is any solution of (1), then from (3)

$$(x + 1 + \sqrt{18})(x + 1 - \sqrt{18}) = 0,$$

and hence one of these two factors must be zero, showing that either $x = -1 - \sqrt{18}$ or $x = -1 + \sqrt{18}$.

As another example, we solve

(4) $$x^2 - 3x + \tfrac{13}{4} = 0.$$
$$x^2 - 3x + \tfrac{13}{4} = x^2 - 3x + \tfrac{9}{4} + 1$$
(5) $$= (x - \tfrac{3}{2})^2 + 1$$
$$= (x - \tfrac{3}{2} + i)(x - \tfrac{3}{2} - i).$$

The solutions are $\tfrac{3}{2} - i$ and $\tfrac{3}{2} + i$.

Note that in both examples we split the constant term, the term not containing an x, into a sum of two numbers in such a way that the first of these together with the terms containing x could be expressed as the square of a single quantity. This "completion of the square" can be effected by choosing the first number as the square of half the coefficient of x. The quadratics in (1) and (4) are now expressed in (2) and (5) as sums or differences of two squares (in (2) 18 can be considered as the square of $\sqrt{18}$) and in this form are easily factored using non-real numbers if necessary.

Illustration 1.   Factor $x^2 + 10x + 42$.

The square of half the coefficient of x is $(\tfrac{10}{2})^2 = 25$. Splitting 42 into $25 + 17$, we have

$$x^2 + 10x + 42 = x^2 + 10x + 25 + 17$$
$$= (x + 5)^2 + 17$$
$$= (x + 5 + i\sqrt{17})(x + 5 - i\sqrt{17}).$$

Illustration 2.   Factor $2x^2 - 5x + \dfrac{9}{4}$.

The rule given above for completing the square by squaring half the coefficient of x does not apply when, as here, the coefficient of x^2 is different from 1. But if one first removes this coefficient by factoring, the method can be used on the polynomial inside the bracket:

$$2x^2 - 5x + \frac{9}{4} = 2\left[x^2 - \frac{5}{2}x + \frac{9}{8}\right]$$

$$= 2\left[\left(x^2 - \frac{5}{2}x + \frac{25}{16}\right) - \frac{25}{16} + \frac{9}{8}\right]$$

$$= 2\left[\left(x - \frac{5}{4}\right)^2 - \frac{7}{16}\right]$$

$$= 2\left(x - \frac{5}{4} + \frac{\sqrt{7}}{4}\right)\left(x - \frac{5}{4} - \frac{\sqrt{7}}{4}\right).$$

The solutions of the equation $2x^2 - 5x + \frac{9}{4} = 0$ are therefore

(6)
$$\frac{5}{4} - \frac{\sqrt{7}}{4} \quad \text{and} \quad \frac{5}{4} + \frac{\sqrt{7}}{4}.$$

At the beginning of this section we remarked that any quadratic polynomial with real coefficients could be factored. To show this, we first point out that any quadratic polynomial can be expressed in the form $ax^2 + bx + c$, where $a \neq 0$. Now factor this by proceeding as in Illustration 2,

$$ax^2 + bx + c = a\left[x^2 + \frac{b}{a}x + \frac{c}{a}\right]$$

$$= a\left[\left(x^2 + \frac{b}{a}x + \frac{b^2}{4a^2}\right) - \frac{b^2}{4a^2} + \frac{c}{a}\right]$$

$$= a\left[\left(x + \frac{b}{2a}\right)^2 - \frac{b^2 - 4ac}{4a^2}\right]$$

$$= a\left(x + \frac{b}{2a} - \frac{\sqrt{b^2 - 4ac}}{2a}\right)\left(x + \frac{b}{2a} + \frac{\sqrt{b^2 - 4ac}}{2a}\right).$$

From this we see that the solutions of the equation $ax^2 + bx + c = 0$, $a \neq 0$, are

(7)
$$\frac{1}{2a}\left(-b + \sqrt{b^2 - 4ac}\right) \quad \text{and} \quad \frac{1}{2a}\left(-b - \sqrt{b^2 - 4ac}\right).$$

The expressions in (7) can be used to solve a quadratic equation directly. For example, for the equation $2x^2 - 5x + \frac{9}{4} = 0$ in Illustration 2 we note that $a = 2$, $b = -5$, and $c = \frac{9}{4}$. The solutions therefore as given by (7) are

$$\frac{1}{2 \cdot 2}\left(5 + \sqrt{(-5)^2 - 4(2)(\tfrac{9}{4})}\right) = \tfrac{1}{4}(5 + \sqrt{7})$$

and

$$\frac{1}{2 \cdot 2}\left(5 - \sqrt{(-5)^2 - 4(2)(\tfrac{9}{4})}\right) = \tfrac{1}{4}(5 - \sqrt{7}),$$

agreeing with (6).

If $b^2 - 4ac$ is negative—say $-d$, where d is positive—it is better to express $\sqrt{b^2 - 4ac}$ as $i\sqrt{d}$ rather than use the form $\sqrt{-d}$. Using (7), the solutions of the equation $x^2 + 10x + 42 = 0$ in Illustration 1 are

$$\tfrac{1}{2}(-10 + \sqrt{-68}) = \tfrac{1}{2}(-10 + i\sqrt{68})$$
$$= \tfrac{1}{2}(-10 + i\sqrt{4}\sqrt{17}) = -5 + i\sqrt{17},$$

and

$$\tfrac{1}{2}(-10 - \sqrt{-68}) = \tfrac{1}{2}(-10 - i\sqrt{68})$$
$$= \tfrac{1}{2}(-10 - i\sqrt{4}\sqrt{17}) = -5 - i\sqrt{17}.$$

A quadratic equation may have only one solution. Consider, for example, the equation $9y^2 - 12y + 4 = 0$. Since

$$9y^2 - 12y + 4 = (3y - 2)^2,$$

we see that $\frac{2}{3}$ is the only solution.

PROBLEMS

Factor the following quadratic polynomials:

1. $9x^2 - 30x + 25$.
2. $w^2 - 9w + 20$.
3. $x^2 + 4x + 1$.
4. $4x^2 - 4x - 6$.
5. $\frac{16}{9}x^2 + 36$.

6. $2z^2 + 11$.
7. $x^2 - 8x + 41$.
8. $9x^2 - 6x + 2$.
9. $6y - 4y^2 + 7$.
10. $x^2 + 14x + 52$.

Solve the following quadratic equations, first by completing the square and factoring, and then by use of expressions (7):

11. $z^2 + 2z - 1 = 0$.
12. $x^2 + 6x - 7 = 0$.
13. $4x^2 - 12x = 11$.
14. $x^2 + 10 = -6x$.
15. $3y^2 + 21 = 0$.
16. $3y^2 - 8y + 9 = y^2 - 2$.
17. $x^2 + x + c = 0$.

18. $4x^2 = 36$.
19. $3ax^2 = 0, \qquad a \neq 0$.
20. $u^2 + 13 = 6u$.
21. $8w + 1 = -16w^2$.
22. $cx^2 + 2cx + 2 = 0, \qquad c \neq 0$.
23. $x^2 + 2ax + cx + 2ac = 0$.

24. Solve $x^2 - x - 20 - y = 0$ for x in terms of y.
25. Solve $4x^4 - 12x^2 + 4 = 0$ for x^2.
26. Solve $4x^4 + 31x^2 - 90 = 0$ for x.

27. Solve $3x^2 + 4xy - 2y^2 = 0$ for y.
28. Solve $x^2 - 2xy + y^2 - 4x + 4y = -4$ for x.
29. Solve $x^2 - 2xz + z^2 - 3x + 2z - 3 = 0$ for z.
30. Solve $y^2 + 2xy + 3y = -x^2 - 3x + 4$ for y.
31. Determine b so that the equation

$$\frac{3x + b}{2x + 3} = x - b$$

has just one solution.
32. Determine k so that the equation $12x^2 - 6kx + k^2 - 4 = 0$ has just one solution.
33. Find a value of c for which the equation $x^2 + 2x + 4 - c = 0$ has real roots.
34. Determine a so that 2 will be a solution of the equation $3ax^2 - 5x + 2a = 0$.
*35. Find a condition on the real numbers $a \neq 0$, b, and c in order that the solutions of the equation $ax^2 + bx + c = 0$ be (a) real; (b) non-real. When will the equation have just one solution?
36. Show that if a quadratic equation with real coefficients has a non-real solution, the conjugate is also a solution. Give an example showing that this may not be true if some of the coefficients are not real.
37. Show that the equation $x^2 - 4x + 4 - k^2 = 0$ has two solutions for all real non-zero values of k.
38. Find two numbers whose sum is 45 and product 434.
39. Find two consecutive integers whose product is 240.
40. Find two numbers whose sum is 3 and the sum of whose squares is 7.

Solve the equations:

41. $\dfrac{6}{z + 1} + \dfrac{2 + 3z}{3z + 4} = -1.$

42. $\dfrac{4}{3 - y} + \dfrac{2y}{y + 5} = 1.$

43. $\dfrac{1}{x^2 - 4} - \dfrac{3x}{x - 2} = -2.$

44. $\dfrac{y + 3}{(y + 1)(y - 4)} = \dfrac{2y}{y - 4}.$

4.4 Complex Equations

Since the set of all complex numbers forms a field, it is possible to extend the concept of an equation to one containing not just real numbers but complex numbers. Examples of such equations are

(1) $$\frac{i}{3}x = 2 - 7i,$$

(2) $$x^2 - (6 - i)x - 6i = 0,$$

and

(3) $$\frac{5(x^2 - i)}{5x + 2(3 + i)} = -(1 + 3i).$$

As with equations containing only real numbers, they may or may not have solutions.

To solve the first equation, we proceed exactly as we would if the coefficients were real, replacing the equation by a sequence of progressively simpler equivalent equations:

$$\frac{i}{3}x = 2 - 7i,$$

$$x = \frac{2 - 7i}{\dfrac{i}{3}} = \frac{3(2 - 7i)}{i}$$

$$= \frac{6}{i} - 21 = -6i - 21.$$

Equation (2) can be solved by factoring:

$$x^2 - (6 - i)x - 6i = (x - 6)(x + i) = 0.$$

The solutions are 6 and $-i$.

Complex numbers were introduced to solve the equation $x^2 + 25 = 0$, but we have seen that many other equations with real coefficients have complex numbers as solutions. The question now arises whether every equation with complex coefficients has a solution in the field of complex numbers or whether for some equations we must look in a still larger field for a solution. The answer is that we have now reached the end. More precisely, every polynomial equation

$$a_n x^n + a_{n-1} x^{n-1} + \cdots + a_1 x + a_0 = 0,$$

where n is a positive integer and the a_i's are complex numbers with $a_n \neq 0$, has a complex number as a solution. The proof of this is too advanced to give here. One of the most important theorems in algebra, it forms the basis for much of the material in the next chapter.

PROBLEMS

Simplify:

1. $(x^2 + ix - 5) + [(2 + i)x^2 + 3x - 2]$.
2. $(x^3 + 5x^2 - x + 3) - [i^2 x^3 - (5 + 2i)x^2 - x + 2 - i\sqrt{3}]$.

Express as a sum and simplify:

3. $(x + \frac{1}{2} - i)(x + \frac{1}{2} + i)$.
4. $(ix + 3)(x + 2 - i)$.
5. $[(1 - 2i)x + 5][(1 + 2i)x - 5]$.
6. $[2x^2 + (1 - 4i)x + 3](x^2 - i)$.
7. $(x + 3i)(x - 5)[x - (2 - i)]$.

Show that each equation has the corresponding complex numbers as roots:

8. $\frac{x}{3} - 7i = 0$; $21i$.
9. $2x^2 + (14 - i)x - 7i = 0$; $-7, \frac{i}{2}$.
10. $(5 + i)y^2 + (6 - i)y = -i + 3$; $\frac{5}{13} - \frac{i}{13}$.
11. $u^3 + 2(i - 1)u^2 - (3 + 4i)u - 6i = 0$; $3, -1, -2i$.

Solve the equations:

12. $\frac{3}{2}x + 5i = 0$.

13. $\frac{2}{i}x + 3 - i = 7$.

14. $(1 - 3i)y + 4i = 0$.

15. $z^2 + (5 - i)z - 5i = 0$.

16. $\dfrac{2x - 6i}{x + i} = 1$.

17. $2x^2 - ix + 4 = 0$.

18. $(1 + i)x^2 + ix + 1 - i = 0$.

Factor each of the following using complex numbers:

19. $x^2 - 49$.

20. $x^2 + 49$.

21. $x^2 + 17$.

22. $x^2 - 17$.

23. $x^2 + (i - 3)x - 3i$.

24. $x^2 - 4x + 5$.

25. $x^2 + 6ix - 8$.

26. $ix^2 - x + 6i$.

27. Solve equation (3).

28. Show that $-2 + i$ is a solution of $x^2 - (1 - 4i)x - 1 + 13i = 0$. Use this to factor the left side of the equation and hence find the other solution.

29. Find a complex number α in the form $a + bi$, a and b real, for which $\alpha^2 = i$. (*Hint:* Solve the equation $(a + bi)^2 = i$ for a and b.)

4.5   Construction of the Complex Field

Formally, what we did in Section 4.1 was to postulate the existence of a field C containing the real field and for which properties I, II, and III are valid. These three properties then are really axioms for C, the first implying all the axioms necessary to ensure that C is a field.

Postulating the existence of anything as abstract as a field can be a form of wishful thinking, for there may not be a field with the desired properties. In this instance the difficulty can be overcome by actually constructing the complex field from the real field. We shall outline a method for doing this.

Let C' be the set of all pairs (a, b) of real numbers a and b. Thus $(1, 2)$, $(1 + \sqrt{3}, -\frac{7}{10})$, and $(0, \pi)$ are in C'. Two pairs shall be considered equal if and only if their respective components are equal; that is, $(a, b) = (c, d)$ if and only if $a = c$ and $b = d$.

We now define two ways of combining pairs to get other pairs in C' and call these two operations "addition" and "multiplication":

$$(a_1, b_1) + (a_2, b_2) = (a_1 + a_2, b_1 + b_2),$$
$$(a_1, b_1) \cdot (a_2, b_2) = (a_1a_2 - b_1b_2, a_1b_2 + b_1a_2).$$

For example,

$$(1, 7) + (-3, 2) = (1 - 3, 7 + 2) = (-2, 9),$$

and

$$(1, 7) \cdot (-3, 2) = [1(-3) - 7 \cdot 2, 1 \cdot 2 + 7(-3)] = (-17, -19).$$

Certainly C' is closed under this addition and multiplication of pairs. It is easy to see that these are commutative operations, and with a little effort one can show them to be associative and that the distributive law holds. The pair $(0, 0)$ has the property that for any pair (a, b),

$$(a, b) + (0, 0) = (a + 0, b + 0) = (a, b).$$

It thus behaves like a zero element. In short, all the axioms for a field can be verified for C'. It is this field that we can take to be the field of complex numbers.

Let R' be the subset of C' composed of all pairs of the form $(a, 0)$. The sum and product of two such pairs are again in R':

$$(a, 0) + (b, 0) = (a + b, 0),$$
$$(a, 0) \cdot (b, 0) = (ab, 0),$$

showing that the subset R' is closed under these operations.

There is a natural correspondence between the elements of R' and the real numbers indicated by pairing $(2, 0)$ with 2, $(-\frac{3}{7}, 0)$ with $-\frac{3}{7}$, and in general, $(a, 0)$ with a. Note then that $(a + b, 0)$ will correspond to $a + b$. That is, the sum of $(a, 0)$ and $(b, 0)$ corresponds to the sum of a and b. Since $(ab, 0)$ corresponds to ab, there is a similar result for products. Because of this, the arithmetic of R' must be exactly like that of the real field R; it is only the notation that is more complicated. We see that although C', being composed of pairs of numbers, cannot contain R, it does contain a subset that behaves exactly like R.

The pair $(0, 1)$ is not in R'. Its square, however, is in R',

$$(0, 1)^2 = (0, 1)(0, 1) = (-1, 0),$$

and is the element corresponding to -1 in R. The pair $(0, 1)$ shall be denoted by i. Lastly, any pair (a, b) in C' can be expressed in the form

$$(a, b) = (a, 0) + (b, 0)(0, 1),$$

where we note that $(a, 0)$ and $(b, 0)$ are the elements of R' corresponding to a and b in R.

To sum up, we have constructed a field C' containing a subfield R' essentially indistinguishable from R; C' contains an element i for which $i^2 = (-1, 0)$; and for each element $\alpha = (a, b)$ in C' there are "numbers" $(a, 0)$ and $(b, 0)$ in R' such that

$$(1) \qquad\qquad \alpha = (a, 0) + (b, 0)i.$$

The final step is to agree to use the same notation for the elements of R and R', enabling us to write $a + bi$ for the element α in (1).

We see that, properly interpreted, the set C' satisfies axioms I, II, and III in Section 4.1 and is essentially the field C. Also, if one takes an abstract view of numbers, the construction shows that imaginary complex numbers are just as tangible as real numbers. There is nothing imaginary about them except their name, an inheritance from the past.

PROBLEMS

Perform the indicated operations. In the first part of each problem the complex numbers are represented by pairs of real numbers, and in the second by the conventional $a + bi$ notation.

1. (a) $(1, 4) + (\frac{7}{2}, -6)$;
   (b) $(1 + 4i) + (\frac{7}{2} - 6i)$.

2. (a) $(1, 4) - (2, 0)$;
   (b) $(1 + 4i) - 2$.

3. (a) $(-1, 2)(3, \frac{1}{2})$;
   (b) $(-1 + 2i)(3 + \frac{1}{2}i)$.

4. (a) $(-1, 0)(4, 0)$;
   (b) $(-1) \cdot 4$.

5. (a) $(0, 5)(0, -7)$;
   (b) $5i(-7i)$.

6. Show that $(0, 1)^3 = -(0, 1)$.

In the following problems C' is the set of all pairs (a,b) of real numbers referred to in the text.

7. Prove that addition and multiplication in C' are commutative.

8. Verify the associative and distributive laws, $\alpha(\beta\gamma) = (\alpha\beta)\gamma$ and $\alpha(\beta + \gamma) = \alpha\beta + \alpha\gamma$, for $\alpha = (3, 1)$, $\beta = (1, -2)$, $\gamma = (2, 2)$.

9. Prove that addition and multiplication in C' are associative.

10. Show that the distributive law holds in C'.

11. Find an element (x, y) of C' such that $(5, -3) + (x, y) = (0, 0)$. It would be natural to denote this element by $-(5, -3)$.

12. Show that for each (a, b) of C' there is an (x, y) for which $(a, b) + (x, y) = (0, 0)$. Why is it reasonable to denote this (x, y) by $-(a, b)$?

13. Define subtraction in C'. That is, explain what is meant by $(a, b) - (c, d)$.

14. Find an element in C' that behaves like a unit element; that is, a pair (x, y) such that $(a, b)(x, y) = (a, b)$ for all pairs (a, b).

15. Show that $(a, b)^{-1}$ exists if a and b are not both zero.

Chapter 5

Polynomials

5.1 Functions

Scarcely less important than the concept of a set is that of a correspondence between two sets. Let X be the set of numbers $\{0, 10, -\frac{7}{2}, -19, 8\}$.
With each of these numbers we shall associate a number, as indicated by
the following table:

(1)

X	0	10	$-\frac{7}{2}$	-19	8
Y	-2	11	3	-19	10

Thus to 0 corresponds -2, to 10 corresponds 11, -19 to -19, and so on.
This correspondence, which associates a number with each number of X, is
an example of a function. Functions are basic in much of present day
mathematics.

The association in (1) was arbitrary in the sense that there was nothing
special about the numbers chosen to be the correspondents of those in X;
any others could have served equally well. To each of the numbers in X
we could have let correspond a number as follows:

(2)

X	0	10	$-\frac{7}{2}$	-19	8
Y	-19	-2	3	11	10

This correspondence is also a function. Although the set Y of correspondents is the same as before, the correspondence is not the same and the
function is considered as different from the first.

Definition. A *function* is a correspondence that associates to each
number x of some given set X of numbers one and only one number.

The condition that to each number x in X corresponds only one number

101

is important. The correspondence indicated by table (3) is not a function because to 1 in X corresponds both 0 and $\frac{1}{2}$.

(3)

X	5	1	4	1
Y	-7	0	6	$\frac{1}{2}$

It is permissible, however, to have the same number as the correspondent of more than one x in X. The correspondence in (4) is a function in which -7 is the correspondent of 5, 0, and -3 in X.

(4)

X	5	1	4	0	-3
Y	-7	0	4	-7	-7

As in the above examples, the set X may have one or more numbers in common with the set Y of correspondents; indeed, X and Y are often the same set. Note that a number may correspond to itself. Usually X and Y will be infinite because the more interesting and useful functions are correspondences between infinite rather than finite sets.

Illustration 1. Let X be the set of all real numbers between -2 and 2, inclusive. To each x in X, let correspond the square of x. Thus to $-\frac{1}{2}$ in X corresponds

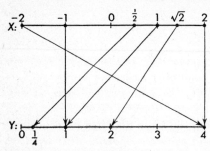

Figure 5.1

$\frac{1}{4}$, and to 1 in X corresponds 1. This correspondence satisfies our definition of a function. It is pictured schematically in Figure 5.1, where the numbers in X and Y are represented by points on the lines and an arrow is drawn from each number in X to its correspondent.

Although in our examples the sets X and Y contained only real numbers, they may for some functions contain non-real numbers as well.

Exercise A.   Describe a third function, using the sets X and Y in (1).

Exercise B.   Consider the function in Illustration 1.

(a) What number corresponds to $1\frac{2}{3}$ in X?

(b) Find two numbers in X whose correspondents are $\frac{9}{4}$.

(c) Some numbers correspond to two different numbers in X. Which ones are they?

(d) What number corresponds to 1.732 in X? To which positive number in X does 3 correspond?

It is convenient to have a means of designating functions, and letters are used for this purpose. The function in (1) might be indicated by the letter f. The letter f when so used does not stand for a number, as it has in earlier chapters, but for the correspondence itself as described by (1). If one wishes to consider another function at the same time, a different letter, such as g, must be used to avoid confusion.

For a function to be completely described, not only must the correspondence be given, but also the description of the set X. Let g be the function in Illustration 1. This function is not sufficiently described by the phrase, "g is the function that associates to each real number its square," because this does not specify the nature of the set X. If we say, "g is the function that associates to each real number between -2 and 2, inclusive, its square," X is specified and g completely described. The function u defined by "to each x between -1.5 and 6, inclusive, corresponds x^2" is a different function even though the nature of the correspondence is the same as that for g.

If f is a function, the number that corresponds to a particular number x in X is denoted by $f(x)$ (read "f of x") and is called the *value of f at x*. Thus if f is the function in (1), then $f(0) = -2$, $f(10) = 11$, $f(-19) = -19$; that is, the value of f at 0 is -2, the value of f at 10 is 11, and so on. Of course, when it is used in this sense, the notation $f(x)$ does not mean the product of f and x. Surprisingly, there is almost no confusion arising from this double use of the parentheses; the context generally makes clear whether a function or a product is intended.

If g is the function described in Illustration 1, then $g(\frac{4}{3}) = \frac{16}{9}$, $g(0) = 0$, $g(-1) = 1$, and more generally, $g(x) = x^2$, where x is between -2 and 2, inclusive. Note that $g(5)$ is not defined, since 5 is not in X. It is important to keep in mind the distinction between a function f, which is a correspondence, and its value $f(x)$, which is a number.

If f is a function, the set X is called the *domain* of the function and the set of those numbers that correspond to some x in X—that is, the set of all $f(x)$—is called its *range*. The domain of the function in (1) is the set $\{0, 10, -\frac{7}{2}, -19, 8\}$, and the range is $\{-2, 11, 3, -19, 10\}$. The function in (2) has the same domain and range. In (4) the domain is $\{5, 1, 4, 0, -3\}$, and the range is $\{-7, 0, 4\}$. The domain of the function g in Illustration 1 is the set of all real numbers between -2 and 2, inclusive. Its range is the set of all real numbers between 0 and 4, inclusive.

Two functions f and g are considered the same if and only if they have the same domain X, and for each x in X the number that corresponds to x under f is the same as the number that corresponds to x under g; that is, $f(x) = g(x)$ for all x in X.

The function in Illustration 1 is completely described by the statement, "Let g be the function defined by $g(x) = x^2$, where x is between -2 and 2, inclusive," or more briefly, by, "Let g be the function defined by $g(x) = x^2$, $-2 \leq x \leq 2$." Usually functions are described in this manner.

When the domain of a function f is not specified, it will be understood to consist of all real numbers for which the expression defining the function is meaningful and the values $f(x)$ are real. For example, the domain of the function f defined by $f(x) = \dfrac{3}{x-1}$ would be understood to be all real $x \neq 1$, since x is not otherwise restricted. The function h defined by $h(x) = \sqrt{16 - x^2}$ would be understood to be defined only for x between -4 and 4, inclusive, since $h(x)$ is non-real for all other x. However, for polynomial functions, a type of function described in the next section and which will be our special concern for the remainder of this chapter, we shall make an exception and allow complex numbers in the domain and range.

There is nothing special about the letter x, and other letters are often used when discussing functions. For example, the function f defined by $f(x) = x^2 - \dfrac{3}{x} + 5$, $x \neq 0$, can equally well be defined by $f(t) = t^2 - \dfrac{3}{t} + 5$, $t \neq 0$.

An important yet simple function is the one that associates with each real number the number 3. If h denotes this function, then $h(1) = 3$, $h(-10) = 3$, $h(2 + \sqrt{3}) = 3$, $h(3) = 3$, and in general, $h(x) = 3$ for all x. Any such function f for which $f(x) = c$ for all x, where c is some fixed number, is called a *constant function*.

PROBLEMS

1. If f is the function defined by $f(x) = -2$ for all x, what is the domain and range of f? Draw a diagram for this function similar to Figure 5.1.

2. Let X be the set of all real numbers and f the function such that to each x in X corresponds the number formed by multiplying x by 3 and then subtracting 1 from this product.
   (a) Find $f(2), f(0), f(-10), f(a), f(x)$.
   (b) Which numbers in X have 8 as their correspondent?
   (c) What is the domain and range of f?
   (d) For which x is $f(x) = x$?
   (e) Draw a diagram for f similar to Figure 5.1.

3. If g is the function defined by $g(t) = 3 - \dfrac{t}{2}$, $t \geq 0$, find $g(1)$, $g(0)$, $g(-a)$, where $a \leq 0$. Is there a value of g at -4? What is the domain and range of g?

4. Let u be the function defined by $u(x) = x^2 + 3x - 10$. Find $u(0)$, $u(2)$, $u(-5)$, $u(-\tfrac{1}{2})$. Find an x, if any, for which $u(x) = 18$.

5. If f is the function defined by $f(z) = \dfrac{4}{z^2 - 1}$, $z \neq \pm 1$, find $f(2)$, $f(0)$, $f(-5)$. Is there a z for which $f(z) = 0$?

6. Let p be the function defined by $p(x) = 2x^2 + 5x - 3$.
   (a) Find $p(0)$, $p(1)$, $p(10)$, $p(a)$, $p(1) + p(10)$, $p(1 + 10)$, $-p(4)$, $p(-4)$.
   (b) Explain the difference between $p(a) + p(b)$ and $p(a + b)$.

(c) Is $p(2) + p(3) = p(2 + 3)$?

(d) Why does the distributive law not apply to the example in (c)?

(e) Find a number a such that $p(a) = 0$. (The number a is called a *zero* of the function.)

7. Let q be the function defined by $q(x) = x^2 + x - 7$.

(a) Explain the difference between $q(2a)$ and $2q(a)$.

(b) Is $2q(a) = q(2a)$ for all a?

8. Is it true that $f(-2) = -f(2)$ for all functions f?

9. Find a function f such that $f(-x) = -f(x)$ for all real numbers x?

10. (a) If f is a function whose domain contains complex numbers, explain the meanings of $f(\alpha)$, $f(\bar\alpha)$, $\overline{f(\alpha)}$, where $\bar\alpha$ is the conjugate of α.

(b) If p is the function defined by $p(x) = 3x^2 + 2x + 7$, where x is any complex number, find $p(i)$, $p(-3)$, $p(5i)$, $p(2 + i)$, $p(\overline{2 + i})$, $\overline{p(2 + i)}$.

5.2 Polynomials

Functions and their properties are the subject of the branch of mathematics known as analysis, the study of which is begun in the calculus. We shall be interested here only in the type of function exemplified by those with defining expressions of the form $f(x) = 4x - \frac{1}{3}$ and

$$(1) \qquad\qquad g(x) = 2x^5 - 4x^4 + 5x^2 - x + 7.$$

Such functions are called polynomial functions, and the expressions on the right of the equals signs are called polynomials.

Definition. A *polynomial in x* is an expression of the form

$$(2) \qquad\qquad a_n x^n + a_{n-1} x^{n-1} + \cdots + a_1 x + a_0,$$

where the a_i's are complex numbers and n is a non-negative integer.

Other examples of polynomials are

$$(3) \qquad\qquad x^3 + \tfrac{17}{5} x^2 + \sqrt{2} x$$

and

$$(4) \qquad\qquad 2x^4 + x^3 - (\tfrac{2}{3} + \sqrt{17i}) x^2 - \log 8.$$

The following are not polynomials:

$$x^2 - 6x + \frac{12}{x} + 5,$$

$$\log(x + 1) - 10,$$

$$4x^3 - 2\sqrt{x} + 5x - 2.$$

When there is no ambiguity about the letter x, a polynomial in x is generally called simply a *polynomial*.

Exercise A. Find n and identify a_n, a_{n-1}, $\cdots$, a_1, a_0 for the following polynomials:

(a) $3x^2 - 5x + \frac{6}{4}$;

(b) $4x - \frac{1}{3}$;

(c) The polynomials in (3) and (4).

Definition. A *polynomial function* is a function p defined by

$$p(x) = a_n x^n + a_{n-1} x^{n-1} + \cdots + a_1 x + a_0,$$

where the expression on the right is a polynomial and x is any complex number.

Definition. Let $a_n x^n + a_{n-1} x^{n-1} + \cdots + a_1 x + a_0$ be a polynomial. The number a_j in the term $a_j x^j$ is the *coefficient* of x^j. If $a_n \neq 0$, the integer n is the *degree* of the polynomial.

For the polynomial $g(x)$ in (1) the coefficient of x^4 is -4 and the coefficient of x^3 is 0. The degree of $g(x)$ is 5. In (4) the coefficient of x^3 is 1 and that of x^2 is $-(\frac{2}{3} + \sqrt{17i})$. The degree of the polynomial is 4. The polynomial $0 \cdot x^4 - 6x^3 + x - 3$ is of the third degree. The polynomial a_0 has degree 0 if $a_0 \neq 0$. Thus zero degree polynomials are just the complex numbers themselves, sometimes called *constants* in this connection. The polynomial 0 does not have a degree.

Polynomials of the first degree are sometimes called *linear* polynomials, those of the second degree *quadratic*, and those of the third degree *cubic*. The term a_0 in (2) is called the *constant term* of the polynomial, the term $a_1 x$ the *linear* or *first degree term*, $a_2 x^2$ the *quadratic* or *second degree* term, etc.

A polynomial whose coefficients are complex numbers is called a *complex polynomial* or a *polynomial over C*, where C is the field of complex numbers. If all of the coefficients are real, it is a *real polynomial* or a *polynomial over R*, the field of real numbers. Obviously, any real polynomial is also a complex polynomial. The polynomial in (4) is a polynomial over C; it is not a polynomial over R. The polynomial in (3) is a real as well as a complex polynomial. An example of a *rational polynomial* is $\frac{1}{2}x^3 - 5x^2 + x$. It is also a real and a complex polynomial. When the coefficients of a polynomial are unspecified, it will be assumed that they are complex. It is quite permissible for x in a real or rational polynomial function to be a complex number.

If $p(x)$ is a polynomial, the equation $p(x) = 0$ is called a *polynomial equation*; for example, $x^2 + 3x - 4 = 0$. Any complex number that is a solution of a polynomial equation is called a *root* of the equation and a *zero* of the polynomial. The polynomial

$$q(x) = x^2 + 3x - 4$$

has 1 and -4 as zeros, since $q(1) = 0$ and $q(-4) = 0$.

Although frequently it is difficult, if not impossible, to find explicit expressions for the zeros of a polynomial, considerable information about the zeros can be found by examining the polynomial.

PROBLEMS

1. What is the coefficient of x in the polynomial in Problem 6? What is the constant term?
2. What are the coefficients of x^3, x^4, and x in the polynomial in Problem 5? What is the constant term?

Give the degree of each of the following polynomials, and state whether it is a polynomial over the rational, real, or complex field:

3. $2x^3 + 1$.

4. 4.

5. $ix^4 - \sqrt{3}x^3 + 2x^2 + x$.

6. $\dfrac{(1 + \sqrt{7})}{8} x + \dfrac{3}{2}$.

7. $\dfrac{2}{15} x^2 - \dfrac{1}{3} x - \dfrac{7}{3}$.

8. If $p(x) = x^2 + x - 2 - 3i$, find the value of p at 6; at -1; at $-4i$; at $\overline{5 + 2i}$.

9. If $q(x) = 2x^3 - 3ix^2 + x - 1$, find $q(2), q(1 - i), q(\overline{1 - i}), \overline{q(1 - i)}$.

Show that each polynomial below has the corresponding complex numbers as zeros:

10. $x^2 - 5x - 6$; 6, -1.

11. $3x + 7$; $-\frac{7}{3}$.

12. $x^3 - 2x^2 - 3x + 6$; $-\sqrt{3}$, 2.

13. $x^2 + 10x + 26$; $-5 + i$, $-5 - i$.

14. $x^2 + (3 - i)x + 2 - i$; $-2 + i$, -1.

15. $x^2 + (7 - a)x + 12 - 4a$; $a - 3$, -4.

5.3   Factors of Polynomials

Definition.   If $p(x)$, $s(x)$, and $t(x)$ are polynomials such that

$$(1) \qquad\qquad p(x) = s(x)t(x),$$

$s(x)$ and $t(x)$ are *factors* or *divisors* of $p(x)$.

Thus $x - 1$ and $x^2 - x - 2$ are factors of $x^3 - 2x^2 - x + 2$, since

$$(2) \qquad\qquad x^3 - 2x^2 - x + 2 = (x - 1)(x^2 - x - 2).$$

Since

$$x^2 + (5 - \sqrt{2})x - 5\sqrt{2} = (x - \sqrt{2})(x + 5),$$

$x - \sqrt{2}$ and $x + 5$ are divisors of $x^2 + (5 - \sqrt{2})x - 5\sqrt{2}$. Note that here we are using the word "factor" in a broader sense than in Section 2.11, where we were concerned for the most part with finding just the rational factors of rational polynomials.

Every polynomial has trivial factorizations; as, for example,

(3) $$x^3 - 2x^2 - x + 2 = -\tfrac{1}{3}(-3x^3 + 6x^2 + 3x - 6).$$

Since these are of little interest, we distinguish between them and a factorization such as that in (2) by calling the factors in (2) proper and those in (3) improper. More generally, $s(x)$ in (1) is a *proper* factor if its degree is less than that of $p(x)$ but is not zero.

Definition. A polynomial of degree greater than zero with coefficients in a field K is *irreducible over* K if it has no proper factors whose coefficients are in K.

Thus $x^2 - 3$, a polynomial over F, the rational field, is irreducible over F, since it cannot be factored as a product of polynomials with *rational* coefficients. So also are $2x + 8$ and $x^2 + 2x + 5$. In fact, $x^2 + 2x + 5$ is also irreducible over the real field R. The polynomial $x^2 - x - 2$ is reducible over F, since

$$x^2 - x - 2 \doteq (x - 2)(x + 1).$$

A polynomial may be irreducible over one field and yet be reducible over a larger field. For example, $x^2 - 3$, which is irreducible over F, does have proper factors over R:

$$x^2 - 3 = (x + \sqrt{3})(x - \sqrt{3}).$$

The same equation shows that it is also reducible over C. Over R, $x^2 + 2x + 5$ is irreducible, but it is reducible over the complex field:

$$x^2 + 2x + 5 = (x + 1 + 2i)(x + 1 - 2i).$$

Obviously, a first degree polynomial is irreducible over every field.

Irreducible polynomials are the analogue of prime numbers, and there is a striking parallel between their theories.

A polynomial is *completely factored over a given field* when it is expressed as a product of factors each of which is irreducible over the field. If we express $p(x) = 2x^4 - 18$ as

$$2x^4 - 18 = 2(x^2 + 3)(x^2 - 3),$$

the right side of the equation is the complete factorization of $p(x)$ over the rational field. Over the real field, however, it is not complete, since $x^2 - 3$ is reducible over R. The complete factorization over the real field is

(4) $$2x^4 - 18 = 2(x^2 + 3)(x + \sqrt{3})(x - \sqrt{3}).$$

Further factorization is possible if we admit complex polynomials as factors,

$$2x^4 - 18 = 2(x + i\sqrt{3})(x - i\sqrt{3})(x + \sqrt{3})(x - \sqrt{3}),$$

and now $p(x)$ is completely factored over the complex field.

It is true, but we shall not prove it here, that there is essentially only one complete factorization of a given polynomial over a field in the sense that no matter how the reduction of the polynomial to a product of irreducible factors is accomplished, the resulting products will always contain the same factors, though these may occur in a different order and some may be multiplied by numbers. For example,

$$2x^4 - 18 = -(2x + 2\sqrt{3})(x^2 + 3)(-x + \sqrt{3})$$

is also a complete factorization of $2x^4 - 18$ over the real field, but it is essentially the same as (4). The situation is quite analogous to the unique factorization of integers as products of primes.

It is often difficult to find proper factors of a given polynomial or even to determine whether it is reducible. We saw in Section 2.11 that certain simple polynomials could be factored by inspection. Although these occur frequently, they are hardly typical of the class of all polynomials, and the techniques used there are rarely successful with polynomials of degree higher than the second. In the following sections we shall see to what extent real and complex polynomials are reducible and derive a few results about them that are occasionally useful in effecting their factorization.

PROBLEMS

1. Show that $x - 6$ and $x + 1$ are factors of $x^2 - 5x - 6$.

Verify the following factorizations:

2. $x^2 + 2x + 5 = (x + 1 + 2i)(x + 1 - 2i)$.
3. $3x^2 + 49 = (\sqrt{3}x + 7i)(\sqrt{3}x - 7i)$.
4. $x^2 + x + 1 + i = (x + i)(x + 1 - i)$.
5. Explain how one can find the factor $t(x)$ in (1) if $s(x)$ is known.
6. Show that $x + 5$ is a factor of $p(x) = x^3 + 8x^2 + 16x + 5$, and express $p(x)$ as $p(x) = (x + 5)q(x)$ for some polynomial $q(x)$.
7. Show that $x - 1$ is a factor of $x^3 - 1$. What is the other rational polynomial factor? Express $x^3 - 1$ as a product of two proper rational polynomial factors.
8. Given that $x^2 + x + 1$ is a factor of $x^4 + 3x^2 + 2x + 3$, find the other rational polynomial factor.
9. Show that $x + \sqrt{3}$ and $x - 2$ divide $x^3 - 2x^2 - 3x + 6$. Find the third factor and hence a third zero of the polynomial in Problem 12 in Section 5.2.
10. Show that $q(x) = x^3 + 2x^2 - 3$ is a factor of $p(x) = x^7 + x^6 - 7x^5 - 12x^4 + 4x^3 + 13x^2 - 3x + 3$ by expressing $p(x)$ as a product $q(x)t(x)$.
11. Show that $x - 2i$ is a factor of $p(x) = x^2 + (3 - i)x + 2 - 6i$ by expressing $p(x)$ as $p(x) = (x - 2i)q(x)$ for some polynomial $q(x)$.

Factor completely over R:

12. $x^2 - 8$.   13. $(x + 1)^2 - 7$.

14. $x^2 + 5x$.   15. $x^2 + 6x - 3$.

16. $x^2 - 2x + 19$.   17. $3x^2 + 8$.

         18. $x^3 + 20x$.

Factor completely over C:

19. $x^2 + 8$.   20. $x^2 + 5x$.

21. $(x + 1)^2 - 7$.   22. $3x^2 + 8$.

23. $x^3 + 20x$.   24. $2x^4 + 32x^2$.

25. $2x^2 - 10$.   26. $x^2 - 4x + 13$.

27. Factor $x^2 - x - 12$ over C. Show that -3 and 4 are its only complex zeros. (*Hint:* First show that they are zeros. Then suppose that a is any zero, and use Theorem 9, Section 2.13).

28. Find two complex zeros of $x^2 - 6$ and show that they are unique.

29. Find three complex zeros of $x^3 + 4x$ and show that they are unique.

30. Show that the set of all polynomials over I, the set of integers, is closed under addition and multiplication. Is it closed under subtraction and division? Is the larger set of all polynomials over R closed under subtraction and division?

31. Let $p(x) = x^2 + x + 1$ and $q(x) = -3x + 2$.

    (a) Find the polynomials $r(x) = p(x) + q(x)$ and $s(x) = p(x) \cdot q(x)$. What are their degrees?

    (b) Find $p(2)$, $q(2)$, $r(2)$, $s(2)$.

32. If $p(x) = a_n x^n + a_{n-1}x^{n-1} + \cdots + a_1 x + a_0$ and $q(x) = b_n x^n + b_{n-1}x^{n-1} + \cdots + b_1 x + b_0$, express $p(x) + q(x)$ as a polynomial. Does $p(x) + q(x) = q(x) + p(x)$ for all x? Which axioms for the real numbers are you using here? What can you say about the degree of $p(x) + q(x)$?

33. If the degrees of $p(x)$ and $q(x)$ are n and m, respectively, what is the degree of $p(x) \cdot q(x)$; of $p(x) + q(x)$?

5.4   Synthetic Division

The labor involved in dividing a polynomial by one of the form $x - a$ can be considerably shortened by using the method called *synthetic division*. The usual procedure for dividing $3x^3 - 11x^2 + 14x + 5$ by $x - 2$ looks like this:

$$
\begin{array}{r}
3x^2 - 5x + 4 \\
x - 2\,\overline{\smash{\big)}\,3x^3 - 11x^2 + 14x + 5} \\
\underline{3x^3 - 6x^2} \\
-5x^2 + 14x + 5 \\
\underline{-5x^2 + 10x} \\
4x + 5 \\
\underline{4x - 8} \\
13 \; .
\end{array}
$$

(1)

Much of the writing in this is repetitious. For example, the numbers 3,

−5, and 4 in the quotient are each written three times. Also the powers of x, which serve no more useful purpose than to separate the coefficients, are repeated several times.

Consider the following arrangement:

$$3 \quad -11 \quad 14 \quad 5 \quad \underline{\big|\,2}$$

$$\overline{3} \qquad \qquad .$$

The first row consists of the coefficients of the polynomial $3x^3 - 11x^2 + 14x + 5$ in order of decreasing powers of x, together with the 2 from the divisor $x - 2$. The 3 below the line is the first number of the upper row repeated.

The synthetic division process leads to the following array

(2)
$$\begin{array}{rrrr|r} 3 & -11 & 14 & 5 & 2 \\ & 6 & -10 & 8 & \\ \hline 3 & -5 & 4 & 13 & \end{array} \quad ,$$

obtained as follows. The 3 in the third row is multiplied by 2 in the divisor, and the product 6 placed in the second row below −11. We now add 6 and −11, and place the sum −5 directly below in the third row. The process is now repeated, with −5 being multiplied by 2 and the product placed in the second row below 14. The sum of −10 and 14 is placed below them in the third row. We continue in this fashion until the end is reached with 13.

The first three numbers in the third row are the coefficients, in order, of the quotient $3x^2 - 5x + 4$. The last number is the remainder 13.

Comparison with (1) will show that in essence synthetic division is the same as the longer method. Superfluous repetitions have been omitted and the work arranged in a more compact form. The only significant difference is the reversing of the sign of the constant term −2 in the divisor. This minor change enables us to replace the operation of subtraction of polynomials in (1) by the addition of the second row to the first in (2).

Illustration. Use synthetic division to find the quotient and remainder in the division of $x^4 + 5x^3 - 5x - 6$ by $x + 3$.

We must be careful when writing down the coefficients of the polynomial to supply a zero for the coefficient of the missing x^2 term. The number to the right in the first row will be −3.

$$\begin{array}{rrrrr|r} 1 & 5 & 0 & -5 & -6 & -3 \\ & -3 & -6 & 18 & -39 & \\ \hline 1 & 2 & -6 & 15 & -45 & \end{array} \quad .$$

The quotient is $x^3 + 2x^2 - 6x + 13$, and the remainder is −45.

PROBLEMS

Use synthetic division to find the quotient and remainder in the division of the first polynomial by the second.

1. $2x^3 + x^2 - 4x$; $x - 4$.
2. $x^4 - x^2 + 5$; $x + 2$.
3. $x^3 + 2x^2 - x - 3$; $x - \frac{3}{2}$.

4. $3x^3 - \frac{1}{2}x^2 + \frac{1}{4}x - 1$; $x + 1$.
5. $x^4 + 6$; $x + 3$.
6. $2x^5 - 2x^4 - 3x + 7$; $x - 2$.

Use synthetic division to show that the first polynomial is divisible by the second, and express the first polynomial as a product of rational polynomials.

7. $x^3 + 3x^2 - x - 3$; $x - 1$.
8. $2x^4 + x^3 + 4x^2 - 8x - 5$; $x + \frac{1}{2}$.

9. $x^4 - x^3 + x - 1$; $x - 1$.
10. $x^5 + 32$; $x + 2$.

11. Show that $x^8 - 1$ is divisible by $x - 1$.

5.5   Remainder and Factor Theorems

In Equation (5) of Section 2.12 we showed that for any two polynomials $p(x)$ and $d(x)$ the division of $p(x)$ by $d(x)$ could be expressed as

$$(1) \qquad\qquad p(x) = d(x)q(x) + r(x),$$

where the polynomials $q(x)$ and $r(x)$ are the quotient and remainder, respectively. Moreover, we remarked that the division process could be continued until the remainder was either zero or of degree less than that of the divisor $d(x)$. From now on, we shall assume that this has been done.

If $d(x)$ is the first degree polynomial $x - a$, where a is any number, the remainder is either 0 or has degree zero and in either case is simply some number b. We can write (1) as

$$(2) \qquad\qquad p(x) = (x - a)q(x) + b.$$

Now (2) is true for every value of x and in particular when $x = a$. Therefore

$$p(a) = 0 \cdot q(a) + b,$$

and $b = p(a)$, the value of p at a. Substituting $p(a)$ for b in (2), we have

$$(3) \qquad\qquad p(x) = (x - a)q(x) + p(a).$$

This is the formal statement of the remainder theorem:

Theorem 1 (Remainder Theorem). If the polynomial $p(x)$ is divided by $x - a$, the remainder is the number $p(a)$.

For example, if

$$(4) \qquad\qquad p(x) = x^3 - 2x^2 + 5x - 6,$$

the remainder on dividing $p(x)$ by $x - 3$ is $p(3) = 18$. Although the remainder is seldom desired for itself, the theorem is useful as an alternative to direct substitution when finding the value of p at a. In the example above we could have found $p(3)$ by actually dividing $p(x)$ by $x - 3$ and noting the remainder. In this instance there would have been no saving of time, but if a were 2.716, it would be quicker to find $p(2.716)$ by this method than by direct substitution of 2.716 in (4). In the remainder theorem the coefficients need not be real numbers; the theorem is valid for complex polynomials and any complex number a.

The most important theoretical application of the remainder theorem is to the proof of its corollary, the factor theorem.

Theorem 2 (Factor Theorem).   Let $p(x)$ be a polynomial with complex coefficients and a a complex number.

(a) If $x - a$ is a factor of $p(x)$, then a is a zero of $p(x)$.
(b) If a is a zero of $p(x)$, then $x - a$ is a factor of $p(x)$.

To prove (a), suppose $x - a$ is a factor of $p(x)$. Then the remainder in the division of $p(x)$ by $x - a$ is zero. Hence by the remainder theorem $p(a) = 0$; that is, a is a zero of $p(x)$. For the second part of the theorem, suppose that a is a zero of $p(x)$. Then $p(a) = 0$, and (3) becomes $p(x) = (x - a)q(x)$, showing that $x - a$ is a factor of $p(x)$.

Illustration.   Let

$$p(x) = 3x^4 - 6x^3 + 2x^2 + x - 10.$$

Since $p(2) = 0$, we know that $x - 2$ is a factor of $p(x)$. In fact,

$$p(x) = (x - 2)\,(3x^3 + 2x + 5).$$

Exercise.   Let $p(x) = x^3 - x^2 - 18x - 18$. Verify that $p(-3) = 0$ and $x + 3$ is a factor of $p(x)$. Express $p(x)$ as $(x + 3)q(x)$ for some $q(x)$.

PROBLEMS

1. If $p(x) = -x^3 + 4x^2 - x + 2$ and $x + 1$ is the divisor, express $p(x)$ in the form (2). Find a for this problem, and verify the remainder theorem.
2. Do the same for $p(x) = x^3 - 6x^2 + 14x - 12$ and divisor $x - 2$.
3. Without actually performing the division, find the remainder if $x^2 + x + 1$ is divided by $x + 3$.
4. Without actually performing the division, find the remainders if $2x^4 - 9x^3 - 5x^2 - 2x + 10$ is divided by (a) $x - \frac{1}{2}$; (b) $x - 5$; (c) $x + 2$.
5. If $p(x) = 3x^4 - 6x^3 - 7x^2 + 10x + 8$, use the remainder theorem to evaluate $p(1), p(2), p(-2)$.
6. If $p(x) = x^2 - 3x - 3$, use the remainder theorem and synthetic division to evaluate $p(7), p(-4.2), p(1.16)$.
7. If $q(x) = 2x^3 - x^2 - 3x + 1$, use the remainder theorem and synthetic division to evaluate $q(2), q(2.7), q(2.744)$.
8. Show that $x^3 + 5ax^2 + (4a^2 + 6)x + 6a$ is divisible by $x + a$.
9. Show that 2 is a zero of $3x^2 - x - 10$, and factor this polynomial over R. Find the other zero.
10. Verify that -5 is a zero of $2x^2 + \frac{22}{3}x - \frac{40}{3}$, and factor this polynomial over R. Find another zero of the polynomial.

11. Show that $x - 4$ and $x + 1$ are factors of $x^3 - 6x^2 + 5x + 12$. Find all the zeros of this polynomial.

12. Show that 1 and -3 are zeros of $2x^3 + 5x^2 - 4x - 3$, and hence factor it completely over R.

13. Verify that $3 + \sqrt{2}$ is a zero of $x^2 - 6x + 7$, and factor this polynomial over C.

14. Verify that $-2 + i$ is a zero of $x^2 + 4x + 5$, and factor this polynomial over C.

15. Let r be a zero of the polynomial $p(x)$ whose degree n is greater than zero. Then $p(x) = (x - r)q(x)$ for some polynomial $q(x)$. What is the degree of $q(x)$? If s is a zero of $p(x)$ different from r, show that s is a zero of $q(x)$.

16. Show that 6 is a zero of $x^3 - 10x^2 + 25x - 6$, and find two more zeros by solving a quadratic equation.

17. Show that $2i$ and $-2i$ are zeros of $x^4 + 2x^3 - 40x^2 + 8x - 176$, and find two more zeros by solving a quadratic equation.

18. Find the roots of $x^2 - 4x - 45 = 0$.

19. Find the roots of $-2x^3 + 26x^2 - 60x = 0$.

Find the complex zeros of the following polynomials by factoring:

20. $x^2 + 3x + 2$.   21. $x^2 - 25$.

22. $15x^2 + x - 2$.   23. $2w^3 + 11w^2 + 15w$.

24. $5x^4$.   25. $24z^2 - 6$.

26. $b^2x^2 + 2bcx - 3c^2$, $b \neq 0$.   27. $3x + 4x^2$.

28. Show that $3 - 4i$ is a root of $x^3 - 6x^2 + 25x = 0$, and find the other roots. Express the polynomial as a product of factors irreducible over C. Express it as a product of factors irreducible over R.

29. Verify that $3i$ is a zero of $x^3 - (1 + 2i)x^2 + (3 + 2i)x - 3$, and factor this polynomial over C.

30. Show that $5 - i$ and $5 + i$ are zeros of $x^3 - 3x^2 - 44x + 182$, and find the other zero. Express this polynomial as a product of factors irreducible over C. Express it as a product of factors irreducible over R.

31. Show that $(3x + 2)$ is a double factor of the polynomial $9x^4 + 21x^3 + 34x^2 + 28x + 8$. Factor the polynomial completely over R.

32. Factor $x^3 + 3x^2 - 24x + 28$ completely over R.

33. Show that $x - a$ is a factor of $x^5 - a^5$.

34. Show that $x - a$ is a factor of $x^n - a^n$, where n is a positive integer.

35. For which positive integers n is $x^n + a^n$ divisible by $x + a$?

36. Find a third degree polynomial whose zeros are $5, \frac{2}{3}, -1$.

37. Find a quadratic equation whose roots are $7 + \sqrt{5}$ and $7 - \sqrt{5}$.

38. Find a fourth degree polynomial whose zeros are $3, 4, 3i, -3i$.

5.6 Theorems and Their Converses

Theorem 2 can be rephrased as

Theorem 2'. Let $p(x)$ be a polynomial with complex coefficients and a a complex number.

(a') a is a zero of $p(x)$ if $x - a$ is a factor of $p(x)$.

(b') a is a zero of $p(x)$ only if $x - a$ is a factor of $p(x)$.

Although (a′) is just a rearrangement of sentence (a) in Theorem 2, (b′) is more than a rearrangement of (b). Careful comparison, however, of (b) and (b′) should convince one that their meanings are exactly the same. Parts (a′) and (b′) can now be combined in a single sentence to give a third and more convenient form of Theorem 2:

Theorem 2″. Let $p(x)$ be a polynomial with complex coefficients. The complex number a is a zero of $p(x)$ if and only if $x - a$ is a factor of $p(x)$.

Theorem 2 really consists of two separate theorems. In Theorem 2(a) the phrase, "$x - a$ is a factor of $p(x)$," is called the *hypothesis* of the theorem and, "a is a zero of $p(x)$," the *conclusion*. In Theorem 2(b), "a is a zero of $p(x)$," is the hypothesis and, "$x - a$ is a factor of $p(x)$," is the conclusion. The hypothesis and conclusion of 2(b′) are the same as those for 2(b), since the two forms have the same meaning. If the hypothesis and conclusion of one theorem are, respectively, the conclusion and hypothesis of another, each theorem is said to be the *converse* of the other. Thus 2(b) is the converse of 2(a), and vice versa. Similarly, 2(a′) and 2(b′) are converses of each other. One does not speak of a hypothesis and conclusion in connection with an "if and only if" theorem such as Theorem 2″. Such theorems embody two statements, each with its own hypothesis and conclusion.

It is important to distinguish between a theorem and its converse, because the converse of a true theorem is not necessarily true, although often it will be. The theorem, "If two triangles are congruent, they are similar," has the converse, "If two triangles are similar, they are congruent," which is false. However, the theorem, "If a triangle is equilateral, it is equiangular," has a true converse. This last theorem and its converse can be combined as, "A triangle is equilateral if and only if it is equiangular."

It is standard mathematical practice to interpret all mathematical statements literally, subject to certain implicit conventions. This may make for monotony of style, but experience has taught mathematicians that only in this way can confusion and misunderstanding be avoided. Consequently, a theorem is considered true only if it is correct in every detail. If it fails in so much as a single case, even though true for thousands of others, the theorem is technically false. In this respect, particular attention must be paid to the word "all" and its mathematical synonyms "any," "each," and "every." As used in mathematics, the word "all" means just that and not "almost all" or "all but one." The assertion, "$a^2 > 0$ for all real numbers a," is false. True for most numbers, it fails when $a = 0$, and hence is not true for all a. The statement, "$a^2 > 0$ for all real numbers, $a \neq 0$," is true, since the exceptional case is specifically excluded. Another true statement is, "$a^2 > 0$ or $a^2 = 0$ for every real number a."

For an "if and only if" theorem to be true, both parts must be true. If either fails, the whole theorem fails. Of course, it may be possible to salvage part of the theorem by breaking it up into parts and stating each separately with suitable restrictions. Usually each part of an "if and only if" theorem must be proved separately.

PROBLEMS

Identify the hypothesis and conclusion of each statement below. Determine the truth or falsity of each (do not give proofs). State the converse of each and indicate whether it is true or false. If both the statement and its converse are true, combine them in an "if and only if" statement.

1. If a is an even integer, $4a$ is an even integer.
2. a^2 is an even integer if a is an even integer.
3. An integer $p + 2$ is prime if p is prime.
4. The integer $5a$ is odd only if the integer a is odd.
5. The product $ab = 0$ only if $a = 0$.
6. A parallelogram is a square if it has equal sides.
7. Two circles have equal areas if they are similar.
8. If $a > 5$ or $a < -5$, then $a^2 > 25$.
9. If $a^2 = a$, then $a = 1$.
10. Let n be a real number. If n is positive, $n < n^2$.

Which of the following are true (omit proofs)?

11. All squares are rectangles.
12. For any real number a, $\dfrac{a}{a} = 1$.
13. There is a positive real number u such that $u < 1$ and $u^2 > 1$.
14. $u^2 > 0$ if and only if $u > 0$.
15. At each point on the earth's surface an arrow can be drawn pointing north.
16. If $a > 3$ and $a < 7$, then $a^2 > 4$.
17. For all real numbers u, $(u + 1)(u - 6) = u^2 - 5u - 6$.
18. $x^2 - 11x + 24 = 0$ if and only if $x = 8$.
19. A convex polygon is a triangle if and only if the sum of its interior angles is 180°.

5.7   Rational Roots

Suppose we wish to solve the polynomial equation

$$(1) \qquad\qquad p(x) = x^3 - 2x^2 - 33x - 14 = 0.$$

If we can find one root r, then it will be easy to find the others. For by the factor theorem

$$p(x) = (x - r)q(x),$$

and the remaining roots of $p(x) = 0$ must be the roots of the quadratic equation $q(x) = 0$. If the root r is irrational, it would be almost impossible to find it by guessing, but if $p(x)$ has rational zeros, they can in most cases be found without too much effort. It is easy to see that 5 is not a root of $p(x) = 0$. If it were, we should have from (1)

$$5^3 - 2 \cdot 5^2 - 33 \cdot 5 = 14.$$

But the left side is a multiple of 5 and hence cannot possibly equal 14. Similarly, -3 can not be a zero. In fact, no integer can be a zero unless it divides 14. Therefore the only possible integral zeros are ± 1, ± 2, ± 7, ± 14. Trying each in turn, we see that $p(7) = 0$ and

$$p(x) = (x - 7)(x^2 + 5x + 2).$$

The other zeros, found by solving the equation

$$x^2 + 5x + 2 = 0,$$

are

$$-\tfrac{5}{2} + \tfrac{1}{2}\sqrt{17} \quad \text{and} \quad -\tfrac{5}{2} - \tfrac{1}{2}\sqrt{17}.$$

Theorem 3 is a useful theorem generalizing the above reasoning. First, we remind the reader that a rational number b/c, where b and c are integers, is said to be in *lowest terms* if b and c have no common factor greater than 1. For example, $\tfrac{20}{3}$ is in lowest terms but $\tfrac{80}{12}$ is not.

Theorem 3. If the rational number b/c, in lowest terms, is a root of the polynomial equation

$$(2) \qquad a_n x^n + a_{n-1} x^{n-1} + \cdots + a_1 x + a_0 = 0$$

with integral coefficients, then b divides a_0 and c divides a_n.

For example, consider the equation

$$(3) \qquad 2x^3 + 9x^2 + 5x - 6 = 0.$$

By direct substitution or synthetic division we see that $\dfrac{-3}{2}$ is a root of (3). Note that the numerator divides the constant term of the polynomial and the denominator divides the coefficient of x^3. As an illustration of how this theorem is used, let us now suppose that we do not know that $-\tfrac{3}{2}$ is a root. The factors of -6 are ± 1, ± 2, ± 3, ± 6, and any rational root of (3) when reduced to lowest terms must have one of these eight integers as its numerator. The factors of 2 are ± 1, ± 2, and any rational root must have one of these as its denominator. Thus the only possible rational roots are $\tfrac{1}{2}$, 1, $\tfrac{3}{2}$, 2, 3, 6, and their negatives. Of course, it may be that none of these is a root. The theorem does not say that the equation must have a rational root; it merely describes the nature of whatever rational roots the equation may have. Trying each possibility in turn, we see that $-\tfrac{3}{2}$ is a root. The other roots, if desired, can now be found by using the factor theorem. Theorem 3 is often helpful in finding the roots of polynomial equations, though its usefulness is naturally limited to those equations having rational roots. Note that to use Theorem 3 the co-efficients of the polynomial must be integers and b/c be in lowest terms.

To prove the theorem, we see that if b/c is a root of equation (2), then

$$a_n \frac{b^n}{c^n} + a_{n-1} \frac{b^{n-1}}{c^{n-1}} + \cdots + a_1 \frac{b}{c} + a_0 = 0.$$

Multiplying both sides by c^n, we have

(4) $$a_n b^n + a_{n-1} b^{n-1} c + \cdots + a_1 b c^{n-1} + a_0 c^n = 0.$$

This can be written as

$$b(a_n b^{n-1} + a_{n-1} b^{n-2} c + \cdots + a_1 c^{n-1}) = -a_0 c^n.$$

Since b, c, and a_0, a_1, $\cdots$, a_n are integers, the left side is a product of two integers, showing (Section 1.3) that b is a factor of the integer $-a_0 c^n$. Now b and c have no factors in common, and hence neither do b and c^n. If b divides $-a_0 c^n$ and has no factor in common with c^n, then b must divide a_0, proving the first conclusion.† By writing (4) in the form

$$a_n b^n = -(a_{n-1} b^{n-1} + \cdots + a_1 b c^{n-2} + a_0 c^{n-1})c,$$

a similar argument can be used to show that c divides a_n.

Exercise A. Let $b = 21$, $a_0 = 84$, $c = 10$. Show that b divides $-a_0 c^4$. Express b and $a_0 c^4$ as products of primes. Note that every prime factor of b is a factor of a_0.

Illustration 1. Solve the equation

(5) $$p(x) = x^4 + 4x^3 - 3x^2 - 14x - 8 = 0.$$

We look first for rational roots. The only possible rational roots are those integers that divide 8, that is, ± 1, ± 2, ± 4, ± 8. By direct substitution we see that 1 is not a root, but that -1 is. Hence

$$p(x) = (x + 1)(x^3 + 3x^2 - 6x - 8).$$

The remaining zeros of $p(x)$ must be zeros of the second factor. Again, -1 is a zero, and

$$x^3 + 3x^2 - 6x - 8 = (x + 1)(x^2 + 2x - 8).$$

Since $x^2 + 2x - 8 = (x + 4)(x - 2)$, the roots of (5) are -1, -4, and 2. The factorization of $p(x)$ is

$$p(x) = (x + 1)^2(x + 4)(x - 2).$$

Except in the simplest cases, it generally is difficult, if not impossible, to find exact expressions for the irrational roots of a polynomial equation. In Chapter 8 we shall show how approximations to such roots can be

†This argument tacitly makes use of the fact that a positive integer can be expressed as a product of positive primes in only one way. If b divides $-a_0 c^n$, every prime factor of b is a factor of $a_0 c^n$. Since b and c^n have no factors in common, every prime factor of b must appear among the prime factors of a_0. Hence b divides a_0.

found by graphing the polynomial, and in Chapter 11 we shall give an algebraic method by which approximations to any desired degree of accuracy can be obtained.

PROBLEMS

Find all the rational roots of each of the following polynomial equations:

1. $2x^3 - 7x^2 + 10x - 6 = 0$.
2. $2y^3 - y^2 - 4y + 2 = 0$.
3. $x^4 - x - 2 = 0$.
4. $x^3 - 3x = 1$.
5. $z^3 + 3z^2 - 4z = 12$.
6. $3x^4 - 40x^3 + 130x^2 - 120x + 27 = 0$.
7. $4w^3 - \frac{1}{3}w^2 - \frac{5}{6}w + \frac{1}{6} = 0$.

Find the complex zeros of each polynomial, and factor the polynomial completely over C: (*Hint:* First find all rational zeros.)

8. $2x^3 + 3x^2 - 2x - 3$.
9. $x^4 + 6x^3 - 16x^2 - 150x - 225$.
10. $3x^3 - 5x^2 - 14x - 4$.
11. $8x^4 - 22x^3 + 29x^2 - 66x + 15$.
12. $x^3 - \frac{7}{2}x^2 + \frac{3}{2}x - \frac{21}{4}$.
13. Find three consecutive integers the sum of whose reciprocals is $\frac{13}{12}$.
14. Find the dimensions of a rectangular box containing 60 cubic inches if the length is 1 inch more than the width and 2 inches more than the depth.
15. Solve the equation $\dfrac{x^3 + 27}{x + 3} = 0$ for its complex roots.
16. Show that $\sqrt{5}$ is irrational. (*Hint:* Consider the equation $x^2 - 5 = 0$.)
17. Show that $\sqrt[3]{2}$ is irrational.
18. Complete the proof of Theorem 3 by showing that c divides a_n.

5.8   Complex Polynomials

We know that every polynomial equation of the first or second degree has a solution, since we are able actually to find the roots. Also, in the course of our work, we have found the roots of many higher degree equations. We have seen, however, that some equations do not have solutions. For example, there is no complex root of the equation $\dfrac{6x + 7}{2x - 3} = 3$, nor does the equation $2^x = 0$ have a solution. Even if there is no explicit expression for the roots, it is still a matter of some interest to know whether an equation has a solution. For polynomials this question has been answered:

Theorem 4. Every polynomial with complex coefficients and degree greater than zero has at least one complex zero.

The proof of this important theorem, which is fundamental in the theory of polynomials, was first given by the German mathematician Gauss in 1799. Since it is too difficult to give here, we shall assume the validity of the theorem. The theorem says that an equation such as $2x^6 + \sqrt{3}x^4 - ix + 5\pi = 0$ has at least one complex number as a root. It does not tell us what the root is or even how to find it. It does not claim that the root will have a conventional symbol as a name, such as $\sqrt{5}$ or $\dfrac{1 + \log 3.7}{11^{2/3}}$. Usually it will not, since only the more important numbers have names.

Such a theorem is called an *existence* theorem, as opposed to a constructive theorem, which shows how to find the object the theorem says exists. Existence theorems are not as useless as they might appear. Often in a new theory they provide the first step from which one can then go on to deduce results of a more practical nature. As we develop the theory of polynomials, we shall see that this is the case here.

Let $p(x)$ be a polynomial of degree $n > 0$ with complex coefficients. By the above theorem it has at least one complex zero; call it r_1. By Theorem 2, $x - r_1$ is a factor of $p(x)$ so that

$$(1) \qquad\qquad p(x) = (x - r_1)q_1(x)$$

for some polynomial $q_1(x)$ of degree $n - 1$. If $n = 1$, so that $q_1(x)$ is a constant (that is, some fixed complex number), we stop. But if $n > 1$, $q_1(x)$ is a non-constant polynomial, which by Theorem 4 must have a complex zero r_2, and hence

$$q_1(x) = (x - r_2)q_2(x)$$

for some polynomial $q_2(x)$ of degree $n - 2$. Substituting for $q_1(x)$ in (1), we have

$$p(x) = (x - r_1)(x - r_2)q_2(x).$$

If $n = 2$, then $q_2(x)$ is a constant and we stop. If $n > 2$, the process is repeated with the non-constant polynomial $q_2(x)$. Continuing in this fashion, we eventually reach a polynomial $q_n(x)$ that is a non-zero constant. Denoting this by c, we have

$$p(x) = (x - r_1)(x - r_2)\cdots(x - r_{n-1})(x - r_n)c.$$

Except for the part about the uniqueness of the factorization, this establishes the next theorem.

Theorem 5. Let $p(x)$ be a polynomial of degree $n > 0$ with complex coefficients. Then $p(x)$ has a factorization over C as a product of a complex number $c \neq 0$ and n linear factors each of the form $x - r_i$:

$$(2) \qquad p(x) = c(x - r_1)(x - r_2)\cdots(x - r_{n-1})(x - r_n), \qquad c \neq 0.$$

This factorization is unique except for the order in which the factors occur.

Let us illustrate with the polynomial

(3) $$p(x) = 5x^3 + (-3 + 10i)x^2 - (2 + 6i)x - 4i.$$

Here $n = 3$. Since $p(1) = 0$, $x - 1$ must be a factor of $p(x)$ and we have

(4) $$p(x) = (x - 1)[5x^2 + (2 + 10i)x + 4i].$$

Let

$$q_1(x) = 5x^2 + (2 + 10i)x + 4i.$$

It has $-2i$ as a zero, and therefore

$$q_1(x) = (x + 2i)(5x + 2).$$

The polynomial $q_2(x) = 5x + 2$ has $-\frac{2}{5}$ as a zero, and hence

$$q_2(x) = (x + \tfrac{2}{5})5.$$

For comparison with the proof of Theorem 5, $q_3(x) = c = 5$. Substitution in (4) gives us the following factorization over C of $p(x)$:

(5) $$p(x) = 5(x - 1)(x + 2i)(x + \tfrac{2}{5}).$$

Theorem 5 is also an existence theorem in that it does not explain how to find the factors of $p(x)$. It merely asserts that there are linear factors c, $x - r_1$, $x - r_2, \cdots$, $x - r_n$ whose product is $p(x)$. The problem of actually finding the factors in any particular instance is another matter and may be difficult. The example above was simple enough so that the zeros of $p(x)$ could be found by guessing.

The factorization in (2) is complete since each of the polynomial factors is linear. We point out, however, that not all the factors are necessarily distinct; two or more of the r_i's may be equal. An immediate consequence of Theorem 5 is that only linear polynomials are irreducible over C.

Exercise A.   Verify (5) by expressing the product there as a sum.

Exercise B.   Factor $p(x)$ in (3) completely over C, starting this time with the factor $x + \dfrac{2}{5}$. Compare the result with that in (5).

Exercise C.   Show that $5x^3 - 15x + 10 = 5(x - 1)\,(x - 1)\,(x + 2)$.

Let s be any zero of the polynomial $p(x)$ in Theorem 5. Then by (2),

$$p(s) = c(s - r_1)(s - r_2)\cdots(s - r_{n-1})(s - r_n) = 0,$$

and hence at least one of the factors of this product must be zero (see Problem 31 in Section 2.13). Since $c \neq 0$, some one of the other factors—say $s - r_i$—must be zero, and hence $s = r_i$. This shows that any zero of $p(x)$ must be one of the numbers $r_1, r_2, \cdots, r_n$, proving the following theorem:

Theorem 6. A polynomial of degree $n > 0$ with complex coefficients cannot have more than n complex zeros.

Since two or more of the r_i's may be equal, the polynomial may well have fewer than n zeros. Also, since $x - r$ is a factor of $p(x)$ only if r is a zero, we see that $x - r_1, x - r_2, \cdots, x - r_n$ are the only linear factors of $p(x)$.

This last result still does not prove that the factorization in (2) is unique, for it is possible that some of the factors there are equal. For example, a cubic polynomial $h(x)$ might have just two distinct zeros a and b, and a factorization

$$(6) \qquad h(x) = (x - a)(x - a)(x - b).$$

On the other hand, it is conceivable that $h(x)$ also has a factorization

$$(7) \qquad h(x) = (x - a)(x - b)(x - b).$$

We shall show now that such a situation cannot exist by proving that the factorization in (2) is unique except for the order of the factors.

Let $p(x)$ also have a factorization

$$(8) \qquad p(x) = d(x - s_1)(x - s_2)\cdots(x - s_n), \qquad d \neq 0.$$

Suppose that (2) and (8) have exactly m factors in common and that the factors in (2) and (8) have been rearranged and renumbered so that these m common factors come first. (For $h(x)$ above, $m = 2$ and (6) would be rearranged as $h(x) = (x - a)(x - b)(x - a)$.) Then

$$(9) \qquad x - r_1 = x - s_1, \quad x - r_2 = x - s_2, \cdots, \quad x - r_m = x - s_m.$$

Also, if we let

$$(10) \qquad u(x) = c(x - r_{m+1})(x - r_{m+2})\cdots(x - r_n)$$

and

$$(11) \qquad v(x) = d(x - s_{m+1})(x - s_{m+2})\cdots(x - s_n)$$

(with the understanding that if $m = n$, $u(x)$ is simply c and $v(x)$ is d), then none of the factors in (10) appears in (11) and conversely, with the possible exception of c and d. We shall show that $m = n$ and $c = d$. In other words, every factor in (8) must occur equally often in (2) and vice-versa.

From (2) and (10)

$$p(x) = (x - r_1)(x - r_2)\cdots(x - r_m)u(x),$$

but also from (8), (9), and (11)

$$p(x) = (x - r_1)(x - r_2)\cdots(x - r_m)v(x).$$

The difference of these,

$$(12) \qquad (x - r_1)(x - r_2) \cdots (x - r_m)[u(x) - v(x)],$$

must equal 0 for every x since it is equal to $p(x) - p(x)$. This implies
that the polynomial form of $u(x)$ is identical with that of $v(x)$, for otherwise (12) would be a non-zero polynomial with more zeros than its degree.
Thus $u(x)$ and $v(x)$ have the same zeros.

If $m < n$, $u(x)$ has at least the proper factor $x - r_n$, which does not
appear in the factorization (11). Therefore $u(r_n) = 0$, but $v(r_n) \neq 0$, which
is a contradiction. If an argument based on the supposition that $m < n$
leads to a contradiction, then we must have $m = n$. We now have
$u(x) = c$ and $v(x) = d$, and since $u(x)$ and $v(x)$ are identical, $c = d$. Thus
the factorization in (8) is the same as that in (2) except for the order of
the factors. This completes the proof of Theorem 5.

We have seen that a factor in (2) may occur more than once. The
number of times a factor $x - r$ occurs is called the *multiplicity* of the zero r.
If $q(x)$ is a polynomial with the factorization

$$(13) \quad q(x) = -3(x - 1)(x - 1)x(x - \tfrac{7}{2})x(x - 1)(x + 2)(x - \tfrac{7}{2}),$$

then -2 is a zero of multiplicity 1, 0 and $\tfrac{7}{2}$ are zeros each of multiplicity 2,
and 1 has multiplicity 3. Since $(x - 1)^3$ is a more convenient notation for
$(x - 1)(x - 1)(x - 1)$, generally (13) would be written as

$$q(x) = -3(x - 1)^3 x^2 (x - \tfrac{7}{2})^2 (x + 2).$$

This is considered as entirely equivalent to (13) and in no sense a different
factorization of $q(x)$.

PROBLEMS

Give the degree of each of the following polynomials and find all its zeros,
together with the multiplicity of each zero:

1. $(x + 10)(x - 1)^2$.
2. $(x + \sqrt{2})^3 \, 5(x - 6)^6$.
3. $2^2(x - 4)^6 \, x$.
4. $(x + 2 + 4\sqrt{3})(x + 2 - 4\sqrt{3})$.
5. $(x - 3i + 7)(x - 3i - 7)$.
6. 8^3.
7. $(x - \tfrac{3}{7})(x + \tfrac{7}{3})^2(x + \pi)^2(x - 3 + i\sqrt{6})(x + \tfrac{7}{3})$.
8. $-(x - a)^2(x + b)$, (two cases).
9. $x^2 - a^2$, (two cases).
10. $x(x + 3 + \sqrt{2})^2 x^2 (x + \tfrac{7}{2}i)^2$.

Factor the polynomials completely over C and find the zeros of each:

11. $2y^2 + 6y + 5$.
12. $x^3 + x^2 - 8x - 12$.
13. $x^3 - 3x^2 - 4x + 12$.
14. $x^3 - 3x^2 + 4x - 12$.
15. $3x - 15$.
16. $2x^2 - 9$.

17. $x^2 + 18$.
18. $x^5 + 10x^4 + 25x^3$.
19. $x^2 - x - \frac{3}{4}$.
20. $x^2 + 6x - 41$.
21. $-8x^3 + 1$.
22. $x^2 + 8x + 17$.
23. $(y + \frac{7}{2})^4$.

24. $x^3 + 2x^2 - 17x$.
25. $ix^2 + ix - 6i$.
26. $x^3 - 6x^2 + 12x - 8$.
27. $z^3 + (1 - 3i)z^2 - 3iz$.
28. $x^2 - 3ix + 4$.
29. $2x^2 - ix + 4$.
30. $x^3 + 4x^2 - 6x - 20$.

31. $x^2 + ax - 2a^2$.

32. Show that $x^2 + 9$ is irreducible over R. (*Hint:* Consider the factorization of the polynomial over C.)

33. Show that 3 has only two complex square roots; that is, there are two and only two complex numbers whose squares are 3. (*Hint:* Consider the equation $x^2 - 3 = 0$.)

34. Find the three complex cube roots of -8. (*Hint:* Solve a polynomial equation.)

35. Show that $\dfrac{1}{\sqrt{2}} + \dfrac{1}{\sqrt{2}} i$ is a square root of i. Find another square root of i. Is there a third?

36. Show that there are no more than five complex fifth roots of 17.

37. If a is any complex number different from zero, what can you say about the number of nth roots of a, where n is a positive integer?

38. Find the three complex cube roots of i. (*Hint:* Consider the appropriate polynomial, and guess one of its zeros.)

39. Is there a value of c for which the equation $x^2 + 2x + 4 - c = 0$ has a root of multiplicity 2?

40. Find a condition on a, b, and c in order that the equation $ax^2 + bx + c = 0$, $a \neq 0$, have a root of multiplicity 2.

41. Let $p(x)$ and $q(x)$ be polynomials of degree n. Show that if they have equal values for more than n values of x, they are identical. (*Hint:* Consider the polynomial $p(x) - q(x)$.)

5.9 Real Polynomials

As we have seen from previous examples, a polynomial with real co-efficients may have non-real as well as real zeros. The reader may have noticed, however, that whenever a polynomial with real coefficients has a non-real zero, the conjugate number is also a zero. For example, $3 + 2i$ and $3 - 2i$ are both zeros of

$$p(x) = x^3 - 7x^2 + 19x - 13$$
$$= (x - 3 - 2i)(x - 3 + 2i)(x - 1).$$

In order to prove that this is typical, we need a preliminary result.

We denote by $\bar{\alpha}$ the conjugate of a complex number α. Thus $\overline{1 - 3i} = 1 + 3i$. If $p(x)$ is a polynomial, then $p(\bar{\alpha})$ is the value of p at $\bar{\alpha}$, and $\overline{p(\alpha)}$ is the conjugate of the value of p at α. For example, if

(1) $$p(x) = 2x^2 + ix - 4$$

and $\alpha = 1 - 3i$, then

$$p(\bar{\alpha}) = 2(1 + 3i)^2 + i(1 + 3i) - 4 = -23 + 13i,$$

and

$$\overline{p(\alpha)} = \overline{2(1 - 3i)^2 + i(1 - 3i) - 4}$$
$$= \overline{-17 - 11i} = -17 + 11i.$$

Although in general $p(\bar{\alpha}) \neq \overline{p(\alpha)}$, the two will be equal for every complex number α if the coefficients of the polynomial are real.

Lemma.† If $p(x)$ is a polynomial with real coefficients and α any complex number, then $p(\bar{\alpha}) = \overline{p(\alpha)}$.

Proof. Let

$$p(x) = a_n x^n + a_{n-1} x^{n-1} + \cdots + a_1 x + a_0,$$

where all the a_i's are real. Then

$$p(\alpha) = a_n \alpha^n + a_{n-1} \alpha^{n-1} + \cdots + a_1 \alpha + a_0,$$

and

$$\overline{p(\alpha)} = \overline{a_n \alpha^n + a_{n-1} \alpha^{n-1} + \cdots + a_1 \alpha + a_0}.$$

Using Problem 31(a) in Section 4.2, this becomes

$$\overline{p(\alpha)} = \overline{a_n \alpha^n} + \overline{a_{n-1} \alpha^{n-1}} + \cdots + \overline{a_1 \alpha} + \overline{a_0},$$

which by Problem 30(b) in the same section can be further reduced to

$$\overline{p(\alpha)} = \bar{a}_n \overline{\alpha^n} + \bar{a}_{n-1} \overline{\alpha^{n-1}} + \cdots + \bar{a}_1 \bar{\alpha} + \bar{a}_0.$$

Now $\bar{a}_r = a_r$, since a_r is real for each $r = 0, 1, 2, \cdots, n$, and $\overline{\alpha^r} = (\bar{\alpha})^r$ (why?), giving us

$$\overline{p(\alpha)} = a_n (\bar{\alpha})^n + a_{n-1} (\bar{\alpha})^{n-1} + \cdots + a_1 \bar{\alpha} + a_0,$$

which is simply $p(\bar{\alpha})$.

Exercise A. If $p(x) = -x^2 + \sqrt{3}x + 7$, find $p(1 + 2i)$, $p(\overline{1 + 2i})$, and $\overline{p(1 + 2i)}$.

Exercise B. Try to carry out the details of the proof of the lemma for the polynomial (1) and $\alpha = 1 - 3i$. Where does the proof break down?

Theorem 7. The conjugate of each zero of a polynomial with real coefficients is also a zero.

Proof. If α is a zero of the real polynomial $p(x)$, then $p(\alpha) = 0$ and hence $\overline{p(\alpha)} = \bar{0}$. But $\bar{0} = 0$ (why?), and by the lemma $\overline{p(\alpha)} = p(\bar{\alpha})$. Therefore $p(\bar{\alpha}) = 0$; that is, $\bar{\alpha}$ is a zero of $p(x)$.

---

†A lemma is a minor theorem of little interest in itself but useful in proving other theorems.

Exercise C. Where in the proof of Theorem 7 did we use the fact that $p(x)$ is a real polynomial?

Exercise D. Show by an example that Theorem 7 may not hold if some of the coefficients are non-real.

Let $p(x)$ be a polynomial with real coefficients and suppose it has a non-real zero α. Then $\bar{\alpha}$, which is different from α, is also a zero. Since the factorization (2) in Section 5.8 is unique, α and $\bar{\alpha}$ must be among the r_i's there. The corresponding factors $x - \alpha$ and $x - \bar{\alpha}$ are distinct and, after rearrangement of the factors in (2) in Section 5.8, can be multiplied to give the quadratic factor:

$$(2) \qquad q(x) = (x - \alpha)(x - \bar{\alpha}) = x^2 - (\alpha + \bar{\alpha})x + \alpha\bar{\alpha}.$$

Let α be expressed in standard form, $\alpha = a + ib$, where a and b are real. Then $\bar{\alpha} = a - ib$, and $\alpha + \bar{\alpha} = 2a$, $\alpha\bar{\alpha} = a^2 + b^2$, showing that $q(x)$ has real coefficients. It is also irreducible over the real field. For a factorization of $q(x)$ over R could be only as a product of two linear factors and would also be a factorization over C. But $(x - \alpha)(x - \bar{\alpha})$ is the unique factorization over C, and these factors are not real.

Thus to each non-real zero α corresponds another non-real zero $\bar{\alpha}$, and together these determine a real quadratic factor of $p(x)$ irreducible over R. A real zero, of course, determines a real linear factor. We have shown the following theorem:

Theorem 8. Every polynomial of degree greater than zero with real coefficients has a unique factorization over R as a product of irreducible quadratic and linear factors.

The uniqueness follows from the uniqueness of the factorization over C. We shall not do so here, but it can be shown that if α is a non-real zero of multiplicity m, then so is $\bar{\alpha}$, and hence the corresponding real quadratic factor will be repeated m times.

Illustration. Let $p(x)$ be the real polynomial whose complete factorization over C is

$$p(x) = (x + 2)^2(x + 2 - i)^3(-4)(x - \sqrt{3})(x + 2 + i)^3.$$

The non-real factors $(x + 2 + i)$ and $(x + 2 - i)$ can be multiplied to give the real quadratic factor

$$q(x) = (x + 2 - i)(x + 2 + i) = x^2 + 4x + 5,$$

and therefore

$$p(x) = -4(x^2 + 4x + 5)^3(x + 2)^2(x - \sqrt{3}).$$

This is the complete factorization of $p(x)$ over R since $q(x)$ is irreducible over R.

It is a corollary of Theorem 8 that quadratic and linear polynomials are the only real polynomials that are irreducible over R. This does not mean that all quadratic polynomials are irreducible, but rather that every real polynomial of the third or higher degree is reducible over R.

PROBLEMS

Show that each of the polynomials $p(x)$ below has the corresponding number and its conjugate as zeros. Find the real quadratic factor $q(x)$ determined by them and write $p(x)$ as $p(x) = q(x) \cdot d(x)$.

1. $3x^3 - 3x^2 + 3x - 3; i$.
2. $x^2 - 4x + 13; 2 - 3i$.
3. $x^6 + 13x^4 + 56x^2 + 80; -2i$.
4. Prove that $x^2 + 3x + 5$ is irreducible over R.
5. Find a condition on the real numbers $a \neq 0$, b, and c for the polynomial $ax^2 + bx + c$ to be irreducible over R.

Factor completely over R and also over C:

6. $x^4 + x^3 + 2x - 4$.
7. $x^3 - 3x^2 + 2x - 6$.
8. $6x^4 - 19x^3 - 7x^2$.
9. $x^3 + 2x^2 - 3x - 10$.
10. $x^3 + 10x^2 + 31x$.
11. $3x^4 - 3x^3 - 12x^2 + 6x + 12$.
12. $x^4 + 3x^2 - 4$.
13. $x^5 + 6x^3 + 9x$.
14. $x^3 + 8$.
15. $x^3 - x^2 - 10x + 12$.
16. $x^4 + 7x^3 - 15x^2 - 127x - 154$.
17. $x^5 - 7x^4 + 19x^3 - 25x^2 + 16x - 4$.

18. If $p(x) = 2x^2 + (3 - 2i)x - 3i$, show that $p(i) = 0$ and $p(-i) \neq 0$. Why does this not contradict Theorem 7?
19. Prove that a real polynomial of odd degree must have at least one real zero.
20. Is Theorem 7 still correct if the zero is real?

21. Factor $x^4 + 1$ over the real field. (*Hint:* $\dfrac{1}{\sqrt{2}}(1 + i)$ is a zero.)

5.10   Algebraic Expressions for the Roots

Although we have shown how to solve certain simple polynomial equations, we have not given a systematic method for finding the zeros of any polynomial. What would be desirable is a formula that expresses the roots of the general polynomial equation

$$(1) \qquad a_n x^n + a_{n-1} x^{n-1} + \cdots + a_1 x + a_0 = 0$$

in terms of its coefficients. For equations of the first and second degrees we have such formulas. The solution of

$$ax + b = 0, \qquad a \neq 0,$$

is given by $-b/a$. The general quadratic equation

$$ax^2 + bx + c = 0, \qquad a \neq 0,$$

has roots

$$\frac{1}{2a}(b + \sqrt{b^2 - 4ac}) \quad \text{and} \quad \frac{1}{2a}(b - \sqrt{b^2 - 4ac}).$$

Do there exist similar expressions for the roots of higher degree polynomial equations? They do if the polynomial is of the third or fourth degree. For the general polynomial of the fifth and higher degree, however, no such expression exists.

To explain exactly what is meant by this, we need a definition. An *algebraic expression in the quantities* $a_0, a_1, \cdots, a_n$ is an expression built up from these quantities by repeated use of the operations of addition, subtraction, multiplication, division, and the taking of roots. For example,

$$b^2, \qquad b^2 - 4ac, \qquad \sqrt{b^2 - 4ac}, \quad \text{and} \quad \frac{-b + \sqrt{b^2 - 4ac}}{2a}$$

are all algebraic expressions in the letters involved. So also is

$$\left[\frac{\sqrt{a_2 + a_1{}^2} + a_0 \sqrt[3]{(a_1 - a_0\sqrt{2})^2}}{a_3} - \frac{5a_2}{3} \right]^{\frac{1}{7}}.$$

The next theorem is a precise formulation of our statement about the roots of higher degree polynomials.

Theorem 9. For each integer $n \geq 5$, there are real polynomial equations of degree n whose roots cannot be written as algebraic expressions in the coefficients.

We emphasize that the question is not one of the existence of roots— this is guaranteed by Theorem 4—but with their representation in a particular form. Theorem 9 does not say that no such expression for the roots has yet been found. It asserts flatly that no such expression can exist. Statements that say that something does not exist are generally difficult to prove, and this theorem is no exception. Indeed, until the theorem was discovered in 1824 by the Norwegian mathematician Abel, most mathematicians had believed that such expressions must exist and had directed their efforts to finding them.

Some equations of the fifth and higher degree do have roots expressible in terms of their coefficients. The equation $2x^7 + 3 = 0$ has $(-\frac{3}{2})^{1/7}$ as one of its roots. Since not all polynomial equations have this property, however, there is no possibility of the existence of general formulas for the roots such as we have for linear and quadratic equations.

The question as to which equations do have their roots expressible in terms of the coefficients was settled by the French mathematician Galois shortly after Abel announced his theorem. Like Abel's theorem, the proof is difficult, and even its statement is too involved to be given here.

The expressions for the roots of the general equation of the third and fourth degree will not be given since we shall have no use for them. They can be found in many texts on higher algebra.†

---

†See Garrett Birkhoff and Saunders MacLane, *A Survey of Modern Algebra*, rev. ed.; New York: Macmillan, 1953; pp. 112-115.

Chapter 6

Inequalities

6.1 Order Axioms

In Chapter 2 we discussed in considerable detail some of the properties of real numbers. There are others, however, that we have not yet mentioned. It is one of the most familiar properties of real numbers that for any two distinct numbers one will be larger than the other. We use the notation $a > b$ to indicate that the real number a is greater than the real number b. For example, $7 > 3$ and $-\frac{5}{3} > -10$. In this chapter we examine this basic property and its consequences.

To have a solid foundation, we proceed axiomatically. The axioms in Chapter 2 made no mention of the ordering of the real number field, and it can be shown that this property cannot be deduced from them. Indeed, four additional axioms are needed if the real field is to behave as we should expect in this regard. Specifically, we assume that any two real numbers a and b can be compared and that one and only one of the following three possibilities can hold: $a = b$, a is greater than b (in symbols, $a > b$), or $b > a$. This is our first assumption, and we shall refer to it as the trichotomy axiom. We list it and the other three below, followed by some remarks on their significance.

Order Axioms for the Real Numbers

Trichotomy.   For any two real numbers a and b, one and only one of the following holds: $a = b$, $a > b$, or $b > a$.

Transitive.   If $a > b$ and $b > c$, then $a > c$.

Additive.   If $a > b$, then $a + c > b + c$ and $c + a > c + b$ for any real number c.

Multiplicative.   If $a > b$ and $c > 0$, then $ac > bc$ and $ca > cb$.

We shall assume, as can be easily shown, that a quantity can be substituted for an equal quantity in any inequality. For example, if $a > b$ and

129

$c = a$, then $c > b$. The additive and multiplicative axioms connect the ordering of the real numbers with their arithmetic properties. From the additive axiom we know that if $10 > 4$, then $10 + 3 > 4 + 3$, that is, $13 > 7$. The multiplicative axiom is similar, but the restriction that c be greater than zero is important. It is true that from $10 > 4$ follows $10 \cdot 3 > 4 \cdot 3$, since $30 > 12$, but note that $10(-3) \not> 4(-3)$.†

We use the notation $a < b$ to indicate that a is less than b. Thus $3 < 7$. Obviously, $a < b$ if and only if $b > a$. It is trivial to show that the first three axioms are still valid if the symbol $>$ is replaced by $<$. The corresponding form of the multiplicative axiom is, "If $a < b$ and $c > 0$, then $ac < bc$ and $ca < cb$." Although these are theorems, provable from the axioms, for simplicity we shall consider them as alternate forms of the axioms.

Definition. An *ordered field* is a field with an order relation $>$ satisfying the four order axioms, the letters there representing elements of the field.

The real numbers form an ordered field as do the set of rational numbers. There are many other ordered fields. The complex field, however, is not ordered (see Problem 43).

Definition. A real number a is *positive* if $a > 0$, and *negative* if $a < 0$.

Zero is neither positive nor negative. The trichotomy axiom implies that every real number except zero is either positive or negative. Do not confuse the "negative of a number" with a "negative number." The former may indeed be positive as with the negative of -5.

Definition. Two real numbers are said to have the *same sign* if both are positive or both are negative. If one is positive and the other is negative, they have *opposite signs*.

For example, $-\sqrt{2}$ and $-\frac{4}{13}$ have the same sign, but $-\sqrt{2}$ and 5 are of opposite sign.

Exercise A. Indicate the order relation between the numbers in each of the following pairs (for example, in (a) $5 > 3$):

(a) $3, 5$. (e) $\pi, 3.141$.

(b) $7, -4$. (f) $-\frac{1}{2}, -\frac{2}{3}$.

(c) $\frac{9}{10}, \frac{9}{10}$. (g) $-2.1, -2$.

(d) $0, 13$.

Exercise B. Arrange the following numbers in ascending order: $2, 1, -\frac{8}{3}, -78,$ $17, 2, 0, \frac{3}{5}, -\frac{4}{3}, \frac{\pi}{2}, \sqrt{2}, -3$.

---

†The notation $a \not> b$ means that a is not greater than b; for example, $-4 \not> 1$.

Exercise C. Verify the additive axiom for various positive, negative, and zero choices of a, b, and c.

Exercise D. Verify the multiplicative axiom for positive, negative, and zero choices of a and b.

*Exercise E. If $a > b$, show that $a - c > b - c$.

Theorem 1. $a > b$ if and only if $a - b > 0$.†

For example, since $10 > 4$, then $6 = 10 - 4 > 0$.

The proof is trivial. If $a > b$, then by Exercise E, $a - b > b - b = 0$. Conversely, if $a - b > 0$, then $(a - b) + b > 0 + b$ and $a > b$.

The next theorem confirms a well-known observation.

Theorem 2. $a > b$ if and only if $-a < -b$.

Thus $7 > 3$ and $-7 < -3$. We leave the proof to the reader.

Corollary. $a > 0$ if and only if $-a < 0$, and $a < 0$ if and only if $-a > 0$.

Theorem 3.

(a) The product ab is positive if and only if a and b are both positive or both negative.

(b) The product ab is negative if and only if one of the factors is positive and the other is negative.

To prove this theorem, suppose that $a > 0$ and $b > 0$. Then, multiplying both sides of the inequality $b > 0$ by the positive number a, we have $ab > a \cdot 0 = 0$. If $a < 0$ and $b < 0$, then $-a > 0$ and $-b > 0$, and by the preceding case $ab = (-a)(-b) > 0$. If a and b have opposite signs— say $a > 0$ and $b < 0$—then on multiplying $b < 0$ by a, we have $ab < a \cdot 0 = 0$. This proves the "if" part of both sections of the theorem. To show the "only if" part, suppose $ab > 0$. Then neither a nor b can be zero. We have just shown that if a and b have opposite signs, then $ab < 0$. Hence a and b must be both positive or both negative. Similarly, if $ab < 0$, then a and b must have opposite signs.

Several important results follow almost immediately from this theorem.

Corollary 1. If $a \neq 0$, then $a^2 > 0$; that is, the square of any non-zero real number is positive.

Proof. $a^2 = aa$. Now use the first part of Theorem 3.

Corollary 2. $1 > 0$.

Proof. $1 = 1^2$.

The fact that 1 is positive is not trivial. Until now we have not used nor needed this property in our work except for illustrative purposes.

†Throughout this chapter lower case letters will stand for real numbers.

Corollary 3. If $a \neq 0$, then a and $1/a$ have the same sign.

Proof. $a(1/a) = 1 > 0$.

The next theorem extends the multiplicative axiom.

Theorem 4.

(a) If $c > 0$, then $ca > cb$ if and only if $a > b$.
(b) If $c < 0$, then $ca < cb$ if and only if $a > b$.

Proof. Suppose $a > b$. Then $a - b > 0$. If $c > 0$, we have $c(a - b) > 0$ by Theorem 3(a), and hence by Theorem 1, $ca > cb$. If $c < 0$, then $c(a - b) < 0$ and $ca < cb$. The proofs of the converses are left to the reader.

Exercise F. Illustrate Theorem 4(b) with $c = -4$ and specific numbers for a and b such that:

(a) $a > 0, b > 0$;   (c) $a < 0, b < 0$;
(b) $a > 0, b < 0$;   (d) $a = 0, b < 0$.

Exercise G. State carefully those parts of Theorem 4 that have been proved in the text. State and prove the remaining parts of the theorem.

The notation $a \geq b$ indicates that either $a > b$ or $a = b$. Thus $2 \geq -7$ and $2 \geq 2$. The set of all integers n for which $n \geq 6$ is the set $\{6, 7, 8, 9, \cdots\}$, and the set of all integers n for which $n > 6$ is $\{7, 8, 9, \cdots\}$.

If $x \geq 0$, we say that x is *non-negative*. A non-negative number is therefore either positive or zero.

Many of the theorems in this section will, with slight modifications, be true if the symbol $>$ is replaced by $\geq$. Some are given as problems at the end of this section, but most we leave for the reader to discover. Similar remarks apply to the notation $\leq$, which is defined analogously.

If a, b, and c are numbers for which $a < b$ and $b < c$, these two inequalities are often combined into the continued inequality $a < b < c$. If $a < b$ and $b > d$, however, this is never written $a < b > d$, since the relation of a to d is ambiguous. By using the continued inequality, the set of all numbers between a and b, inclusive, can be described more succinctly as "the set of all x, $a \leq x \leq b$."

In Problem 44 it is stated that for positive a and b, $\sqrt{a} > \sqrt{b}$ if and only if $a > b$. This result can be used to find decimal approximations to the square root of a number. Let us illustrate by approximating $\sqrt{2}$.

Since $1 < 2 < 4$, we have, by using the above result on each part of the inequality, $1 < \sqrt{2} < 2$. By squaring the successive tenths between 1 and 2—namely, 1.1, 1.2, and so on—we find that $1.4^2 < 2 < 1.5^2$ and hence $1.4 < \sqrt{2} < 1.5$. We can say that 1.4 (or 1.5) is an approximation to $\sqrt{2}$. Now by trying the successive hundredths between 1.4 and 1.5, we can narrow down still further the interval within which $\sqrt{2}$ lies and find that

$1.41 < \sqrt{2} < 1.42$, giving 1.41 (or 1.42) as a better approximation. The process can be continued to give approximations to any desired degree of accuracy. A similar procedure can be used to approximate cube and higher roots of numbers.

PROBLEMS

Indicate the order relation between the numbers in each pair.

1. $\frac{9}{13}, \frac{7}{11}$.

2. $-.0357, -.041$.

3. $\dfrac{1}{\sqrt{2}}, \dfrac{3}{5}$.

4. $\dfrac{1 - \sqrt{3}}{5}, -1$.

Express the relationship of the numbers in each set by a continued inequality.

5. $10, -5, -\frac{1}{2}$.

6. $1, 2, 0, 4$.

7. $\frac{3}{4}, \frac{2}{3}, 0, -1$.

8. $-9, -\frac{3}{5}, -\frac{5}{3}, -2$.

9. $1, \frac{1}{5}, \frac{10}{3}, -16, -7, 0$.

10. Show that $a > b$ if and only if $a + c > b + c$.

*11. Show that if $a - c < b - c$, then $a < b$.

12. Prove Theorem 2. (*Hint:* If $a > b$, then $a - b > 0$. Add a suitable quantity to each side of this inequality.)

13. If $a \leq b$ and $b < c$, what is the relation between a and c?

14. State a transitive law for $\leq$.

15. If b is a number such that $b \leq 1$ and $b \geq 1$, what is b? Is there a number b such that $b < 1$ and $b > 1$?

16. A certain non-negative number is smaller than every positive number. What is the number?

*17. If $a \leq b$, show that $a + c \leq b + c$.

18. If $a < b < c$, show that $a + u < b + u < c + u$ for any real number u, and $av < bv < cv$ for any positive real number v.

*19. If $a \leq b$, for which c is $ac \leq bc$?

*20. If $ab \geq 0$, what can you say about a and b?

21. If $a \leq b$, $b \leq c$, $c \leq d$, and $d \leq a$, show that $a = b = c = d$.

*22. Show that $-1 < 0$.

23. If 2 is defined to be the number $1 + 1$, show that $2 > 0$.

24. If $0 < a < 1$, show that $a^2 < a$ and illustrate with an example. What is the relation of a^2 to a if $a > 1$?

25. If $a > 0$, show that $a^m > 0$ for all positive integers m.

26. If $a < 0$, show that
    (a) $a^3 < 0$;
    (b) $a^m < 0$ for any odd positive integer m.

*27. Show that for any positive integer m
    (a) $a^m > 1$ if $a > 1$.
    (b) $0 < a^m < 1$ if $0 < a < 1$.

28. Describe the set of all x for which (a) $x \not> \frac{5}{2}$, (b) $x \not\leq \frac{5}{2}$.

*29. If $a < b$ and $c < d$, show that $a + c < b + d$. (*Hint:* First show $a + c < b + c$ and then $b + c < b + d$.) Illustrate with $a = -5$, $b = -2$, $c = 1$, $d = 7$.

30. If $a > b > 0$ and $x > y > 0$, show that $ax > by$. Give an illustration showing that the result may not be true if b or y is negative.

*31. If $a > b > 0$, show that $a^2 > b^2$ and $a^3 > b^3$. State a corresponding theorem for negative a and b.

*32. Let $b \neq 0$. Show that

   (a) $\dfrac{a}{b} > 0$ if and only if a and b have the same sign.

   (b) $\dfrac{a}{b} < 0$ if and only if a and b have opposite signs.

33. (a) Which is larger: $\dfrac{4}{6}$ or $\dfrac{7}{6}$; $\dfrac{3}{5}$ or $\dfrac{-2}{5}$; $\dfrac{a}{b}$ or $\dfrac{2a}{b}$, where $b > 0$?

   (b) If $c > 0$ and $a > b$, show that $\dfrac{a}{c} > \dfrac{b}{c}$.

   (c) Give an example showing that the restriction $c > 0$ in (b) is necessary.

   (d) How would you proceed if asked to compare two fractions with equal negative denominators?

34. (a) Which is larger: $\frac{2}{7}$ or $\frac{5}{14}$; $\frac{2}{3}$ or $\frac{3}{4}$?

   (b) Show how to compare two fractions with unequal denominators by replacing them by equivalent fractions with equal denominators.

35. Which is smaller: $\dfrac{10}{19}$ or $\dfrac{7}{16}$; $\dfrac{2}{-11}$ or $\dfrac{15}{-78}$?

*36. If a and b are positive, show that $a < b$ if and only if $\dfrac{1}{a} > \dfrac{1}{b}$. Illustrate with $a = \frac{1}{5}$ and $b = \frac{3}{2}$. If a and b are negative and $a < b$, what is the relation between $\dfrac{1}{a}$ and $\dfrac{1}{b}$?

37. Find all x for which (a) $x - 1 < 0$, (b) $x - 1$ is non-positive.

38. For which numbers x is $x^2 - 1$ (a) positive; (b) negative; (c) zero?

Find all x for which:

39. $x + 7 > 11$.   41. $7x > -23$.

40. $3x \leq 12$.   42. $-4x \leq 20$.

43. Show that no ordering is possible in the complex field. (*Hint:* Use Corollary 1 to Theorem 3).

*44. Let a and b be positive real numbers. Show that $\sqrt{a} > \sqrt{b}$ if and only if $a > b$. (*Hint:* Use Problem 31.)

45. Show that $\sqrt[3]{a} < \sqrt[3]{b}$ if and only if $a < b$.

46. Determine which is larger:

   (a) $\dfrac{1}{\sqrt{2}}$, $\sqrt{\dfrac{5}{3}}$;   (b) $\dfrac{\sqrt{29}}{9}$, $\dfrac{5}{9}$.

Locate between consecutive thousandths:

47. $\sqrt{3}$.   48. $\sqrt{5}$.   49. $\sqrt{10}$.   50. $\sqrt{6.8}$.

Use Problem 45 to locate between consecutive thousandths:

51. $\sqrt[3]{2}$.   52. $\sqrt[3]{7}$.   53. $\sqrt[3]{1.5}$.

54. (a) Prove that $(x - 1)^2 > 0$ for any number $x \neq 1$.

    (b) Use this to show that $x + \dfrac{1}{x} > 2$ if $x > 0$, $x \neq 1$; that is, the sum of any positive number different from 1 and its reciprocal is greater than 2.

55. Prove that $a^2 - 4a + 9 > 0$ for all real a. (*Hint:* Write the left side as $(a - 2)^2 + 5$.)

56. Show that there is no real x for which $4x^2 + 4x \leq -5$.

57. If $a \geq 0$ and $b \geq 0$, prove that $a + b \geq 2\sqrt{ab}$. (*Hint:* Consider the inequality $(\sqrt{a} - \sqrt{b})^2 \geq 0$.) Illustrate with suitable a and b.

58. If x and y are positive, show that $x + y \geq \dfrac{4xy}{x + y}$.

59. Assuming that each positive real number has a positive square root, use Problem 44 to show that it has only one positive square root.

60. If x_1, x_2, y_1, y_2 are non-negative, show that $x_1 y_1 + x_2 y_2 \leq \sqrt{x_1^2 + x_2^2}\sqrt{y_1^2 + y_2^2}$.

61. Assuming that each real number b has a real cube root, show that it has only one; that is, there is just one real number x for which $x^3 = b$. (*Hint:* Suppose also $y^3 = b$ and consider the implications of $x > y$.)

6.2   The Order of the Integers

In Chapter 1 we discussed from a rather intuitive point of view the integers and their arithmetic. We are now able to derive their natural ordering. A careful perusal of Chapter 2 will show that although we were dealing there with numbers, only two numbers, 0 and 1, were explicitly mentioned in the axioms and subsequent formal development of the properties of real numbers. If other specific numbers were mentioned, it was only for illustrative purposes.

The real number represented by the symbol $1 + 1$ occurs so frequently that it is convenient to have a simpler symbol for it. We use the symbol 2 for this purpose, and it is in this sense that $2 = 1 + 1$. In the last section we showed that $1 > 0$. Therefore $1 + 1 > 1 + 0 = 1$ and hence $2 > 1$. The transitive axiom together with $1 > 0$ now shows that $2 > 0$. Similarly, $2 + 1 = (1 + 1) + 1$ is a real number, which by associativity can be written as $1 + (1 + 1)$ or $1 + 1 + 1$. We denote this sum by the symbol 3. Since $2 > 1$, then $3 = 2 + 1 > 1 + 1 = 2$, which in turn implies that $3 > 0$.

In the same manner we assign in turn symbols to the other positive integers:

$$4 = 3 + 1 = 1 + 1 + 1 + 1,$$
$$5 = 4 + 1 = 1 + 1 + 1 + 1 + 1,$$
$$6 = 5 + 1 = 1 + 1 + 1 + 1 + 1 + 1,$$
$$\cdots$$

and have

$$0 < 1 < 2 < 3 < 4 < \cdots.$$

Elementary arithmetic can now be easily developed. For example, to find the sum of the numbers whose symbols are 3 and 2, we write

$$3 + 2 = (1 + 1 + 1) + (1 + 1) = 1 + 1 + 1 + 1 + 1.$$

A more convenient symbol for this last expression is 5. Likewise,

$$3 \cdot 2 = (1 + 1 + 1) \cdot 2 = 1 \cdot 2 + 1 \cdot 2 + 1 \cdot 2$$
$$= 2 + 2 + 2 = (1 + 1) + (1 + 1) + (1 + 1)$$
$$= 1 + 1 + 1 + 1 + 1 + 1 = 6.$$

A similar procedure will show that if a is any real number, then $3a = a + a + a$:

$$3a = (1 + 1 + 1)a = 1 \cdot a + 1 \cdot a + 1 \cdot a = a + a + a.$$

This is the justification of the practice of reading $3a$ as "three a's."

Since $1 > 0$, $-1 < 0$ by the corollary to Theorem 2. Likewise, $2 > 1$ implies $-2 < -1$, and so on. This gives the ordering of the negative integers:

$$\cdots < -4 < -3 < -2 < -1 < 0 < 1 < 2 < 3 < \cdots.$$

PROBLEMS

1. Show that if $0 < c$, then $0 < \dfrac{c}{2} < c$.

2. If $a < b$, show that $a < \dfrac{a + b}{2} < b$. Illustrate with $a = -9$, $b = 4$. (The number $\dfrac{a + b}{2}$ is called the *mean* or *average* of a and b. The former term is preferable, since statistics uses many kinds of averages.)

3. If n is a positive integer, show that $0 < \dfrac{1}{n} \leq 1$. When, in particular, would we have $0 < \dfrac{1}{n} < 1$?

4. Prove that $0 < \dfrac{1}{n^2} \leq \dfrac{1}{n}$ if n is a positive integer.

5. If $3x - 9y > 12$, show that $x > 4 + 3y$.

6. If $-2a + 5b < 4$, show that $a > \frac{5}{2}b - 2$.

7. If $a > 0$ and $b > 0$, show that $(a + b)^2 > a^2 + b^2$.

8. Show that $ab \leq \frac{1}{2}(a^2 + b^2)$.

9. If n is a positive integer, prove that

$$1 < \left(1 + \frac{1}{n}\right)^2 \leq 1 + \frac{3}{n}.$$

(*Hint:* Use Problem 4.)

10. Show that $3 + 5 = 8$ and $3 \cdot 5 = 15$.

11. If a is a positive number such that $a^2 \not< 2$ and $a^2 \not> 2$, what is a? Which order axiom are you using here?

12. If a, b, and c are three numbers such that $a < b < c$, show that
$$a < \frac{a+b+c}{3} < c.$$

13. Show that the set S of all x for which $x < 4$ has no largest element. (*Hint:* Suppose c were the largest number in S. Use Problem 2 to construct a number between c and 4.) Find an upper bound of S; that is, a number u such that $u \geq s$ for all s in S. Are there others? What is the smallest number that is an upper bound of S? (This number is called the *least upper bound of S.*) Is the least upper bound of S an element of S?

14. Discuss Problem 13 if S is the set of all x for which $x \leq 4$.

15. Give an example of a set of real numbers with no upper bound.

16. By analogy with upper bounds, define lower bound and greatest lower bound of a set T of real numbers. Give an illustration.

6.3   The Coordinate Line, Intervals, and Absolute Values

It is possible to give a pictorial representation of the real numbers that is not only useful in geometry, but also helpful in understanding theorems and proofs on the ordering of the real numbers.

On a line L extending indefinitely in both directions choose a point O, called the *origin*. To facilitate discussion, we shall assume that line L is positioned so that it is horizontal, extending to the right and left of the viewer. Choose another point I anywhere to the right of O. We shall let the number zero correspond to the point O and the number 1 to the point I, and write these numbers below their respective points to remind us of this (Figure 6.1).

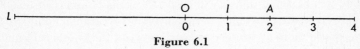

Figure 6.1

Now mark a third point A on the line to the right of I such that the distance from I to A equals that from O to I, and let the number 2 correspond to A. Continue this process, selecting points at equally spaced intervals on L to the right of O and extending indefinitely to the right. We assign the whole numbers in their natural order to these points in the same manner as above.

Similarly, to those points to the left of O that are spaced a distance OI apart can be assigned the negative integers -1, -2, -3, $\cdots$, as indicated in Figure 6.2.

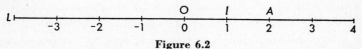

Figure 6.2

If the number x is assigned to the point P, we call x the *coordinate* of P and indicate this symbolically by $P(x)$. Thus for Figure 6.2, $A(2)$ means that the point A has coordinate 2. Instead of speaking of a point as "the point whose coordinate is 3," it is more convenient to say just "the point 3."

To the number $\frac{1}{2}$ we let correspond the point midway between O and I, and to the number $2\frac{4}{5}$ the point $\frac{4}{5}$ of the way between 2 and 3. To the number $-\frac{4}{3}$ we assign the point that is $\frac{1}{3}$ of the way between -1 and -2 and nearer -1. In this way every rational number can be assigned to some point on L. These points can be located geometrically by following the construction given in plane geometry texts for dividing a given line segment in a given ratio. For example, in order to locate the point to which $2\frac{4}{5}$ is to correspond, divide the segment between 2 and 3 into five equal subsegments. The right end point of the fourth of these is the desired point. The existence of a correspondence between numbers and points is quite independent of this geometrical construction, however; there would be a correspondence even if there were no way of locating the points using only ruler and compass.

The irrational numbers can also be assigned to points on the line, though to do this in a manner that will ensure that no point has more than one number assigned to it requires a more careful study of the nature of the irrational numbers and the axioms of geometry than we can undertake here.

If a number a is greater than the number b, then the point to which it is assigned will lie to the right of the point corresponding to b; that is, the ordering of the points on the line corresponds to the ordering of the real numbers. This means that the point corresponding to π will lie between the points corresponding to 3 and 4. The decimal expansion of π correct to six decimal places is 3.141593. We can use this to locate the point more precisely by observing that it will lie between the points corresponding to 3.1 and 3.2, since 3.141593 lies between these two rational numbers. It can be placed still more accurately as lying between the points 3.14 and 3.15. In this way, the point corresponding to π can be located to any desired degree of accuracy.

We shall assume that each real number can be assigned to a point on the line in the manner described above. We shall go one step further and assume that when this is done there are no points left over. This means that every point on the line will have some number assigned to it. This too can be justified by careful analysis. Thus every real number corresponds to one and only one point, and conversely, every point corresponds to one and only one real number. This correspondence is such that the point P with coordinate a lies to the left of the point Q with coordinate b if and only if $a < b$. Such a line in correspondence with the set of real numbers is called a *coordinate line* or in some branches of mathematics the *real line*. It is basic to the study of the graphing of equations and its extension, analytic geometry.

Let a and b be two real numbers with $a < b$. The set of all numbers between a and b is called an *interval*. An interval is indicated by the phrase, "the set of all numbers x for which $a < x < b$," or more briefly, "the interval $a < x < b$." Note that the numbers a and b are not in this interval. To indicate that the interval includes both a and b, we write $a \leqq x \leqq b$.

We can indicate geometrically the set of all points x for which $x > 3$ by an arrow, as in Figure 6.3, where the curved bracket at the point whose coordinate is 3 indicates that this point is not in the set. We shall use a square bracket to show that the end point is a member of the set. The set of all points x for which $x \leqq 0$ would be pictured as in Figure 6.4.

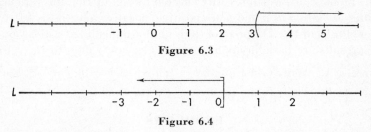

Figure 6.3

Figure 6.4

If a is not zero, just one of the pair a and $-a$ is positive. The notation $|a|$ is used to indicate this positive member and is called the *absolute value* or *numerical value* of a. For example, $|5| = 5$, and $|-6| = 6$ since 6 is the positive member of the pair -6 and $-(-6)$. We define $|0| = 0$.

The symbol $|x|$ is really a functional notation. It can be considered as the function f that associates to each real number x the number x itself if x is positive or zero, and $-x$ if x is negative. That is,

$$f(x) = |x| = \begin{cases} x, \text{ if } x \geqq 0, \\ -x, \text{ if } x < 0. \end{cases}$$

The vertical bars take the place of the letter f. It should be obvious that in order to evaluate $|a|$ for a given number a, one must first determine whether a is positive, negative, or zero.

Illustration.

(a) Since $\frac{1}{4} > 0$, $|\frac{1}{4}| = \frac{1}{4}$.

(b) Since $\sqrt{2} - 1 > 0$, $|\sqrt{2} - 1| = \sqrt{2} - 1$.

(c) Since $3 - \pi < 0$, $|3 - \pi| = \pi - 3$.

The set of all numbers x for which $|x| < 4$ consists of all numbers between -4 and 4, exclusive; that is, it is the interval $-4 < x < 4$. The requirement that a number z be such that $|z| \leqq 10$ is just another, and often more convenient, way of saying that it must lie between -10 and 10, end points included.

We have defined $\sqrt{b}$ for $b \geqq 0$ to be that non-negative number whose square is b. The statement, frequently seen, that $\sqrt{a^2} = a$ is then not always correct; for example, if $a = -5$, $\sqrt{a^2} = \sqrt{25} = 5 = -a$. Using absolute values, we can express $\sqrt{a^2}$ correctly in terms of a as $\sqrt{a^2} = |a|$.

The absolute value of a product or sum is related to the absolute values of the individual factors or terms by the following theorem.

Theorem 5.

(a) $|ab| = |a| \cdot |b|$,

(b) $|a + b| \leq |a| + |b|$.

The proof of (a), which is easily effected by considering the various possibilities according as a and b are positive, negative, or zero, is left to the reader (Problem 47). The proof of (b) is not too difficult but will be omitted. These results are basic in applications of absolute values to the calculus.

Exercise A.   Verify (a) for $a = 4$, $b = \frac{1}{3}$; $a = -2$, $b = 10$; $a = -5$, $b = -3$.

Exercise B.   Verify (b) for the above choices of a and b.

PROBLEMS

1. On a coordinate line mark as accurately as possible the points with coordinates 0, 1, 5, -4, $\frac{13}{4}$, $-3\frac{1}{5}$, π, $-\sqrt{3}$.

2. Does the point P with coordinate $\frac{11}{7}$ lie to the right or left of (a) the point Q whose coordinate is $\frac{23}{14}$; (b) the point $R(1.571)$; (c) the point $S(-\frac{11}{7})$; (d) the point $T\left(\frac{21}{15}\right)$?

3. Indicate on a coordinate line the set of all points x for which (a) $x < 2\frac{1}{2}$; (b) $x \geq -1$.

4. Indicate on a coordinate line the set of all points y for which $-3 < y < 5$.

5. Which of the following numbers are contained in the interval $-1 < x \leq 3$: 5, 0, $\frac{1}{2}$, 3, π, $\sqrt{2}$, -1, $-\frac{1}{4}$?

6. Is $\frac{17}{23}$ in the interval $-1 \leq x < \frac{3}{4}$?

7. Write the notation for the interval consisting of all numbers between (a) $\frac{3}{8}$ and 15, inclusive; (b) $-\frac{4}{5}$ and 7, excluding the left but including the right end point; (c) -5 and -4.9, excluding the end points. Indicate these intervals on a coordinate line and find two numbers in each of them.

8. Show on the real line the relation of a^2 to a if $a > 1$; if $0 < a < 1$. (*Hint:* See Problem 24 in Section 6.1.) Illustrate with $a = 3$, $\frac{1}{2}$, $\frac{1}{5}$.

Express without absolute value signs:

9. $|3|$.

10. $|-10|$.

11. $\left|\frac{16}{5}\right|$.

12. $-|-2|$.

13. $|-\sqrt{2}|$.

14. $|1|$.

15. $\left|-\frac{10}{4}\right|$.

16. $-\left|\frac{10}{4}\right|$.

17. $\left|\frac{3}{2} - 1\right|$.

18. $\left|\frac{33}{100} - \frac{1}{3}\right|$.

19. $\left|\dfrac{2 + \frac{1}{2} - 3}{8}\right|.$

22. $|\sqrt{3} - \sqrt{2}|.$

20. $|1.732 - \sqrt{3}|.$

23. $-\left|2\pi - \dfrac{58}{7}\right|.$

21. $\left|\sqrt{3} - \dfrac{1}{2}\right|.$

24. $|(1 - \sqrt{5})^2 - 1|.$

*25. When is $|a| = a$ and when is $|a| = -a$?

26. If $|c| = |d|$, what can you say about the relation of c to d?

27. Mark on a coordinate line the points (a) 3, $|3|$; (b) -3, $|-3|$; (c) $-\frac{1}{2}$, $|-\frac{1}{2}|$.

28. Describe the set of all real numbers x for which $x^2 < 9$. Show this set on a coordinate line.

29. (a) Indicate on a coordinate line the set of all x for which $|x| < 3$. Does this set contain a largest element? (b) Do the same for $|x| \leq \frac{5}{2}$.

30. If $|y| < 6$, within what interval must y lie?

31. Describe the set of all numbers x for which $|x| > 2$. Mark this set on the real line. Does this set contain a largest element; a least element?

32. Let $b > 0$. Within what interval must a lie if $|a| < b$?

33. Using absolute values, express the relationship $-7.1 \leq w \leq 7.1$.

Find the numbers, if any, in the set of all x such that:

34. $|x| \leq 0.$

35. $|x| = 1.7.$

36. $|x| < -1.$

37. $|x| = -1.7.$

38. Indicate on a coordinate line the set of all x for which $|x - 4| < 1$. Express this relationship using the interval notation.

39. Indicate on a coordinate line the set of all z for which $|3z| \leq 7$.

40. If $-3.01 \leq x \leq -2.99$, show that $|x + 3| \leq .01$.

41. Find the set of all x for which $|x + \frac{1}{2}| \geq 2$.

42. Show that $|-a| = |a|$.

*43. Prove that $|a - b| = |b - a|$.

44. Show that $|a^2| = a^2 = |a|^2$.

45. For which numbers a is $|a^3| = a^3$?

46. Show that $a \leq |a|$ and $-|a| \leq a$.

*47. Prove $|ab| = |a| \cdot |b|$. (*Hint:* Consider the four possible cases according as a or b is positive or negative.)

*48. Prove $\left|\dfrac{a}{b}\right| = \dfrac{|a|}{|b|}$ if $b \neq 0$. $\left(Hint:\ \text{Show first that } \left|\dfrac{1}{b}\right| = \dfrac{1}{|b|}.\right)$

49. If $|a + b| = |a| + |b|$, what can you say about a and b?

50. Using Theorem 5(b), show that if $|x - a| < \frac{1}{20}$ and $|a - y| < \frac{1}{20}$, then $|x - y| < \frac{1}{10}$. (*Hint:* Express $x - y$ as $x - a + a - y$.)

51. If $|f(x) - b| < \frac{1}{100}$ and $|g(x) - c| < \frac{1}{100}$, show that $|[f(x) + g(x)] - (b + c)| < \frac{1}{50}$.

52. Using Theorem 5(b), show that $|a - b| \leq |a| + |b|$.

53. Simplify $\sqrt{(x - y)^2}$.

54. The decimal expansion of $\sqrt{5}$ correct to six decimal places is 2.236068. Locate $\sqrt{5}$ between two rational numbers that are no more than $\frac{1}{10}$ apart. Do the same if the rational numbers are no more than $\frac{1}{100}$ apart; $\frac{1}{1000}$ apart.

55. Do the same for $-\frac{\pi}{2}$.

56. Find all numbers x for which (a) $-1 < x - 2 \leqq 4$; (b) $|x - 1| < 3$; (c) $|5x| \geqq 14$; (d) $|2x + 6| < 11$.

57. Describe the set of all real numbers x for which $x^2 < 2$. Show this set on a coordinate line. Does this set contain a largest element?

58. Does the set of all rational numbers r for which $r^2 \leqq 2$ have a largest element?

59. Indicate on a coordinate line the intervals $A: -4 \leqq x \leqq 1$ and $B: -\frac{1}{2} \leqq x < 2$. What is the interval consisting of all numbers that are (a) common to A and B; (b) in A or B (or both)?

60. What are the domain and range of the absolute value function?

61. Let $[x]$ define the function that associates to each real number x the largest integer less than or equal to x. Thus to 6.2 corresponds 6, and this correspondence would be indicated by $[6.2] = 6$.

    (a) Evaluate $\left[\dfrac{9}{2}\right]$, $[12]$, $\left[-\dfrac{3}{4}\right]$, $\left[\dfrac{\pi}{2}\right]$.

    (b) What are the domain and range of this function?

    (c) Make a diagram for the function similar to Figure 5.1.

62. Prove that the length of each leg of a right triangle is less than the length of the hypotenuse.

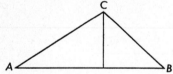

63. Prove that the sum of the lengths of any two sides of a triangle is greater than the length of the third side. (*Hint:* In the triangle ABC drop the perpendicular from C to AB and use Problem 62. Consider also the case in which the perpendicular falls outside the base of the triangle.)

64. Prove that the difference of the lengths of two sides of a triangle is less than the length of the third side. (*Hint:* Use Problem 63.)

6.4   Solution of Inequalities

Instead of asking for all numbers x for which $2x - 3 = 5$, one might seek all numbers x such that

$$(1) \qquad\qquad 2x - 3 < 5.$$

The solution of such inequalities is an increasingly important problem in modern mathematics. As with equations, an inequality may have one, many, or no solutions, and a complete answer should give them all. Any number x for which $x < 4$ is a solution of the above inequality; for example, -1 is a solution, since $2(-1) - 3 = -5$ and $-5 < 5$. However, 6 is not a solution, since $2(6) - 3 = 9$ and $9 \not< 5$. Note that 4 is also not a solution.

The infinite number of solutions of (1) is typical of inequalities. Whereas most equations commonly encountered have only one, two, or a finite number of solutions, most inequalities have an infinite number. Some, however, will have but one answer, as in $x^2 - 2x + 1 \leq 0$ whose only solution is 1. Others may have no answer; for example, $2x - 3 > 2x + 1$.

Exercise A.   By writing $x^2 - 2x + 1$ in the form $(x - 1)^2$, show that 1 is the only solution of $x^2 - 2x + 1 \leq 0$.

Exercise B.   Use the additive order axiom to show that $2x - 3 > 2x + 1$ has no solution.

Linear inequalities can be solved in much the same manner as linear equations. One replaces the inequality by an equivalent yet simpler one and repeats the process until an inequality is found whose solution is obvious. Two inequalities are *equivalent* if their sets of solutions are identical.

The addition of the same number to both sides of an inequality or multiplication of both sides by the same *positive* number leads to an inequality equivalent to the first. That is, if P and Q are expressions involving the unknown x and one wishes to solve the inequality $P < Q$, then $P + c < Q + c$ is an equivalent inequality for any number c, and so is $Pd < Qd$ provided $d > 0$. These are simply restatements of the additive and multiplicative order axioms. If $d < 0$, the inequality sign must be reversed, giving $Pd > Qd$ as the equivalent inequality (Theorem 4(b)). Except for having to note the sign of any multiplicative factor, the procedure for solving a linear inequality is identical with that for a linear equation.

Illustration 1.   Solve the inequality $2x - 3 < 5$.

Adding 3 to both sides, we obtain the equivalent inequality $2x < 8$. Dividing both sides by 2 gives $x < 4$. Thus any number less than 4 is a solution, and these are the only solutions.

Illustration 2.   Solve the inequality $1 - 3x \geq 6$.

Adding -1 to both sides gives $-3x \geq 5$. If we multiply both sides by $-\frac{1}{3}$, a negative number, the equivalent inequality is $x \leq -\frac{5}{3}$, which shows that any number x for which $x \leq -\frac{5}{3}$ is a solution. The reader should substitute in the original inequality numbers both less than and greater than $-\frac{5}{3}$ to convince himself of this.

Illustration 3.   Find all numbers x for which $1 < 2x - 1 < 5$.

Since $1 < 2x - 1 < 5$ stands for the two inequalities $1 < 2x - 1$ and $2x - 1 < 5$, we are to find all x satisfying simultaneously both of these. From the first we have

$$1 < 2x - 1,$$
$$2 < 2x,$$
$$1 < x.$$

Hence x must be a number such that $x > 1$. From the second we see that

$$2x - 1 < 5,$$
$$2x < 6,$$
$$x < 3,$$

and x must also be a number less than 3. Thus the only numbers x satisfying both inequalities are those for which $1 < x < 3$.

Since the same operations were performed at each step in both parts, they can be carried out simultaneously and the work arranged as follows:

$$1 < 2x - 1 < 5.$$

Add 1 to each of the three parts of the inequality, obtaining

$$2 < 2x < 6.$$

Divide by 2:

$$1 < x < 3,$$

and the answer has been obtained directly.

Illustration 4. Find all numbers x for which $\frac{1}{2}x - 5 < 0$ and $3x \leq 4x - 4$.

Any x such that $x < 10$ will satisfy the first inequality. Solving the second, we have $-x \leq -4$ or $x \geq 4$. Therefore the numbers x satisfying both inequalities are those for which $4 \leq x < 10$.

PROBLEMS

Find all solutions of the following inequalities and show the set of solutions on a coordinate line:

1. $x - 2 < 5$.
2. $6x - 5 > 7$.
3. $3x + 4 \leq x$.
4. $5x + 7 \geq x - 4$.
5. $\frac{2}{7}x \geq 3$.
6. $-x < 1$.
7. $x - 8 \geq x - 17$.
8. $-4x \geq 6$.
9. $x + \frac{1}{2} < 7x - 1$.

10. $5x > \frac{3}{2}x + 1$.
11. $x + a \geq 6$.
12. $ax + b < 2$, where $a < 0$.
13. $-6 < x + 4 < -1$.
14. $-3 \leq -x + 2 < 0$.
15. $0 < 2x < 7$.
16. $-2 \leq \frac{1}{2}x < 3$.
17. $-1 \leq x \leq -1$.
18. $11 \leq 3x + 5 \leq 11$.

Find all x for which:

19. $x^2 \leq 9$.
20. $x^2 \leq -2$.
21. $(x - 5)^2 \leq 0$.

Find all solutions of the following inequalities and show the solution set on a coordinate line:

22. $|x| < 2$.
23. $|x - 2| < 4$. (*Hint:* Write the inequality in the form $-4 < x - 2 < 4$.)
24. $|x + 7| \leq 7$.
25. $|2x - \frac{1}{2}| \leq \frac{1}{2}$.
26. $|1 - \frac{1}{3}x| < 15$.
27. $|6x + 5| \leq -2$.

28. $|3x| > 21$.
29. $\left| \dfrac{x - 1}{5} \right| \leq 4$.
30. $|7x - 1| > 6$.

Find all numbers x for which each pair of inequalities below is true and show the solution set on a coordinate line:

31. $3x < 12, \qquad x > 1.$

32. $x + 7 > 2, \qquad 2x < 1.$

33. $-x + 4 \leq 3, \qquad \frac{1}{2}x < 11.$

34. $-2x + 7 > 4, \qquad \frac{2}{3}x > 2.$

35. $3x - 5 \leq 7, \qquad 20 \leq 4x + 5.$

36. $1 \leq \dfrac{x + 9}{3}, \qquad 2x + 7 < -5.$

37. $5x + 2 \geq 3(x + 1), \qquad -2(x - 2) \geq 3.$

38. $\dfrac{2}{3}(x + 1) + \dfrac{1}{3} \leq 7, \qquad \dfrac{x}{2} + 2 < \dfrac{9}{2}.$

39. $-5 < 2x + 3, \qquad \frac{1}{2}(x + 5) > \frac{7}{2}.$

Find all solutions of each set of inequalities:

40. $-4x + 17 > 1, \qquad 2x + 8 < 8, \qquad x - 2 \geq -3.$

41. $\frac{1}{2}(x - 5) \leq 2, \qquad |x - 2| > 4.$

42. For any real number a, let the symbol $[a]$ stand for the largest integer less than or equal to a. For example, $[3\frac{4}{5}] = 3$, $[5] = 5$, $[-\frac{3}{2}] = -2$.
    (a) Solve the equation $[x] = 2$.
    (b) Prove that $0 \leq x - [x] < 1$ for all x.
    (c) Solve the equation $x - [x] = \frac{1}{3}$.

43. Find all c for which the roots of the equation $x^2 + 2x - 4 - c = 0$ are (a) real; (b) non-real.

6.5   Quadratic Inequalities

The quadratic inequality

$$(1) \qquad\qquad 3x^2 + 4x - 4 > 0$$

can be solved without too much difficulty if one first factors the left side:

$$(2) \qquad\qquad (3x - 2)(x + 2) > 0.$$

Any solution x must be a number for which the product in (2) is positive. Therefore by Theorem 3 we must have either

$$(3) \qquad\qquad 3x - 2 > 0 \quad \text{and} \quad x + 2 > 0,$$

or

$$(4) \qquad\qquad 3x - 2 < 0 \quad \text{and} \quad x + 2 < 0.$$

The solution of the first inequality in (3) is $x > \frac{2}{3}$ and of the second $x > -2$. Hence any x for which $x > \frac{2}{3}$ is a solution of both inequalities (3). Similarly, the solution of the pair of inequalities (4) is $x < -2$. Thus any x for which

$x > \frac{2}{3}$ or $x < -2$ is a solution of (1). The solution set is shown on a co-ordinate line in Figure 6.5.

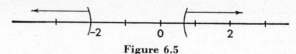

Figure 6.5

Exercise A.   By substituting 1, 5, -5 in (1) and (2), verify that they are solutions. Show that -1 and $\frac{1}{2}$ are not solutions.

Illustration 1.   Solve the inequality

(5) $$x^2 + 8x - 3 < -16.$$

Add 16 to each side so that only 0 is on the right:

(6) $$x^2 + 8x + 13 < 0.$$

The polynomial on the left has no rational factors, but can be factored by the method of completing the square described in Section 4.3. If we do this, (6) becomes

$$x^2 + 8x + 13 = x^2 + 8x + 16 - 3$$
$$= (x + 4)^2 - 3$$
(7) $$= (x + 4 + \sqrt{3})\,(x + 4 - \sqrt{3}) < 0.$$

By Theorem 3 any solution x of (7) must be a number for which either

(8) $$x + 4 + \sqrt{3} < 0 \quad \text{and} \quad x + 4 - \sqrt{3} > 0,$$

or

(9) $$x + 4 + \sqrt{3} > 0 \quad \text{and} \quad x + 4 - \sqrt{3} < 0.$$

There is no solution of the pair of inequalities (8), but the pair in (9) have the solution

$$-4 - \sqrt{3} < x < -4 + \sqrt{3}.$$

Therefore these values of x satisfy (5) and are its only solutions.

Illustration 2.   Solve the inequality

(10) $$x^2 + x + 1 > 0.$$

By completing the square, (10) can be expressed in the form

(11) $$\left(x + \frac{1}{2}\right)^2 + \frac{3}{4} > 0,$$

showing that (10) has only complex factors. Since the first term of (11) is always non-negative and the second positive, any number x is a solution of (11) and hence of (10). If the inequality in (10) had been reversed, there would have been no solution.

Illustration 3.   Solve the inequality

(12) $$\frac{x + 5}{2x - 1} > 3.$$

Since the quantity $(2x - 1)^2$ is positive for all $x \neq \frac{1}{2}$, by multiplying both sides of (12) by $(2x - 1)^2$, we obtain the equivalent inequality

$$(x + 5)(2x - 1) > 3(2x - 1)^2, \quad x \neq \frac{1}{2}.$$

Rearranging and factoring gives us

$$(2x - 1)[(x + 5) - 3(2x - 1)] > 0$$

or

(13) $(2x - 1)(-5x + 8) > 0.$

The solution of (13) is any x for which $\frac{1}{2} < x < \frac{8}{5}$.

PROBLEMS

Solve the following inequalities and show the solution set on a coordinate line:

1. $(x - 2)(x + 3) > 0.$
2. $(x + 5)(x + 7) < 0.$
3. $x^2 - 4x \geq 0.$
4. $x^2 + 10x + 21 \geq 0.$
5. $2x^2 - 9x + 7 \leq 12.$
6. $x^2 - 1 > 8.$
7. $x^2 - 7 > 0.$
8. $x^2 + 2x - 1 > 0.$
9. $x^2 - 3x + 2 \leq 1.$
10. $x^2 + 3x + 1 > 0.$
11. $x^2 + 6x + 9 \leq 0.$
12. $x^2 - 2x - 4 < 0.$
13. $x^2 + 10 > 0.$
14. $(x - 3)^2 + 6 < 0.$
15. $x^2 + 4x + 11 \geq 0.$
16. $x^2 - 2x + 3 < 0.$
17. $x^3 - x^2 + x - 1 < 0.$
18. $x(x - 1)(x + 5) > 0.$
19. $x^3 - 9x \leq 0.$

20. $\dfrac{3}{x} < 6.$

21. $\dfrac{2}{x - 4} > 10.$

22. $\dfrac{x}{x + 3} \geq 7.$

23. $\dfrac{x - 2}{x + 2} < 1.$

24. $\dfrac{3}{x - 3} > \dfrac{2}{x}.$

25. $\dfrac{1}{x - 1} \leq \dfrac{3}{x + 2}.$

26. $\dfrac{7}{4x + 2} > \dfrac{4}{x - 5}.$

27. $\dfrac{x(x + 2)}{x - 6} > 0.$

28. $\dfrac{2x - 5}{x + 4} < x.$

29. $\dfrac{7x + 10}{x + 1} > 2(x + 2).$

30. Find all b for which the equation $x^2 + bx + 9 = 0$ has (a) real roots; (b) non-real roots.
31. For which values of c is $x^2 + 2x + 8 + c > 0$ for all x?

Chapter 7

Graphs

7.1 Coordinates

Although aspects of plane geometry can be traced back to the Egyptians and Babylonians, the ancient Greeks developed most of elementary plane geometry as it is presented today in the average high school course. To Euclid belongs the credit for organizing the theorems into a logical sequence and the realization that the whole must be based on axioms.

After the decline of Greece there was little advance in geometry until the seventeenth century when the French philosopher Descartes conceived the idea of using algebra as an aid in the study of geometry. Unexpectedly, perhaps, it was soon discovered that geometry, in turn, could be used to clarify certain algebraic ideas by furnishing pictures of equations.

The basis of Descartes's method is the use of numbers to identify points in the plane. Let x and y be two coordinate lines in the plane intersecting at right angles at their common origins O and with equal scales (Figure 7.1). We call the two lines the x-axis and y-axis. (For purposes of discussion, it is convenient to imagine the x-axis as horizontal.) With each point P in the plane we associate a pair of real numbers determined as follows. Let P' be the foot of the perpendicular from P to the x-axis and a the coordinate of this point (if P lies on the x-axis, we take P' to be P itself). Similarly, the perpendicular from P to the y-axis intersects the y-axis in a point P'' with coordinate b. The pair of numbers a, b, in that order, we call the *coordinates* of P and write $P(a, b)$ to indicate this. The plane is said to be a *coordinate plane*, and the point O is called the *origin*.

It should be apparent that every point in the plane can have coordinates assigned to it in this manner and that these coordinates are unique. This last is a consequence of the fact that every point on a coordinate line has a unique coordinate. Conversely, given a pair of real numbers—say $(-4, \frac{3}{2})$—there will be a point in the plane, and only one, with these numbers as coordinates. This point will be the intersection of the perpendiculars to the x- and y-axes at the points -4 and $\frac{3}{2}$, respectively. We have then a correspondence between the points of the plane and pairs of numbers such that to each point corresponds just one pair of numbers and conversely. Therefore if the points P and Q have the same coordinates, they must be the same point; only their names are different.

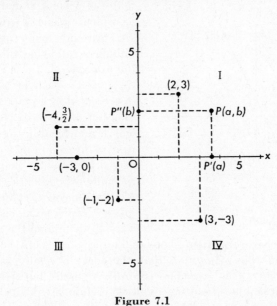

Figure 7.1

The two axes divide the plane into four sections called *quadrants*, labeled as indicated by the roman numerals in Figure 7.1. The points on the axes are not considered as lying in any quadrant.

PROBLEMS

1. Plot on a coordinate plane the points with coordinates: $(3, 1)$, $(-6, 3)$, $(0, 4)$, $(\frac{5}{2}, -7)$, $(-1, 0)$, $(0, 0)$, $(-4, -5)$, $(\sqrt{2}, -\frac{7}{3})$.

2. Give the quadrant in which each of the points in Problem 1 lies.

Plot the following pairs of points and find the distance between them:

3. $(2, 1)$, $(6, 1)$.   6. $(1, 2)$, $(5, 0)$.

4. $(1, -1)$, $(1, 4)$.   7. $(-3, -2)$, $(4, 6)$.

5. $(0, -3)$, $(4, 0)$.

8. The vertices of a triangle are $A(3, 2)$, $B(-1, 7)$, $C(-1, 1)$.
   (a) Find the area of the triangle.
   (b) A median of a triangle is the line segment between a vertex and the midpoint of the opposite side. Find the length of the median through A.
   (c) Find the perimeter of the triangle.
   (d) Find the length of the median through B.

7.2　Graphs of Equations

Consider the equation

(1) $$2x - y + 1 = 0.$$

The pair of numbers $x = 2$, $y = 5$ satisfies this equation, since $2(2) - 5 + 1 = 0$. Let us now interpret this pair of numbers (2, 5) as the coordi-

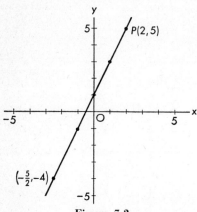

nates of a point P and plot it on a coordinate plane (Figure 7.2).

There are many other pairs of numbers satisfying this equation— for example, $(1, 3), (0, 1), (-1, -1),$ $(-\frac{5}{2}, -4)$—each of which can be represented as a point in the plane. The set of all these points forms a curve and furnishes us with a picture of the equation $2x - y + 1 = 0$, called its graph.† Since one cannot plot all the points whose coordinates satisfy the equation, in practice one plots as many points as seem neces-

Figure 7.2

sary to determine the general character of the curve and then sketches in the curve between the points, proceeding on the assumption that the curve is relatively smooth between the points. This procedure is hardly rigorous, but with the aid of the calculus it can be shown that between certain key points on the curve this will be the case. In Figure 7.2 we have sketched the graph of (1).

Solving (1) for y, we obtain $y = 2x + 1$. From this we see that for every x there is a y satisfying the equation. Geometrically, this means that the curve extends indefinitely to the right and left and that every line parallel to the y-axis must intersect the curve. Similarly, by solving (1) for x, $x = \frac{1}{2}(y - 1)$, we see that the curve extends indefinitely above and below the x-axis and is cut by every line parallel to the x-axis.

It is not difficult to show that the graph of this equation is a line, but we shall not do so here.

Exercise A.　Find the coordinates of the point where the line through the point $(50, 0)$ and parallel to the y-axis intersects the curve in Figure 7.2. Do the same for the line through $(0, -76)$ and parallel to the x-axis.

So that we may graph other equations, let us state precisely what is meant by the graph of an equation.

Definition.　The *graph* of an equation in x and y is the set C of all points (a, b) whose coordinates satisfy the equation.

†In mathematics a curve is not necessarily crooked but may be a line. A line, however, will always mean a straight line. In this example the points seem to lie on a line.

It is convenient to refer to the graph of an equation as a *curve*, even though it may not always resemble one's intuitive idea of a curve. The equation, in turn, is said to be an *equation of the curve C*. Frequently we shall say, for example, the "curve $y = x^2$", meaning "the curve whose equation is $y = x^2$". In this book it will always be understood that a curve is the graph of some equation.

Illustration 1. Sketch the graph of the equation

$$(2) \qquad\qquad\qquad\qquad y = \frac{1}{2}x^2.$$

We make a table of values of x and y satisfying the equation. This can be done most easily by choosing convenient values of x and computing from the equation the corresponding values for y or vice versa:

x	y		x	y
-3	$\frac{9}{2}$		1	$\frac{1}{2}$
-2	2		2	2
-1	$\frac{1}{2}$		3	$\frac{9}{2}$
0	0			

If the points with these numbers as coordinates are plotted, it is fairly clear how the curve should be sketched, except perhaps for the section between $x = -1$ and $x = 1$. By choosing values of x in this range, additional points on the graph in this

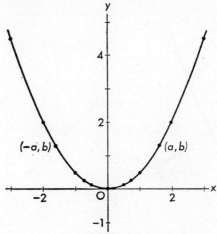

Figure 7.3

region can be found: $(\frac{1}{2}, \frac{1}{8})$, $(-\frac{1}{2}, \frac{1}{8})$, $(\frac{3}{4}, \frac{9}{32})$, $(-\frac{3}{4}, \frac{9}{32})$. With the aid of these, the graph can now be sketched with fair accuracy (Figure 7.3).

Several properties of the curve can be inferred from its equation and used to facilitate the sketching of the graph. If (a, b) is any point on the graph, then $b = \frac{1}{2}a^2$. Since this can be written $b = \frac{1}{2}(-a)^2$, we see that the point $(-a, b)$ must also lie on the curve. This shows that for every point on the graph, the point symmetrically placed with respect to the y-axis is also on the graph. A curve with this property is said to be *symmetric with respect to the y-axis*. For such a curve only one half of it need be plotted with care; the other half can then be quickly sketched in.

Since x^2 is non-negative, the equation of the curve shows that no points with negative y-coordinates can be on the curve, and hence no part of the curve lies below the x-axis. For each x, however, there will be a y satisfying the equation, showing that the curve extends indefinitely to the right and left. The equation also shows that when x is large y is considerably larger. Therefore the curve rises rapidly as x increases.

Illustration 2. Sketch the graph of the equation

(3) $$\sqrt{2y} = x.$$

By convention, the symbol $\sqrt{2y}$ always denotes the non-negative number whose square is $2y$ (see Section 2.19), and thus x can never be negative. This equation is not equivalent to (2) in the sense of Section 3.3 and does not have the same graph. For example, the point $(-3, \frac{9}{2})$ on the graph of (2) is not on the graph of (3). Some points on the graph of (3) are given by the following table:

x	0	$\frac{1}{2}$	1	2	3
y	0	$\frac{1}{8}$	$\frac{1}{2}$	2	$\frac{9}{2}$

Using these, we have sketched the graph in Figure 7.4. It does coincide with the right half of the graph $y = \frac{1}{2}x^2$.

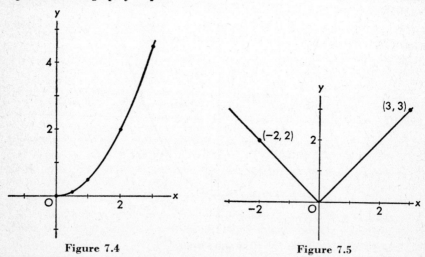

Figure 7.4   Figure 7.5

Illustration 3. Sketch the graph of the equation $y = |x|$.

Whenever $x \geqq 0$, $|x| = x$, and every point on the graph to the right of the y-axis must have equal x- and y-coordinates, as for example, $(3, 3)$. That part therefore is the line bisecting the first quadrant. When $x < 0$, $|x| = -x$, and points on the graph to the left of the y-axis have coordinates $(a, -a)$, where $a < 0$, as for example, $(-2, 2)$. These points lie on the line bisecting the second quadrant. The graph consists of the two rays emanating from the origin bisecting the first and second quadrants (Figure 7.5).

There is nothing in the definition that implies that the graph of an equation must be in one connected piece. Indeed, some common and important curves consist of two pieces.

The set of all points whose x-coordinates are 3 is the line parallel to the y-axis and three units to the right. It is natural then to consider this line as the graph of the equation $x = 3$. More generally, we shall define the graph of an equation containing only x terms to be the set of all points whose x-coordinates satisfy the equation.

Exercise A. Define the graph of an equation containing only y terms. Sketch the graph of the equation $y + 5 = 0$.

PROBLEMS

Sketch the graphs of the following equations. (a) Does the graph rise or fall as x becomes positively large; negatively large? (b) Is the graph cut by every vertical line; every horizontal line? (c) What happens to the steepness of the graph as a point on it moves to the right away from the origin?

1. $y = 3x$.
2. $x + y - 2 = 0$.
3. $2x - y = 3$.
4. $y = x^2$.
5. $y = 9$.
6. $2x + 7 = 0$.
7. $y = 0$.
8. $y^2 = x$.
9. $y = \sqrt{x}$.
10. $y = -\sqrt{x}$.

11. $y = \sqrt{-x}$.
12. $-y + \frac{3}{2}x - 1 = 0$.
13. $5x + 2y - 13 = 0$.
14. $y = \dfrac{6}{x}$.
15. $y = -x^2 + 3x$.
16. $y = x^2 - 9$.
17. $y = x^3$.
18. $y = x + |x|$.
19. $y = \dfrac{12}{x - 1}$.

20. Find the y-coordinate of the point on the curve $x - 3y + 5 = 0$ whose x-coordinate is 7. Find the x-coordinate of the point whose y-coordinate is $\frac{3}{2}$. Where does the curve cross the x- and y-axes? Sketch the graph of the equation.

21. Find the y-coordinate of the point on the curve $y = 4 - x^2$ whose x-coordinate is 1. Find the x-coordinate of the point whose y-coordinate is -12. Is there more than one such point? Where does the curve meet the x- and y-axes? Sketch the graph of the equation.

22. At what points does the curve $y^2 = 5x - 1$ intersect (a) the line $y = 4$; (b) the line $x = 3$; (c) the line $x = -2$?

23. Where does the graph of the equation $y = x^2 - 3x - 10$ meet the x- and y-axes? Sketch the graph.

24. How many times does the graph of $y = x^2 - 3x + 4$ meet the x-axis; the y-axis? Sketch the graph.

25. How many times does the graph of $y = x^2 - 6x + 9$ meet the x-axis; the y-axis?

Sketch the graphs of:

26. $x^2 + y^2 = 17$.
27. $x^2 + y^2 = 0$.
28. $(x - 1)^2 = 0$.
29. $x^2 - 1 = 0$.
30. $y^2 - 2y - 3 = 0$.
31. $x^2 - y^2 = 0$.
32. Show that the equation $x^2 + 3y^2 = -5$ has no graph.
33. Define symmetry of a curve with respect to the x-axis, and give an example.
34. For which values of k does the graph of $y = 4x^2 - 12x + k$ meet the x-axis in (a) one point; (b) more than one point; (c) no points?
35. Sketch the graph of $y = [x]$, where $[x]$ is the largest integer less than or equal to x.

7.3 Equations of Curves

In addition to the problem of finding the graph of an equation, there is the converse problem: given a curve C, to find an equation of the curve, that is, an equation whose graph is the curve C.

An equation of a curve expresses in algebraic language some geometric property that describes the curve. To find the equation of a curve, one first formulates such a geometric property and then translates it into algebraic symbolism. The resulting equation must be such that all points on the curve and no others satisfy it. A curve may have more than one equation, but all such equations are equivalent in the sense that any pair of numbers satisfying one will satisfy the others.

Illustration 1. Find an equation of the line parallel to the y-axis and passing through the point $(-2, 1)$.

The line is completely determined by the property that the x-coordinate of every point on it is -2. The equation $x = -2$ expresses this fact algebraically. Every point on the line and no other point satisfies the equation. It is then an equation of the line. Another equation of this same line is $3x + 6 = 0$.

Illustration 2. Find an equation of the line through the origin bisecting the second and fourth quadrants.

A property of this line that describes it completely is that for every point (a, b) on it the y-coordinate is the negative of the x-coordinate; that is, $b = -a$ (Figure 7.6). All points on the line will therefore satisfy the equation $y = -x$. Before we can claim that this is an equation of the line, we must show that if a point is not on the line, it does not satisfy the equation. We shall do this by showing that if a point satisfies the equation, it must lie on the line. Now, if a point (a, b) satisfies the equation, then $b = -a$, the point has coordinates $(a, -a)$, and therefore lies on the line.

Illustration 3.   Find an equation of the circle with radius 5 and center at the origin.

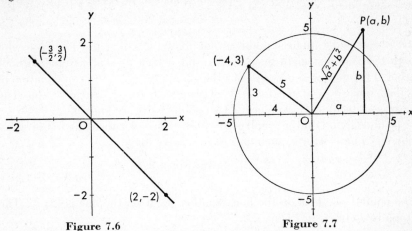

Figure 7.6   Figure 7.7

This circle can be described as the set of all points whose distance from the origin is 5. Let $P(a, b)$ be any point in the plane. By the Pythagorean theorem the length of the line segment joining P and the origin O is $\sqrt{a^2 + b^2}$ (Figure 7.7). If $P(a, b)$ is on the circle, then $\sqrt{a^2 + b^2} = 5$ and the coordinates of P satisfy the equation

(1) $$\sqrt{x^2 + y^2} = 5.$$

Conversely, if $P(a, b)$ is a point whose coordinates satisfy equation (1), then $\sqrt{a^2 + b^2} = 5$. But this says that the length of the line OP is 5 and P is on the circle. This shows that (1) is an equation of the circle. An equivalent equation is $x^2 + y^2 = 25$.

The equation of a curve depends on the location of the curve in the plane. If the circle in the previous illustration is moved, it will have a different equation.

PROBLEMS

1. Find an equation of the line bisecting the first and third quadrants.
2. Find an equation of the line parallel to the x-axis and six units below it.
3. Find an equation of the y-axis.
4. Find an equation of the line through the point $(6, 3)$ and parallel to the line whose equation is $x = 2$.
5. Find an equation of the circle with radius 7 and center at the origin.
6. Find an equation of the line that passes through the origin and rises from left to right three units vertically for every horizontal unit. (*Hint:* Sketch the line, and note the relation of the x- and y-coordinates of every point.
7. Find an equation of the line through the origin and the point $(1, 2)$.
8. Find an equation of the circle with radius 5 and center at the point $(1, 0)$.
*9. Show that the graph of $x^2 + y^2 = r^2$ is a circle with radius r and center at the origin.

7.4 Lines

It can be shown that every equation that can be expressed in the form

(1) $$ax + by + c = 0,$$

where a, b, and c are fixed numbers not involving x or y, and a and b are not both zero, has a straight line for its graph, a fact we shall assume without proof. Therefore we know at once that $2x + 3y - 6 = 0$ is an equation of a line, since it is of the form (1) with $a = 2$, $b = 3$, and $c = -6$. The graph can be quickly sketched if two points on it are known.

To find a point on the graph of $2x + 3y - 6 = 0$, substitute in the equation any number for x, such as -3, and solve for y:

$$2(-3) + 3y - 6 = 0,$$
$$y = 4.$$

The point $(-3, 4)$ is on the line. Another point on the line is $(2, \frac{2}{3})$. The graph is sketched in Figure 7.8.

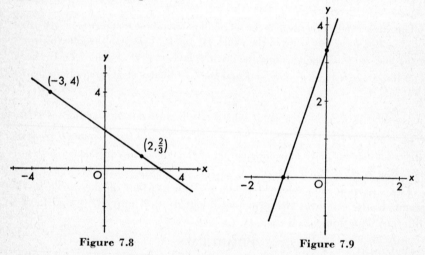

Figure 7.8   Figure 7.9

Two points especially easy to find are the point or points of intersection of the line with the axes. From the equation of the line we see that the line crosses the x-axis at $(3, 0)$ and the y-axis at $(0, 2)$. These points are called the x- and y-*intercepts* of the line.

Illustration 1.   The equation $y = 3x + \frac{10}{3}$ can be put in the form (1) by writing it as $3x + (-1)y + \frac{10}{3} = 0$. Its graph must be a line. The intercepts, found by substituting 0 for x and y in turn in the equation and solving for the other letter, are $(0, \frac{10}{3})$ and $(-\frac{10}{9}, 0)$. Plotting these, we see that the line is as sketched in Figure 7.9.

Since the quantities x and y in (1) are of the first degree, the equation is said to be a *first degree equation in x and y*. Because its graph is a line, (1) or any equation that can be expressed in that form is also called a *linear equation*.

Exercise. Show that the graph of the equation $5y - 17 = 0$ is a line by expressing it in the form (1). What are a, b, and c in this case? Sketch the graph.

Illustration 2. The equation

$$(2) \qquad\qquad 3x^2 + 8y + 7 = 0$$

is not of the form (1), since no choice of a, b, and c will make (1) look like (2).

PROBLEMS

Sketch the following lines and find their intercepts:

1. $x - y + 5 = 0$.
2. $7x - 3y = 0$.
3. $5y + 6x + 13 = 0$.
4. $2x + 2y = 7$.

5. $5y + 8 = -4$.
6. $\frac{1}{2}x - 2y - 3 = 0$.
7. $\frac{1}{2}x = 6 - 2x$.

Determine whether each equation below is linear, and if it is, choose a, b, and c according to (1):

8. $2y + x = 10$.
9. $x^2 - y = 0$.
10. $2x^2 + 3y^2 - 8 = 0$.
11. $0 = 3x + \frac{1}{2}y$.
12. $\frac{1}{2}(x - \sqrt{3}y) - 2 = 0$.

13. $\dfrac{5}{x} = y$.
14. $\frac{3}{5}x = 17$.
15. $4x + 6\sqrt{y} + 1 = 0$.
16. $3x + y - 4 = 2 + x$.
17. $\dfrac{y}{x} = 6$.

18. Find the area of the triangle whose sides have equations $y = \frac{1}{2}x$, $x = 0$, $y = 6$.

19. Sketch the curve $y = x^2 - 16$ and the line $y = x + 4$. At what points do they intersect?

20. For each value of c, the graph of the equation $x - 2y + c = 0$ is a straight line. Thus the equation determines a set of lines, one for each value of c.
    (a) Sketch the three lines corresponding to $c = 0, 6, -8$.
    (b) Is there a line of the set passing through the point $(1, \frac{5}{3})$?
    (c) Is there any special geometric property of the set of lines?

21. The equation $y = mx + m + 3$ determines a set of lines, one for each value of m.
    (a) Sketch the lines corresponding to $m = 1, -2, \frac{1}{3}$.
    (b) Is there any special geometric property of the set of lines?
    (c) Find a line of the set passing through the origin.
    (d) Find a line of the set parallel to the x-axis.

22. Sketch the graph of the equation $y = \dfrac{|x|}{x}(x - 1)$. Which vertical line does not intersect the graph?

23. Sketch the graph of the equation $y = \dfrac{|x|}{x}(x^2 - 1)$.

7.5   Graphical Interpretation of Roots

The root -1 and 3 of the equation $x^2 - 2x - 3 = 0$ are the x-coordinates of the points where the graph of the equation $y = x^2 - 2x - 3$ meets the x-axis (Figure 7.10). Those x's for which the graph lies below the x-axis are the solutions of the inequality $x^2 - 2x - 3 < 0$, namely $-1 < x < 3$.

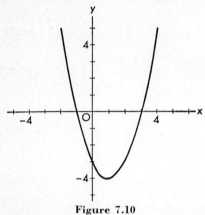

Figure 7.10

Similarly, for any polynomial $p(x)$, that part of the graph of $y = p(x)$ below the x-axis shows the relation of those x's for which $p(x) < 0$. This property can be used to solve, at least approximately, the inequality $p(x) < 0$. By making a careful sketch of the graph, one can estimate from it the x's for which $p(x) < 0$. Because of the labor involved in making a careful sketch, this method is useful only in cases in which it is difficult to solve the inequality by algebraic methods.

The solutions of the equation $x^2 + 2x + 5 = 0$ are non-real. This implies that the graph of

$$(1) \qquad\qquad y = x^2 + 2x + 5$$

does not meet the x-axis. Since the polynomial can be expressed in the form

$$x^2 + 2x + 5 = (x + 1)^2 + 4,$$

we see that it is positive for all x, and therefore the graph of (1) must lie entirely above the x-axis.

It can be shown that for any polynomial $p(x)$ the graph of $y = p(x)$ is in one continuous piece. Hence if the equation $p(x) = 0$ has no real roots, the graph must lie entirely above or entirely below the x-axis.

PROBLEMS

Sketch the graphs of the following equations and determine whether the zeros of the corresponding polynomials are real or non-real. Estimate from the graph those values of x for which each polynomial is positive:

1. $y = 3x - 5$.
2. $y = x^2 - 4x$.
3. $y = 3 - x^2$.
4. $y = 5x^2 - x$.
5. $y = -x^2 - 1$.
6. $y = x^2 + x + 2$.
7. $y = 5x^2 - 29x + 20$.

Chapter 8

Sets of Equations and Inequalities

8.1 Sets of Linear Equations

We have seen that there are many pairs of values of x and y satisfying an equation such as

$$(1) \qquad\qquad 2x - y = 4.$$

Similarly, there are pairs of numbers satisfying

$$(2) \qquad\qquad 6x + 2y = 7.$$

In general, a pair that satisfies (1) will not satisfy (2). We raise the question whether there are pairs satisfying both equations and, if so, how can they be found.

A *solution* of an equation in x and y is a pair of numbers a and b that, when substituted for x and y, respectively, satisfies the equation. The solution can be written in the form (a, b). Thus $(1, -2)$ and $(0, -4)$ are two solutions of (1).† A pair (a, b) satisfying both (1) and (2) is sometimes called a simultaneous solution of the equations, but we shall refer to it as a solution of the set of equations (1) and (2).

Before trying to answer the question posed above, let us consider the problem geometrically. The graphs of (1) and (2) are the lines l_1 and l_2 sketched in Figure 8.1. Solutions of (1) are coordinates of points on l_1, and solutions of (2) are coordinates of points on l_2. A common solution must be

---

†This differs somewhat from our earlier definition of a solution given in Section 3.2. According to that, we would consider $y = 2x - 4$ the solution of (1) in terms of x. There is no real contradiction here, solutions in the second sense being derivable from the first. For if we substitute 1 for x in the solution $y = 2x - 4$, we see that $y = -2$ and obtain $(1, -2)$ as a solution in the second sense.

represented by a point on both l_1 and l_2, that is, their point of intersection. From Figure 8.1 it is apparent that (1) and (2) will have just one common solution.

Our procedure for finding this common solution will be to replace (1) and (2) by another set of equations equivalent to this set, but simpler. As in Section 3.3, we shall say that two sets of equations in x and y are *equivalent* if every solution of one set is a solution of the other and conversely. This second set will be replaced, if necessary, by a third equivalent but simpler set, and the process repeated until a set is reached whose solution is easily found.

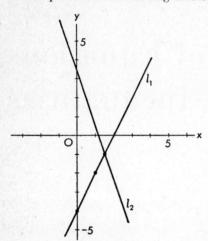

Figure 8.1

To do this, let us take the original set

$$(3) \qquad \begin{aligned} 2x - y &= 4, \\ 6x + 2y &= 7. \end{aligned}$$

As the first equation of the second set we shall choose the first equation in (3) again. The second equation will be formed by multiplying the first equation by -3, obtaining $-6x + 3y = -12$, and adding this equation to the second equation in (3) (by adding their respective left and right sides), giving us $5y = -5$. Our second set of equations equivalent to (3) is

$$(3a) \qquad \begin{aligned} 2x - y &= 4, \\ 5y &= -5. \end{aligned}$$

The third set (3b) equivalent to (3a) we form by repeating the first equation in (3a) as the first equation of (3b), and obtain the second equation by multiplying the second equation of (3a) by $\frac{1}{5}$:

$$(3b) \qquad \begin{aligned} 2x - y &= 4, \\ y &= -1. \end{aligned}$$

We shall explain our guiding principle in forming these equations shortly. The proof of the equivalence of these sets of equations will be left until later. We point out here that since (3) and (3a) are equivalent and (3a) and (3b) equivalent, every solution of the set (3) is a solution of (3b) and conversely. But the solutions of the last set are easy to find. The second equation in (3b) says that the solution must have $y = -1$. Substituting -1 for y in the first equation of (3b) and solving for x, we see that $x = \frac{3}{2}$. This shows that $(\frac{3}{2}, -1)$ is the only solution of (3b) and hence of (3). Geometrically, these are the coordinates of the point of intersection of the lines in Figure 8.1.

Exercise A. Check by direct substitution that $(\frac{3}{2}, -1)$ is a solution of (3b), (3a), and (3).

It will be easier to explain the general principles involved in solving sets of linear equations if first we consider another example, this time involving three equations and three unknowns:

$$
\begin{aligned}
y - z &= -33, \\
2x - 6y - z &= 0, \\
x + y + z &= 11.
\end{aligned}
$$

(4)

Our objective is essentially the same. We wish to find all triples of numbers, a, b, c that, when substituted for x, y, and z, respectively, satisfy the three equations in (4).

If we interchange the first and third equations, we obtain an obviously equivalent set:

$$
\begin{aligned}
x + y + z &= 11, \\
2x - 6y - z &= 0, \\
y - z &= -33.
\end{aligned}
$$

(4a)

The next set of equations will have the same first and third equations, and the second will be formed by multiplying the first equation in (4a) by -2 and adding the resulting equation to the second:

$$
\begin{aligned}
x + y + z &= 11, \\
-8y - 3z &= -22, \\
y - z &= -33.
\end{aligned}
$$

(4b)

For the fourth set, we repeat the first and third equations of (4b) and obtain the second equation by multiplying the third by 8 and adding it to the second:

$$
\begin{aligned}
x + y + z &= 11, \\
-11z &= -286, \\
y - z &= -33.
\end{aligned}
$$

(4c)

Multiplying the second equation by $-\frac{1}{11}$ and interchanging the second and third gives us finally:

$$
\begin{aligned}
x + y + z &= 11, \\
y - z &= -33, \\
z &= 26.
\end{aligned}
$$

(4d)

Since each set is equivalent to the one just before, they all have the same solutions. From the last equation in (4d) we have $z = 26$. Substituting this in the second gives us $y = -7$. And now from the first we see that $x = 11 - y - z = -8$. Thus $(-8, -7, 26)$ is a solution of (4) and the only one. Though logically not necessary, it is wise to guard against arithmetical errors by checking that the answer obtained from the last set is a solution of the original set by substituting directly in it.

It is possible to give a geometric interpretation of this problem, too, but three dimensions are necessary. If a third axis, the z-axis, is erected at the origin perpendicular to the plane determined by the x- and y-axes, then

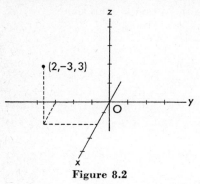

Figure 8.2

points in space can be assigned coordinates that are triples of numbers. The point with coordinates $(2, -3, 3)$, for example, is three units above the point $(2, -3)$ in the x, y-plane (Figure 8.2).

It can be shown that first degree equations in x, y, and z—that is, equations that can be put in the form $ax + by + cz + d = 0$, where a, b, and c are not all zero—have planes for their graphs. In other words, the set of all points whose coordinates satisfy such an equation is a plane. Each equation in (4) is then the equation of a plane. A triple of numbers (a, b, c) satisfying all three equations must be the coordinates of a point lying in all three planes. We have shown that these planes intersect in just the one point $(-8, -7, 26)$.

In these two examples we constructed each equivalent set by performing one of the three following *elementary operations:*

   (i) The interchange of any two equations.
   (ii) The multiplication of an equation by any non-zero number.
   (iii) The addition of a multiple of one equation to another equation.

It is obvious that no solutions of a set of equations are gained or lost if the set is replaced by a set obtained as a result of an operation of type (i) or (ii). To show that an operation of type (iii) also results in an equivalent set, let us represent symbolically the two equations involved by

$$(5) \qquad \begin{aligned} P(x, y, z) &= p, \\ Q(x, y, z) &= q, \end{aligned}$$

where $P(x, y, z)$ and $Q(x, y, z)$ are expressions involving the letters x, y, and z, and p and q are numbers. For example, in the second equation in (4) $P(x, y, z)$ would stand for $2x - 6y - z$, and p would be 0. The number obtained as the result of substituting a, b, and c for x, y, and z in $P(x, y, z)$ can be indicated by $P(a, b, c)$. In the above example $P(1, -3, 4)$ is 16.†

Under an operation of type (iii) in which the first equation in (5) is multiplied by some number k and added to the second, we obtain the set:

$$(5a) \qquad \begin{aligned} P(x, y, z) &= p, \\ Q(x, y, z) + kP(x, y, z) &= q + kp. \end{aligned}$$

†See Section 8.4 for a further discussion of the notation $P(x, y)$.

Now, if (a, b, c) is a solution of (5), then

(6) $$P(a, b, c) = p$$

and

(7) $$Q(a, b, c) = q$$

are true statements. Therefore so is

(8) $$Q(a, b, c) + kP(a, b, c) = q + kp,$$

which together with (6) shows that (a, b, c) is a solution of (5a). Conversely, if (a, b, c) is a solution of (5a), then (6) and (8) are true, and hence so is (7). Therefore (a, b, c) is a solution of (5). This shows that (5) and (5a) are equivalent.

Since any elementary operation leads to an equivalent set of equations, any set obtained by a succession of such operations will also be equivalent to the original set. The same argument holds for sets of any number of linear equations in any number of unknowns, regardless of whether the number of equations is greater or less than the number of unknowns.

Our objective in the two examples considered was to construct by a succession of elementary operations an equivalent set in which each equation had one less unknown than the equation immediately above (cf. (4d) and (3b)). The essential step of this process was multiplying one of the equations by a suitable number and adding it to another. In this way, in the second example we first eliminated x from all equations except the first and then y from the third equation. (If there had been more equations, we would have eliminated y from them too.) If there are more equations and more unknowns, the succeeding unknowns can be eliminated in a like manner until a staggered form similar to that in (3b) and (4d) is obtained. As we did in the second example when obtaining (4d) from (4c), it is quite permissible to combine two or more steps.

Illustration 1.   Solve the set of equations

(9) $$\begin{aligned} 2x + y + z &= 8, \\ x + y + 3z &= 10, \\ -3x - y + z &= -6. \end{aligned}$$

Multiply the first equation by $\frac{1}{2}$, obtaining $x + \frac{1}{2}y + \frac{1}{2}z = 4$. If we add -1 times this to the second equation and then 3 times it to the third, we obtain the equivalent set:

(9a) $$\begin{aligned} x + \frac{1}{2}y + \frac{1}{2}z &= 4, \\[4pt] \frac{1}{2}y + \frac{5}{2}z &= 6, \\[4pt] \frac{1}{2}y + \frac{5}{2}z &= 6. \end{aligned}$$

Now multiply the second equation by -1 and add it to the third:

$$x + \frac{1}{2}y + \frac{1}{2}z = 4,$$

(9b)

$$\frac{1}{2}y + \frac{5}{2}z = 6,$$

$$0 = 0.$$

From the second equation we see that $y = 12 - 5z$. Substituting $12 - 5z$ for y in the first equation in (9b) gives $x = -2 + 2z$. Thus for any number z, if we choose y and x as indicated, that triple is a solution. There is then an infinite number of solutions of (9) all of the form

(10) $(-2 + 2z, 12 - 5z, z),$

where z can be any number. For example, if $z = 1$, (10) is $(0, 7, 1)$; if $z = -2$, it is $(-6, 22, -2)$. Both of these are solutions of (9). If preferred, (10) can be written as

(11) $(-2 + 2t, 12 - 5t, t),$

where t is any number.

Since the three planes whose equations are given by (9) intersect in a line, the existence of more than one solution is not surprising.

Exercise A.   Show by direct substitution that $(0, 7, 1)$ and $(-6, 22, -2)$ are solutions of (9). Show by direct substitution that (11) is a solution of (9) for any t.

Illustration 2.   Solve the set of equations

(12)
$$\begin{aligned} 2x + y + z &= 8, \\ x + y + 3z &= 10, \\ -3x - y + z &= -4. \end{aligned}$$

This set differs from (9) only in the last equation. The same sequence of elementary operations used in reducing (9) to (9b) will when applied to (12) give the equivalent set

$$x + \frac{1}{2}y + \frac{1}{2}z = 4,$$

(12a)

$$\frac{1}{2}y + \frac{5}{2}z = 6,$$

$$0 = 2.$$

Since no choice of x, y, and z can ever make the last equation in this set true, (12a) and hence (12) has no solution. It can be shown that the three planes in (12) intersect each other in three parallel lines.

PROBLEMS

Find all solutions of each set of equations and sketch their graphs:

1. $x - y = 3,$
     $-x + 2y = 1.$

2. $3x + y = 0,$
   $x - y = 8.$

3. $x + 4y = 7,$
   $\qquad x = -3.$

4. $\quad 2x + 5y = 1,$
   $\quad -3x + \ y = 1.$

5. $\quad 6x - 12y = 5,$
   $\quad -2x + \ 4y = 1.$

6. $\quad x + 3y = -8,$
   $\quad 2x + 6y = -16.$

7. $\qquad y = -4x,$
   $\quad x + 3y = 0.$

8. $x - 5 = 0,$
   $\qquad y = 1.$

9. $20x - 10y = 3,$
   $\quad 50x - 30y = 9.$

10. $3y + 5 = 0,$
    $\quad \dfrac{x}{3} + \dfrac{y}{2} = 1.$

11. $\quad x + \tfrac{1}{2}y = 5,$
    $\quad -x + \ 6y = -\tfrac{1}{3},$
    $\quad -x + 19y = 9.$

12. $\quad x - \ y + 5 = 0,$
    $\quad 2x + \ y - 5 = 0,$
    $\quad 4x - 3y \qquad = 0.$

Find all solutions of each pair of equations:

13. $.8x + \ .2y = .2,$
    $\quad .6x + 1.1y = .2.$

14. $\dfrac{2x + 3}{2} + 3y = 2,$
    $\quad \dfrac{2y + 3}{3} - \ x = -7.$

15. $ax - by = m, \qquad a \neq b,$
    $\quad x - \ y = m.$

16. $ux + vy = 2uv,$
    $\quad vx + uy = u^2 + v^2, \qquad u^2 \neq v^2.$

17. $\dfrac{3}{x} - \dfrac{1}{y} = 2,$
    $\quad \dfrac{2}{x} - \dfrac{5}{y} = 1.$

18. $\quad ax + 5y = 6,$
    $\quad 2ax - \ y = 1.$

19. $a_1 x + b_1 y = c_1,$
    $\quad a_2 x + b_2 y = c_2, \qquad a_1 b_2 - a_2 b_1 \neq 0.$

20. Find the coordinates of the vertices of the triangle whose sides have equations
    $4x - 3y = -8, \quad 11x + 8y = 43, \quad 3x + 14y = -6.$

21. Show that the three lines $4x - y = -\tfrac{11}{3}, \ 3x + 3y = -4, \ 3x - 6y = -1$ meet in a point.

Find all solutions of each set of equations:

22. $x + 2y - \ z = 6,$
    $\quad x + \ y + \ z = 4,$
    $\quad 2x - 2y + 3z = 7.$

23. $-2x + \ y + 3z = 5,$
    $\quad 3x + 7y + \ z = 12,$
    $\quad 5x + 5y + \ z = 12.$

24. $x + 2y - \ z = -2,$
    $\quad 2x - \ y + 3z = 11.$

25. $-x + \ y + 2z = 7,$
    $\quad 2x - 2y - 4z = 3.$

26. $3x + 3y + \ z = 0,$
    $\quad x - \ y + 2z = 0,$
    $\quad x + \ y - 6z = 0.$

27. $x - y + 10z = 0,$
    $\quad x + y + \ 3z = 3,$
    $\quad 3x - y + 23z = 7.$

28. $20x + 40y \qquad = 37,$
    $\qquad 8y - 8z = 9,$
    $\quad 5x + \ 8y + 2z = 7.$

29. $2x - y \qquad = 5,$
 $x + y + 3z = 1,$
 $x - y - \quad z = 3.$

31. $- x + 4y - 3z = 2,$
 $3x - 12y + 9z = -6,$
 $-5x + 20y - 15z = 10.$

30. $3x + 4y - z = 1,$
 $9x + 12y - 3z = 3.$

32. $x + y + z = 4,$
 $y - z = 1,$
 $x - 2z = -1,$
 $x + y = 3.$

33. It can be shown that for all t the points $(t, -11 - 3t, 6 - 3t)$ lie on a line. Find the point of intersection of this line with the plane $7x - y + z = 3$.

34. Write an equation of the plane perpendicular to the z-axis at the point $(0, 0, 2)$.

8.2 Sets of Quadratic Equations

When one or more of the equations in a set of equations is of degree higher than the first, the method of equivalent sets is not very useful in effecting their solution. Let us solve the set of equations

(1)
$$x^2 + y^2 = 25,$$
$$2x - y = 5.$$

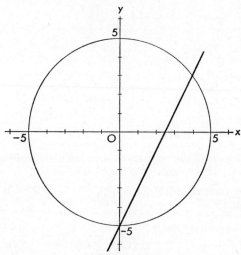

Figure 8.3

The graph of the first is a circle and the second a line (Figure 8.3). We rewrite these in the form

(2)
$$y^2 = 25 - x^2,$$

(3)
$$y = 2x - 5.$$

Squaring both sides of (3) gives us

(4)
$$y^2 = (2x - 5)^2.$$

This equation is not equivalent to (3), but among the pairs (a, b) satisfying it will be found all (a, b) satisfying (3).† Therefore the set of common solutions of (2) and (3) will be a subset of the set of common solutions of (2) and (4), and can be found by finding all common solutions of the latter pair.

To solve the pair (2) and (4), we look for values of x for which the two y's will be the same; that is, x's for which

$$25 - x^2 = (2x - 5)^2.$$

This simplifies to

$$5x^2 - 20x = 0,$$

the roots of which are easily found by factoring to be 0 and 4. From either (2) or (4) the corresponding values of y are ± 5 and ± 3, so that the common solutions (and the only ones) of (2) and (4) are $(0, 5), (0, -5), (4, 3)$, and $(4, -3)$. Of these only $(0, -5)$ and $(4, 3)$ satisfy (3) and hence the set (1).

As another example, we solve the pair of equations

$$y = x^2$$
$$x^2 + y^2 = 20.$$

Values of y giving common values of x are those for which $y = 20 - y^2$, that is, 4 and -5. Corresponding to the first of these, we have for x the values 2 and -2, and to the second the non-real numbers $i\sqrt{5}$ and $-i\sqrt{5}$.

Therefore there are four common solutions: $(2, 4), (-2, 4), (i\sqrt{5}, -5), (-i\sqrt{5}, -5)$. The graphs of the equations are sketched in Figure 8.4. Although they intersect in only two points, there is no contradiction here. All points in the plane have real coordinates, and graphs do not reflect the algebraic situation when non-real numbers are involved. We found a similar situation with the roots of polynomial equations. The real roots corresponded to points of intersection of the graph with the x-axis. There was no geometrical interpretation of the non-real roots.

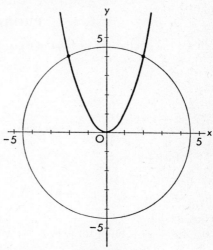

Figure 8.4

Even when logically not necessary, it is advisable, when practicable, to check all solutions by substitution in the original set of equations.

---

†The argument is the same as that used to find the solution of equation (6) in Section 3.5.

Illustration. Find the solutions of the set of equations $xy = 6$ and $2x + y = -6$.

Writing the equations as $x = \dfrac{6}{y}$ and $x = -\dfrac{y}{2} - 3$, we see that for common values of x, y must satisfy

$$\frac{6}{y} = -\frac{y}{2} - 3,$$

or equivalently,

(5) $$y^2 + 6y + 12 = 0, \quad y \neq 0.$$

The left side is easily factored by completing the square (see Section 4.3),

$$[(y + 3) + \sqrt{3}i]\,[(y + 3) - \sqrt{3}i] = 0,$$

showing that the roots of (5) are $-3 - \sqrt{3}i$ and $-3 + \sqrt{3}i$. Alternatively, the roots could have been found by the quadratic formula (7) in Section 4.3. The corresponding values of x can be found from either of the given equations, but the second is the more convenient. It gives for x the values $-\dfrac{3}{2} + \dfrac{\sqrt{3}}{2}i$ and $-\dfrac{3}{2} - \dfrac{\sqrt{3}}{2}i$, respectively. The solutions are

$$\left(-\frac{3}{2} + \frac{\sqrt{3}}{2}i,\ -3 - \sqrt{3}i\right) \quad \text{and} \quad \left(-\frac{3}{2} - \frac{\sqrt{3}}{2}i,\ -3 + \sqrt{3}i\right).$$

Since both solutions are non-real, the graphs of the two equations do not intersect.

PROBLEMS

Find the solutions of each set of equations:

1. $x^2 + y^2 = 52,$
   $5x - y = 26.$

2. $y = x^2,$
   $x - y = -2.$

3. $x^2 + y^2 = 10,$
   $16x^2 + y^2 = 25.$

4. $x^2 + y^2 = 13,$
   $x^2 + y^2 - 2x - 8 = 0.$

5. $x^2 + y^2 = 9,$
   $x^2 + y^2 + 14y + 33 = 0.$

6. $x^2 + y^2 = 10,$
   $xy = 4.$

7. $y = x^3 - 12x,$
   $y = 4x.$

8. $x^2 + y^2 = 4,$
   $y = -2x - 6.$

9. $y^2 = x - 4,$
   $y = \frac{1}{2}x + 1.$

10. $x^2 - y^2 = 36,$
    $y^2 = -5x.$

11. $y = 2x^2,$
    $y^2 = 32x.$

12. $2x^2 + y^2 - 12x + 2y + 2 = 0,$
    $4x + 3y - 26 = 0.$

13. $x^2 + y^2 + 4x - 10y = -16,$
    $x^2 + y^2 + 4x - 10y = -22.$

14. Sketch the graphs of $y = x^3$ and $y = \dfrac{x}{3} + \dfrac{22}{3}$, and find their points of intersection.

15. Sketch the graphs of $y = x^2$ and $y^2 = x$, and find their points of intersection. Are there other solutions of the pair of equations?

16. For each c, the equation $-3x + 4y + c = 0$ has a line for its graph, the lines being all parallel to one another. (a) Determine c so that the line intersects the circle $x^2 + y^2 = 25$ in only one point. Sketch the circle and the line for this value of c. (b) For which values of c will the line intersect the circle in two points?

17. Find the solutions of the set of equations $y^2 = 3x - 3$, $x^2 + y^2 - 2x - 9 = 0$, $y = \dfrac{\sqrt{6}}{2}(x - 1)$.

18. Show that the equations $x^2 + y^2 = 5$, $2y - x = 0$, and $y + x - 2 = 0$ have no common solution.

19. Show algebraically that the graphs of the equations $y^2 = -3x$ and $x^2 + y^2 - 10x + 9 = 0$ do not intersect.

8.3 Equations of Higher Degree

When the degree of an equation in a set of equations in two unknowns is greater than two, the algebraic difficulties in finding a solution of the set are often considerable. Occasionally, some ingenious trick will solve a particular problem, but few general rules can be given. The real solutions can be approximated by making a careful sketch of the graphs and reading from this the approximate coordinates of the points of intersection. This is at best a laborious procedure, but sometimes it is the quickest way, though obviously the accuracy will not be great.

If first a rough sketch is made showing the general features of the curves, the approximate location of the points of intersection can be determined. One need then sketch carefully only those parts of the graphs in the vicinity of these points to find a better approximation.

Illustration. Approximate graphically the real solutions of the pair of equations

$$y^2 = \frac{2}{x}, \qquad x^2 + y^2 = 4.$$

The graph of the second equation is a circle with radius 2 and center at the origin. Hence the points of intersection, if any, will lie near the origin, and a large scale can be used for the sketch. Since no point on the first curve has a zero or negative x-coordinate, the curve lies to the right of the y-axis. Moreover, since for every point (a, b) on this curve the point $(a, -b)$ is also on the curve, the curve is symmetric with respect to the x-axis. Therefore only the part above the x-axis need be sketched.

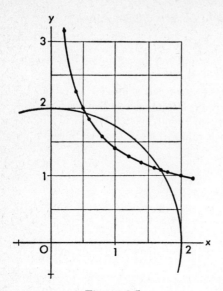

Figure 8.5

A table of values for the first equation is:

x	y	x	y
.2	3.16	1.4	1.20
.4	2.25	1.6	1.12
.5	2.00	1.7	1.08
.6	1.83	1.8	1.05
.8	1.58	2.0	1.00
1.0	1.41	2.2	.95
1.2	1.29		

We use these to sketch that part of its graph lying in the first quadrant and a compass to sketch the circle (Figure 8.5). From the figure we see that the points of intersection are approximately (.54, 1.93) and (1.68, 1.08). By symmetry the number pairs (.54, −1.93) and (1.68, −1.08) are also approximate solutions.

PROBLEMS

Using graphical methods, approximate to within .1 the real solutions of the following sets of equations:

1. $y = \frac{1}{4}x^3$, $y = -x + 3$.

2. $y = \frac{1}{4}x^3$, $y = 2x - 1$.

3. $y = \dfrac{2}{x^2 + 1}$, $x^2 + y^2 = 7$.

4. $y = \dfrac{1}{x}$, $x^2 + y^2 = 3$.

5. $x\sqrt{y} = 1$, $y + 2x = 1$.

6. $y^2 = x^3$, $y^2 = 4 - x$.

Using graphical methods, approximate the real solutions of the following sets of equations, and check by finding algebraically the exact solutions:

7. $2x + 3y = 6$, $-x + 5y = 1$.
8. $x^2 + y^2 = 17$, $y = -x + 1$.
9. $y^2 = 2x$, $y = \frac{4}{5}x$.

8.4 Sets of Inequalities

An expression composed of the sum of one or more terms of the form $cx^m y^n$, dx^m, ey^n, and f, where c, d, e, and f are real numbers and m and n are positive integers, is called a *polynomial in x and y;* for example,

(1) $$5x^3y^2 - \frac{3}{2}xy^2 + \sqrt{2}y - 6x + 1$$

and

(2) $$13x^7 + 8xy^5 - 3xy + y^2.$$

If x or y is missing, it is customary to consider the expression as a polynomial in just one letter.

By extension of the notation $p(x)$ indicating a polynomial in x, we shall let $p(x, y)$ denote a polynomial in x and y, and $p(a, b)$ the value of this polynomial when the numbers a and b are substituted for x and y. If $p(x, y)$ is the polynomial (1), then $p(2, 3) = 322 + 3\sqrt{2}$ and $p(-1, 0) = 7$.

The *degree of a non-zero term* is the sum of the exponents of x and y in that term. The degrees of the terms in (1) are, respectively, 5, 3, 1, 1, 0. The *degree of the polynomial* is the degree of the term of highest degree provided its coefficient is not zero. The degree of the polynomial (1) is 5 and that of the polynomial (2) is 7. Polynomials in x and y can be added and multiplied in the same manner as those in one letter.

If $p(x, y)$ is a polynomial, the graph C of the equation $p(x, y) = 0$ is the set of all points (a, b) for which $p(a, b) = 0$. Generally, C is some curve, as we saw in Section 7.2. In this section we shall determine the set of all points (a, b) for which $p(a, b) > 0$. We shall find the following theorem useful.

Theorem 1. Let $p(x, y)$ be a polynomial and C the graph of the equation $p(x, y) = 0$. If Q and Q' are two points that can be joined by a continuous curve having no point in common with C, then the values of $p(x, y)$ at Q and Q' have the same sign.

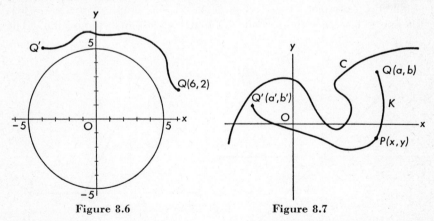

Figure 8.6   Figure 8.7

For example, if $p(x, y) = x^2 + y^2 - 25$, then the graph C of $p(x, y) = 0$ is the circle with radius 5 and center at the origin (Figure 8.6). At the point $Q(6, 2)$ the value of $p(x, y)$ is $p(6, 2) = 15$. Since any point outside the circle can be joined to $Q(6, 2)$ by some continuous curve not touching C, the value of $p(x, y)$ at all such points must also be positive. At the origin $p(0, 0) < 0$. Hence $p(a, b) < 0$ for all points inside the circle.

By a continuous curve we mean a curve that has no gaps or missing points. Roughly speaking, it is one that can be sketched without lifting the pencil from the paper. This is not a precise definition. In order to prove Theorem 1, an algebraic definition of continuity is needed, which we are unable to give here. Although we shall have to assume the validity of the theorem, we can perhaps make it plausible.

Let C be the graph of $p(x, y) = 0$ (Figure 8.7) and $Q(a, b)$ a point for which $p(a, b) > 0$. Let $Q'(a', b')$ be a point that can be joined to Q by a continuous curve K not touching C, and suppose $p(a', b') < 0$. Let $P(x, y)$ be a point that moves along K from Q to Q'. For any polynomial $p(x, y)$, it seems reasonable, and indeed can be shown, that small changes in x and y will produce small changes in the values of $p(x, y)$. This and the continuity of K imply that as P traverses K from Q to Q' the values of $p(x, y)$ will change smoothly, sometimes increasing and sometimes decreasing, but without any sudden jumps. Since $p(x, y)$ has a positive value at Q and a negative value at Q', there must be some point Z on K between Q and Q' at which the value is zero. But such a point Z would also have to be on C, which is impossible since K does not touch C. Hence $p(a', b') > 0$.

Exercise A. Sketch the graph of the circle $x^2 + y^2 - 25 = 0$. Plot the points $(4, 0), (4, -1), (4, -2), (4, -2.8), (4, -3), (4, -3.1), (4, -4), (4, -8)$ and compute the value of $p(x, y) = x^2 + y^2 - 25$ at each of them.

The converse of Theorem 1 may not be true; for some polynomials the sign of $p(x, y)$ may be the same even for points on opposite sides of its graph. For example, let $p(x, y) = (x + y)^2$. The graph of $p(x, y) = 0$ is the line C bisecting the second and fourth quadrants (Figure 8.8). The

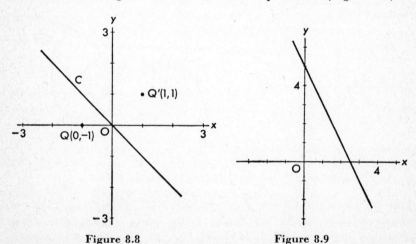

Figure 8.8   Figure 8.9

values of $p(x, y)$ at $Q(0, -1)$ and $Q'(1, 1)$ are both positive, and yet every continuous curve joining the two points must cross C.

Illustration 1. Find all points (x, y) for which $2x + y - 5 < 0$.

The graph of $2x + y - 5 = 0$ is a line (Figure 8.9). The value of $2x + y - 5$ at $(1, 0)$ is -3. Hence all points below the line satisfy the inequality. Since the value is positive at the point $(4, 2)$, which lies above the line, no point above the line satisfies the inequality. Therefore the solution set consists of all points below the line.

Illustration 2. Indicate on a sketch the regions in which the inequalities $4y - x^2 > 0$ and $x + 2y - 4 \leq 0$ have a common solution.

Let $p(x, y) = 4y - x^2$ and $q(x, y) = x + 2y - 4$. The graphs of $4y - x^2 = 0$ and the line $x + 2y - 4 = 0$ are shown in Figure 8.10. Since $p(0, 3) > 0$, $p(x, y) > 0$ for all points inside the curve $4y - x^2 = 0$. It is easy to show that $p(x, y) < 0$ for all points outside. Since $q(0, 0) < 0$, $q(x, y) \leq 0$ for all points on or below the line. For points above the line, $q(x, y) > 0$. Therefore the set of common solutions is the region marked I in the figure bounded by the segment of the line and the arc of the curve between the points A and B. The line segment itself is included, but the arc of the curve is not, since we must have $p(x, y) > 0$. The points A and B are not included for the same reason.

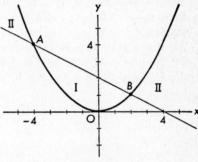

Figure 8.10

If the inequalities in the statement of the problem are reversed, the common solutions of $4y - x^2 < 0$ and $x + 2y - 4 \geq 0$ are all points on or above the line and outside the curve, that is, the two regions marked II.

PROBLEMS

If $p(x, y)$ stands for each of the polynomials below, sketch the graph of $p(x, y) = 0$ and indicate the regions for which the inequality is satisfied:

1. $3x + 5y - 13 < 0$.
2. $-3x - 5y + 13 < 0$.
3. $y - \frac{1}{4}x \leq 0$.
4. $1 - \frac{1}{2}x + 4y \geq 0$.
5. $x^2 + y^2 - 13 < 0$.
6. $y^2 - 4x > 0$.
7. $xy - 6 > 0$.
8. $1 - x^2y > 0$.
9. $x + y^2 + 5 \leq 0$.
10. $3y - x^2 + 25 < 0$.
11. $x^2 + y^2 + 1 > 0$.
12. $(x + y - 2)^2 > 0$.
13. $y - |x| \leq 0$.

14. Indicate the region in the plane for which (a) $x > -3$; (b) $y \leq 0$.
15. Does the point $(\frac{10}{9}, -\frac{11}{4})$ lie above or below the line $x - 4y - 12 = 0$?
16. Does the point $(\frac{10}{3}, \frac{5}{2})$ lie inside or outside the circle $x^2 + y^2 = 18$?
17. Give a definition of a polynomial in three letters and give two examples.
18. If $p(x, y) = x - 3y + 5$ and $q(x, y) = 2x + 3y - 6$, sketch the graphs of $p(x, y) = 0$ and $q(x, y) = 0$. Indicate the regions for which (a) $p(x, y) > 0$ and $q(x, y) > 0$; (b) $p(x, y) < 0$ and $q(x, y) > 0$.

Indicate the regions in which each of the following sets of inequalities has common solutions:

19. $x^2 + y^2 - 25 \leqq 0$, $4x - 3y \geqq 0$.

20. $x^2 + y^2 - 3 < 0$, $y - \frac{1}{3}x + 3 < 0$.

21. $y - x^2 > 0$, $2x + y > 1$.

22. $y - x^2 < 0$, $2x + y > 1$.

23. $x^2 + y^2 > 16$, $x^2 + y^2 < 36$.

24. $y + 2x + 5 \geqq 0$, $y + 2x - 4 \leqq 0$.

25. $y + 2x + 5 < 0$, $y + 2x - 4 > 0$.

26. $y + 2x + 5 > 0$, $y + 2x - 4 > 0$.

27. $3x - 5y - 1 < 0$, $4x + y + 4 > 0$, $y \leqq 2$.

28. $3x - 5y - 1 > 0$, $4x + y + 4 > 0$, $y < 2$.

29. $x + y < 1$, $x > 0$, $y > 0$.

30. $x^2 + y^2 - 25 < 0$, $y^2 - 4x > 0$, $y - \frac{1}{2}x + 3 < 0$.

31. $x \leqq -1$, $x \geqq -4$, $y \leqq 6$, $y \geqq -1$.

32. $y \leqq 0$, $x \geqq 0$, $y \geqq -3$, $x + y - 4 \leqq 0$.

33. $13x - 5y - 65 \leqq 0$, $13x - 5y - 65 \geqq 0$.

34. $2x + 7y + 14 = 0$, $3x - y - 2 < 0$.

35. $y^2 - x \leqq 0$, $6y - x - 9 \geqq 0$.

Chapter 9

Exponents

9.1 Integral Exponents

In Section 2.4 we defined a^n for any real a and positive integral n to be $a \cdot a \cdots a$ (n factors), and proved there and in Section 2.15 the basic laws

$$a^m a^n = a^{m+n}; \qquad \frac{a^m}{a^n} = a^{m-n}, \quad m > n;$$

$$a^n b^n = (ab)^n; \qquad (a^m)^n = a^{mn};$$

$$\frac{a^n}{b^n} = \left(\frac{a}{b}\right)^n, \quad b \neq 0.\dagger$$

It is possible to extend the concept of a power to include negative and rational exponents so that expressions such as $(\frac{1}{2})^{-3}$ and $21^{8/5}$ have meaning. Moreover, this can be done in such a way that the above laws are valid when m and n come from the larger set of rational numbers. This has proved to be a most useful concept. We first define powers with negative integral exponents.

Definition. Let $a \neq 0$. Then $a^{-n} = \dfrac{1}{a^n}$ if n is a positive integer, and $a^0 = 1$.

For example,

$$(-3)^{-4} = \frac{1}{(-3)^4} = \frac{1}{81};$$

$$\left(\frac{2}{3}\right)^{-3} = \frac{1}{\left(\frac{2}{3}\right)^3} = \frac{1}{\frac{8}{27}} = \frac{27}{8};$$

$$(\sqrt{5})^0 = 1.$$

†Some of these were listed as problems.

Since no useful definition of the symbols 0^0 and 0^{-n} for $n \geq 0$ can be given, they are left undefined.

If $n < 0$, then $-n > 0$, and by the definition $a^n = a^{-(-n)} = 1/a^{-n}$, giving us $a^{-n} = 1/a^n$. This shows that the equation $a^{-n} = 1/a^n$, or equivalently, $a^n = 1/a^{-n}$, holds for all integral n.

For any exponent r, $-a^r$ always means $-(a^r)$ and ab^r means $a(b^r)$. For example,

$$-5^{-2} = -(5^{-2}) = -\frac{1}{5^2} = -\frac{1}{25},$$

but

$$(-5)^{-2} = \frac{1}{(-5)^2} = \frac{1}{25}.$$

Also,

$$5 \cdot 2^3 = 5 \cdot 8 = 40.$$

Theorem 1. For all integers r and s and non-zero a and b,

(a) $$a^r a^s = a^{r+s};$$

(b) $$\frac{a^r}{a^s} = a^{r-s} = \frac{1}{a^{s-r}};$$

(c) $$(a^r)^s = a^{rs};$$

(d) $$a^r b^r = (ab)^r;$$

(e) $$\frac{a^r}{b^r} = \left(\frac{a}{b}\right)^r.$$

Thus by (a) $(\frac{1}{2})^7 \cdot (\frac{1}{2})^{-3} = (\frac{1}{2})^{7+(-3)} = (\frac{1}{2})^4$. It is obvious that for some choices of r and s the restriction $a \neq 0$ or $b \neq 0$ can be removed. We shall see later that this theorem is true for any real numbers r and s, provided that a and b are positive if r and s are irrational.

Proof.

(a) The proof of (a) for positive r and s is given in Theorem 1 in Section 2.4. If r and s are both negative, then

$$a^r a^s = \frac{1}{a^{-r}} \cdot \frac{1}{a^{-s}} = \frac{1}{a^{-r} a^{-s}}.$$

Since $-r > 0$ and $-s > 0$, we can apply (a), which we know to be valid for positive exponents, obtaining

$$a^r a^s = \frac{1}{a^{-r} a^{-s}} = \frac{1}{a^{-r+(-s)}} = \frac{1}{a^{-(r+s)}} = a^{r+s}.$$

If $r > 0$ and $s < 0$, suppose $r > -s > 0$. By Theorem 14 in Section 2.15, $a^m/a^n = a^{m-n}$ if $m > n > 0$. Hence

$$a^r a^s = \frac{a^r}{a^{-s}} = a^{r-(-s)} = a^{r+s}.$$

If $-s > r > 0$, the other half of Theorem 14 shows that

$$a^r a^s = \frac{a^r}{a^{-s}} = \frac{1}{a^{-s-r}} = \frac{1}{a^{-(s+r)}} = a^{r+s}.$$

If $r = -s$, then $r + s = 0$ and

$$a^r a^s = \frac{a^r}{a^{-s}} = 1 = a^0 = a^{r+s}.$$

A similar argument will show that (a) is true if $r < 0$ and $s > 0$. Finally, if either or both of r and s is zero, it is almost trivial to show (a) true. Notice that in every case we reduced the problem to one involving positive exponents that could be treated by previously proved cases.

(b) It is easy now to prove (b). We have

$$\frac{a^r}{a^s} = a^r a^{-s} = a^{r-s} = \frac{1}{a^{-(r-s)}} = \frac{1}{a^{s-r}}.$$

(c) If $s > 0$ and $r > 0$, then by definition

$$(a^r)^s = \Big(\overbrace{a \cdot a \cdots a}^{r \text{ factors}}\Big)^s$$
$$= (a \cdot a \cdots a)(a \cdot a \cdots a) \cdots (a \cdot a \cdots a),$$

there being s blocks of r a's each. Altogether there are rs a's, and so the right side is just a^{rs}.

If $r < 0$ and $s > 0$,

$$(a^r)^s = \Big(\frac{1}{a^{-r}}\Big)^s = \frac{1}{(a^{-r})^s} = \frac{1}{a^{-rs}} = a^{rs}.$$

The other possibilities for r and s are handled similarly by changing the expressions so that only positive exponents appear. Again, if either r or s is zero, the theorem is obvious.

(d) and (e) The proofs of these are left to the reader with the suggestion that he consider first the case for $r > 0$ and use the definition of a^r for positive integral r.

In Section 2.13, we introduced the symbol a^{-1} for the reciprocal of a, and in the remark just before Illustration 1 in Section 2.14 we proved that $a^{-1} = 1/a$. As used there, the -1 is not a true exponent, and so this is not a special case of the definition of a^{-n} for negative exponents. The remark does show, however, that the -1 in the expression for the reciprocal can now be treated as an exponent and a^{-1} considered a power of a.

Exercise A. Illustrate the details of the proof of Theorem 1(a) with $r = 6$ and $s = -2$.

Exercise B. Prove Theorem 1(a) if $s = 0$.

Exercise C. Verify Theorem 1(b) if (a) $r = 3$, $s = 8$, and (b) $r = 4$, $s = 3$, by writing the numerator and denominator as products and cancelling.

Illustration 1.

$$a^5 a^{-13} = a^{5-13} = a^{-8} = \frac{1}{a^8};$$

$$(a^{-2})^3 = a^{-6};$$

$$\frac{a^{11}}{a^{-4}} = a^{11-(-4)} = a^{15};$$

$$\frac{a^{11}}{a^{-4}} = \frac{1}{a^{-4-11}} = \frac{1}{a^{-15}};$$

$$\frac{x^3 y^{-3}}{x^{-4} y^{-2}} = x^3 x^4 y^{-3} y^2 = x^7 y^{-1};$$

$$3^{-2} \cdot 5^{-2} = (3 \cdot 5)^{-2} = 15^{-2} = \frac{1}{225};$$

$$\frac{6^3}{2^3} = \left(\frac{6}{2}\right)^3 = 3^3 = 27.$$

As in all our work, it is understood that letters cannot be zero in those expressions that would thereby be undefined.

Illustration 2. Simplify $\dfrac{x^{-2} + y^{-2}}{x^{-2} y^{-2}}$.

$$\frac{x^{-2} + y^{-2}}{x^{-2} y^{-2}} = \frac{\dfrac{1}{x^2} + \dfrac{1}{y^2}}{\dfrac{1}{x^2} \cdot \dfrac{1}{y^2}}$$

$$= \frac{\dfrac{y^2 + x^2}{x^2 y^2}}{\dfrac{1}{x^2 y^2}} = y^2 + x^2.$$

Care must be taken in problems such as this not to make mistakes. A typical common error is to say

$$\frac{2a^{-1} + 7}{b} = \frac{2 + 7}{ab} = \frac{9}{ab}.$$

Proceeding more slowly, we obtain the correct answer:

$$\frac{2a^{-1} + 7}{b} = \frac{\dfrac{2}{a} + 7}{b} = \frac{\dfrac{2 + 7a}{a}}{b} = \frac{2 + 7a}{ab}.$$

Usually mistakes arise because students try to skip steps. The safest way is first to replace each power containing a negative exponent by one with a positive exponent and then simplify the resulting fractions.

PROBLEMS

1. Evaluate 0^1, 1^0, 0^{-5}.

Express as a number without exponents:

2. 5^3.

6. 5^{-3}.

10. $(-2)^{-5}$.

3. $\dfrac{1}{3^2}$.

7. $.01^{-2}$.

11. $\left(\dfrac{1}{8}\right)^{-2}$.

4. $\left(\dfrac{1}{-4}\right)^2$.

8. 9^0.

12. ab^0.

5. 4^{-1}.

9. $(-7)^{-2}$.

13. $\dfrac{4}{2^{-4}}$.

Express with positive exponents:

14. a^{-2}.

20. $\dfrac{1}{b^{-3}}$.

26. $\dfrac{c^{-2}r^3}{2b^{-3}}$.

15. $x^{-3}y^4$.

21. $\dfrac{7}{u^{-7}}$.

27. $\dfrac{6^{-2}x}{4^{-1}b^{-5}}$.

16. $5a^{-1}$.

22. $(5a)^{-1}$.

28. $x^{-1}+y^{-1}$.

17. ax^{-1}.

23. $\dfrac{a^{-2}}{-6}$.

29. $-2(x+y)^{-1}$.

18. by^{-4}.

24. $(-2)^{-1}$.

30. $\left(\dfrac{2}{x-y^2}\right)^{-1}$.

19. $3x^2y^{-3}$.

25. $\dfrac{c^{-3}}{x^{-3}}$.

31. $\left(\dfrac{a^{-2}}{b^{-2}}\right)^{-1}$.

Give an equivalent expression without a denominator:

32. $\dfrac{7}{w^3}$.

35. $\dfrac{3}{20}$.

38. $\dfrac{5a^{-4}}{6b^{-2}}$.

33. $\dfrac{-\frac{3}{5}a}{x^2}$.

36. $\dfrac{a}{-11}$.

39. $\dfrac{3z^6}{4x^2y^{-3}}$.

34. $x-\dfrac{2}{y}$.

37. $\dfrac{7}{(1.03)^{10}}$.

40. $\dfrac{3}{a-2b}$.

Simplify:

41. a^0a^5.

45. $(x^{-2}y)^{-4}$.

48. $\dfrac{c^{-4}z^5}{c^{-1}z^3}$.

42. $(x^{-2})^{-3}$.

46. $\dfrac{(3x^{-2})^2}{x}$.

49. $(4a^{-1}b^7)^3$.

43. $(y^3)^{-2}$.

44. $\dfrac{1}{(b^4b^{-4})^2}$.

47. $\dfrac{x^0}{y^4}$.

50. $\dfrac{5^2 \cdot 5^{-2}}{3^2+3^0}$.

Express with positive exponents and simplify:

51. $a^{-3} + a^3$.

54. $\dfrac{c^{-2} - d}{c^{-2} + d}$.

57. $(a^{-2} + 3b^{-1})^{-1}$.

52. $\dfrac{2^{-2} - 3^{-1}}{4^{-1} + 1}$.

55. $\dfrac{(x + y)^{-1}}{x + y}$.

53. $\dfrac{a^{-2} - b^{-2}}{a - b}$.

56. $\dfrac{x^{-1} + y^{-1}}{x + y}$.

58. Prove that $(a^m)^n = (a^n)^m$, where m and n are integers.

59. Prove Theorem 1(d) and (e).

*60. If $a > 0$, show that $a^m > 0$ for all integers m.

9.2   Rational Exponents

In Section 2.19, we discussed the existence of roots of numbers; that is, given a real number b and a positive integer n, is there a real number a for which $a^n = b$? If n is an odd integer, such an a exists and there is only one. It is positive, negative, or zero according as b is, and we denote it by $b^{1/n}$ or, equivalently, $\sqrt[n]{b}$. If n is even, there is an a only for $b \geq 0$ and there are then two possibilities for a, one positive and one negative (unless $b = 0$). In this case we let $b^{1/n}$ stand for the positive root. Under this convention $\sqrt{\frac{4}{49}} = \frac{2}{7}$ and not $-\frac{2}{7}$. To indicate $-\frac{2}{7}$, we write $-\sqrt{\frac{4}{49}}$.

We see then that for real x and y, $x^n = y^n$ implies $x = y$ if (1) n is odd, or (2) n is even, and x and y are both positive or both negative.

We shall extend the concept of exponent to include rational numbers by making the following definition:

Definition.   If m and n are integers and $n > 0$, then

$$a^{\frac{m}{n}} = \left(a^{\frac{1}{n}}\right)^m = (\sqrt[n]{a})^m.$$

For example,

$$25^{\frac{3}{2}} = \left(25^{\frac{1}{2}}\right)^3 = 5^3;$$

$$(-\tfrac{1}{5})^{2/3} = [(-\tfrac{1}{5})^{1/3}]^2 = (\sqrt[3]{-\tfrac{1}{5}})^2; \quad 7^{3/1} = 7^3;$$

$$8^{-\frac{2}{3}} = 8^{\frac{-2}{3}} = \left(8^{\frac{1}{3}}\right)^{-2} = 2^{-2} = \frac{1}{2^2}.$$

Because we are dealing with real numbers only, the definition is meaningless if $a < 0$ and n is even, or if $a = 0$ and $m \leq 0$. We shall assume henceforth that a, m, and n are numbers for which the definition is meaningful. Since any rational number can be expressed as one with a positive denominator, $a^{m/n}$ will have a meaning even if $n < 0$, subject to the restrictions just mentioned. For example, $13^{-\frac{2}{5}} = 13^{\frac{-2}{5}} = \left(13^{\frac{1}{5}}\right)^{-2}$.

Exercise. Define the following:

$$14^{3/2}, \quad (-4)^{3/1}, \quad 0^{2/3}, \quad 8^{0/4}, \quad a^{3/-7}.$$

The reason for defining $a^{m/n}$ as we did is that with this definition the properties of exponents given in Theorem 1 are valid for rational as well as integral exponents. We shall prove only the first law: $a^r a^s = a^{r+s}$.

Let $r = m/n$ and $s = u/v$, where m, n, u, and v are integers, n and v being positive. Then

$$a^r a^s = a^{\frac{m}{n}} a^{\frac{u}{v}} = a^{\frac{mv}{nv}} a^{\frac{nu}{nv}} = \left(a^{\frac{1}{nv}}\right)^{mv} \left(a^{\frac{1}{nv}}\right)^{nu}.$$

Since mv and nu are integers, we can use Theorem 1(a) to combine the factors in the last product,

$$a^r a^s = \left(a^{\frac{1}{nv}}\right)^{(mv+nu)} = a^{\frac{(mv+nu)}{nv}}$$

$$= a^{\left(\frac{mv}{nv}\right)+\left(\frac{nu}{nv}\right)} = a^{\frac{m}{n}+\frac{u}{v}} = a^{r+s}.$$

Note that the key steps in the proof were the expression of the exponents as ratios of integers and writing $a^r a^s$ in a form involving integral exponents so that Theorem 1(a) could be applied. The other parts of the theorem can be proved by similar techniques with the help of the next theorem and Problem 66.

Theorem 2. $a^{m/n} = (a^m)^{1/n}$, where m and n are integers and $n > 0$.

Because of this we see that $a^{m/n}$ can be considered as the nth root of a^m as well as the mth power of $a^{1/n}$. For example, by definition $27^{2/3} = (27^{1/3})^2 = 3^2 = 9$. By this theorem $27^{2/3} = (27^2)^{1/3} = 729^{1/3} = 9$.

Proof. By definition $a^{m/n} = (a^{1/n})^m$. Hence

$$[a^{m/n}]^n = [(a^{1/n})^m]^n = (a^{1/n})^{mn} = (a^{1/n})^{nm} = [(a^{1/n})^n]^m = a^m.$$

This says that $a^{m/n}$ is the nth root of a^m or, in symbols, $a^{m/n} = (a^m)^{1/n}$.

Theorem 3. If r is a rational number, $a^{-r} = \dfrac{1}{a^r}$.

Proof. Let $r = m/n$, where m and n are integers and $n > 0$. Then

$$a^{-r} = a^{\frac{-m}{n}} = \left(a^{\frac{1}{n}}\right)^{-m} = \frac{1}{\left(a^{\frac{1}{n}}\right)^m} = \frac{1}{a^{\frac{m}{n}}} = \frac{1}{a^r}.$$

Illustration 1.

$$(2^{-4}a^3)^{2/3} = (2^{-4})^{2/3}(a^3)^{2/3} \qquad \text{Theorem 1(d)}$$

$$= 2^{-(8/3)}a^2. \qquad \text{Theorem 1(c)}$$

Illustration 2. Simplify $\dfrac{-7a^2x^{-1}}{2a^{1/2}x^4}$, $a > 0$.

$$\frac{-7a^2x^{-1}}{2a^{1/2}x^4} = \frac{-7a^2a^{-(1/2)}}{2x^4x^1}$$

$$= \frac{-7a^{3/2}}{2x^5}.$$ Theorem 1(a)

Illustration 3.

$$\left(\frac{a^{2/3}b^{1/2}}{3ay^{-(1/8)}}\right)^4 = \left(\frac{b^{1/2}}{3a^{1-(2/3)}y^{-(1/8)}}\right)^4, \quad a > 0,\, b \geqq 0,\, y > 0, \qquad \text{Theorem 1(b)}$$

$$= \frac{(b^{1/2})^4}{3^4(a^{1/3})^4(y^{-(1/8)})^4} \qquad\qquad \text{Theorem 1(e) and (d)}$$

$$= \frac{b^2}{3^4a^{4/3}y^{-(1/2)}} \qquad\qquad\qquad \text{Theorem 1(c)}$$

$$= \frac{b^2y^{1/2}}{3^4a^{4/3}}.$$

When using Theorem 1 to simplify quantities with rational exponents, one must be sure that at every step the corresponding expression is defined. For example, it is not true that $(a^{18})^{1/6} = a^{18/6} = a^3$ for all a. If a is negative, $(a^{18})^{1/6}$ is positive, but a^3 is negative. The first step, which seems to be justified by Theorem 1(c), is not valid if $a < 0$, since $a^{18/6}$ has no meaning.

Illustration 4. Simplify $(25a^2)^{3/2}$.

We remind the reader that $(x^2)^{1/2} = |x|$. Therefore

$$(25a^2)^{3/2} = [(25a^2)^{1/2}]^3 = (5|a|)^3 = 125|a|^3.$$

If preferred, two cases can be considered and the result expressed as $125a^3$ if $a \geqq 0$, and $-125a^3$ if $a < 0$. The absolute value notation, however, subsumes both of these and is more compact.

To multiply sums whose terms have rational exponents, one proceeds exactly as if the exponents were positive integers. For example,

$$(a^{-1} - 2b^{1/2})(a^{-1} + 3b^{1/2})$$
$$= a^{-1}a^{-1} + 3a^{-1}b^{1/2} - 2a^{-1}b^{1/2} - 6b^{1/2}b^{1/2}$$
$$= a^{-2} + a^{-1}b^{1/2} - 6b.$$

PROBLEMS

Change each expression below with fractional exponents to one with radicals and vice versa; for example, $\sqrt[3]{x^5} = x^{5/3}$.

1. $\dfrac{7}{3}x^{1/4}$.   3. $b^{7/-5}$.   5. $-w\sqrt{w}$.

2. $\sqrt{xy}$.   4. $x\sqrt{y}$.   6. $\sqrt[4]{a^3}$.

7. $(2x)^{1/2}$.   10. $(-u)^{7/3}$.   13. $\sqrt[3]{(x+y)^2}$.

8. $2x^{1/2}$.   11. $\sqrt{(ay)^5}$.   14. $\sqrt[3]{-3a^2x}$.

9. $-u^{7/3}$.   12. $(5a^2)^{2/3}$.   15. $a^{1/2}b^{2/3}$.

Express without exponents:

16. $(\frac{1}{16})^{1/2}$.   18. $9^{-(1/2)}$.   20. $(-8)^{2/3}$.

17. 9^{-2}.   19. $32^{7/5}$.

Simplify and express without negative exponents:

21. $(.0001)^{1/4}$.   24. $\dfrac{1}{b^{-(2/3)}}$.   27. $\left(\dfrac{3x^{-(1/2)}}{4x^2y}\right)^2$.

22. $\left(\dfrac{1}{16}\right)^{3/2}$.   25. $4^{-(1/2)}aw^{-3}$.   28. $(a^2 - x^2)^{-(1/2)}$.

23. $(-27)^{-(1/3)}$.   26. $\dfrac{a^{-(1/2)}b^3}{5^{-1}z^{-1}}$.

Give an equivalent expression without a denominator:

29. $\dfrac{1}{10}$.   31. $\dfrac{2x^{3/2}}{y^{-(1/2)}}$.   33. $\dfrac{a}{a+b}$.

30. $\dfrac{1}{a^{1/2}}$.   32. $\dfrac{8x^3}{y^3z^{-2}}$.

Simplify:

34. $\dfrac{8^{2/3} - 8^{-(2/3)}}{4}$.   44. $\dfrac{h^3r^2}{h^{5/2}r^{7/2}}$.

35. $\dfrac{(7^{.878})(7^{-1})}{(7^{2.502})^{1/3}(7^{1.544})(7^{-2})}$.   45. $\dfrac{x^{-(1/3)}y^{2/3}}{\sqrt{2}x^{1/2}y^4y^{-2}}$.

36. $2c^{2/5}xc^{3/10}$.   46. $(-8x)^{-(2/3)}$.

37. $x^{2/3}x^{1/2}x^{-(1/3)}$.   47. $\left(\dfrac{a^{1/2}x^{1/3}}{-2y^{1/2}}\right)^3$.

38. $(w^4)^{3/4}$.   48. $\dfrac{(x+y)^{-(1/2)}x^3}{2^{-1}(x+y)^{3/2}}$.

39. $(27z^6)^{2/3}$.

40. $(c^{7/3}c^{-(7/3)})^2$.   49. $\dfrac{c^{-2} - d^{-2}}{c^{-1}d^{-2} - c^{-2}d^{-1}}$.

41. $\dfrac{a^2}{a^{8/3}}$.   50. $(36y^2)^{-(3/2)}$.

42. $\dfrac{y^{1/3}}{y^{5/6}}$.   51. $\left(\dfrac{x^4b^{-4}}{16}\right)^{1/4}$.

43. $\dfrac{b^{-(4/5)}}{b^{-(1/5)}}$.   52. $\left[\dfrac{10}{(x+y)^2}\right]^{1/2}$.

Express as a sum:

53. $(b^{1/3} + a)^2$.

54. $(5x - y^{1/3})(5x + y^{1/3})$.

55. $(x^{1/2} + y^{1/2})(x^{1/2} - y^{1/2})$.

56. $(a^{-1} + b^{-1})(a^{-1} - b^{-1})$.

57. $(r^4 - 2s^{-1})^2$.

58. $(a + x)(a^{-1} + x^{-1})$.

59. $(a^{-1} + y)^3$.

60. $(e^x - e^{-x})^2$.

61. $(x^{-1} + 3xy^{-1} + y^{-2})(x + y^2)$.

62. $(2x - b^{-(1/2)})(4x^2 + 2xb^{-(1/2)} + b^{-1})$.

63. $\dfrac{a - b}{a^{1/3} - b^{1/3}}$.

64. $\dfrac{3y^3 - y^2 - 18y + 16}{y^{1/2} - 2y^{-(1/2)}}$.

65. Prove Theorem 1(b) when r and s are rational numbers.

66. Prove $a^{1/n}b^{1/n} = (ab)^{1/n}$, n a positive integer. (*Hint:* Consider $(a^{1/n}b^{1/n})^n$.)

67. Use Problem 66 to prove Theorem 1(d) for rational r. (*Hint:* Express r as m/n.)

68. Prove Theorem 1(e) for rational r. (*Hint:* First prove an analogue of the theorem in Problem 66.)

69. If n is an odd integer, show that $\sqrt[n]{-a} = -\sqrt[n]{a}$. Is this true if n is even? Illustrate with examples.

9.3   Radicals

The radical notation is a relic of the past. Fractional exponents are so much more convenient that radicals are seldom used today except for square roots. The easiest way to handle a radical is to change it to the equivalent fractional exponent notation, as in the following illustrations.

Illustration 1.   Simplify $\sqrt[4]{x^6y^{12}}$, $x \geq 0$, $y \geq 0$.

$$\sqrt[4]{x^6y^{12}} = (x^6y^{12})^{1/4} = x^{6/4}y^{12/4} = x^{3/2}y^3.$$

This form of the answer is quite acceptable; there is no need to change back to the radical notation.

Illustration 2.   Simplify $\sqrt[3]{4} \cdot \sqrt[3]{10}$.

$$\sqrt[3]{4} \cdot \sqrt[3]{10} = (2^2)^{1/3}(2 \cdot 5)^{1/3} = 2^{2/3} \cdot 2^{1/3} \cdot 5^{1/3} = 2 \cdot 5^{1/3}.$$

Illustration 3.   Simplify $\dfrac{\sqrt[5]{y^{-3}z^5}}{\sqrt[5]{32y^7z}}$.

$$\frac{\sqrt[5]{y^{-3}z^5}}{\sqrt[5]{32y^7z}} = \frac{(y^{-3}z^5)^{1/5}}{(32y^7z)^{1/5}} = \left(\frac{y^{-3}z^5}{32y^7z}\right)^{1/5}$$

$$= \left(\frac{y^{-10}z^4}{32}\right)^{1/5} = \frac{1}{2}y^{-2}z^{4/5}.$$

As we mentioned earlier, the simplest form is a matter of taste. Also, and perhaps more important, the form in which an expression is left will depend on the uses intended for it; not always is the simplest form the most useful. There is nothing wrong about leaving a radical in the denominator of a fraction. Thus $\dfrac{1}{\sqrt{3}}$ is just as acceptable as $\frac{1}{3}\sqrt{3}$, in addition to being somewhat simpler.

Illustration 4.   Simplify $\sqrt{\dfrac{7}{ab^2}+\dfrac{3}{a^2b}}$, $a > 0, b > 0$.

$$\sqrt{\frac{7}{ab^2}+\frac{3}{a^2b}} = \sqrt{\frac{7a+3b}{a^2b^2}} = \frac{(7a+3b)^{1/2}}{(a^2b^2)^{1/2}} = \frac{1}{ab}(7a+3b)^{1/2}.$$

Illustration 5.   Express $3x\sqrt{a+b}$, $x \geq 0$, $a \geq 0$, $b \geq 0$, as a radical.

$$3x\sqrt{a+b} = (3x)^{2/2}(a+b)^{1/2}$$

$$= [(3x)^2(a+b)]^{1/2} = \sqrt{9x^2(a+b)}.$$

Illustration 6.   Express $\sqrt{a^2+x^2}$, $x \neq 0$, as a product with x as one factor.

$$\sqrt{a^2+x^2} = (a^2+x^2)^{1/2} = \left(x^2\frac{a^2+x^2}{x^2}\right)^{1/2}$$

$$= |x|\sqrt{\frac{a^2+x^2}{x^2}}.$$

Illustration 7.   Express $\sqrt{7}\ \sqrt[3]{x}$, $x \geq 0$, as a power.

$$\sqrt{7}\ \sqrt[3]{x} = 7^{1/2}x^{1/3} = 7^{3/6}x^{2/6} = (7^3x^2)^{1/6}.$$

Illustration 8.   Simplify $\dfrac{(a^2+x^2)^{1/2} - \dfrac{x}{2}(a^2+x^2)^{-(1/2)}2x}{a^2+x^2}$.

The most straightforward procedure is to eliminate all negative exponents and then simplify the resulting fraction.

$$\frac{(a^2+x^2)^{1/2} - \dfrac{x}{2}(a^2+x^2)^{-(1/2)}2x}{a^2+x^2} = \frac{(a^2+x^2)^{1/2} - \dfrac{x^2}{(a^2+x^2)^{1/2}}}{a^2+x^2}$$

$$= \frac{\dfrac{(a^2+x^2) - x^2}{(a^2+x^2)^{1/2}}}{a^2+x^2} = \frac{a^2}{(a^2+x^2)^{3/2}}.$$

Illustration 9. Solve the equation

$$(a - y)\frac{1}{3}(a^2 - y^2)^{-(2/3)}(-2y) - (a^2 - y^2)^{1/3} = 0.$$

First simplify the expression on the left.

$$(a - y)\frac{1}{3}(a^2 - y^2)^{-(2/3)}(-2y) - (a^2 - y^2)^{1/3}$$

$$= \frac{-2y(a - y)}{3(a^2 - y^2)^{2/3}} - (a^2 - y^2)^{1/3} = \frac{-2y(a - y) - 3(a^2 - y^2)}{3(a^2 - y^2)^{2/3}}$$

$$= \frac{5y^2 - 2ay - 3a^2}{3(a^2 - y^2)^{2/3}}.$$

This fraction is zero only if its numerator is zero. Since

$$5y^2 - 2ay - 3a^2 = (5y + 3a)(y - a),$$

this will happen only if $y = a$ or $-\dfrac{3a}{5}$. But if $y = a$, the denominator of the fraction

is zero. Therefore $-\dfrac{3a}{5}$ is the only solution.

A common yet inexcusable mistake is to say $\sqrt{a^2 + b^2} = a + b$. As one can see by trying $a = 3$ and $b = 4$, this is not always true.

When working with square roots it is useful to remember that for positive a and b, $\sqrt{a}\sqrt{b} = \sqrt{ab}$ and $\dfrac{\sqrt{a}}{\sqrt{b}} = \sqrt{\dfrac{a}{b}}$. These were shown in Problems 47 and 48 of Section 2.19, and also follow from Problems 66 and 68 of Section 9.2.

PROBLEMS

Simplify:

1. $\sqrt{12}\sqrt{15}$.

2. $(-7\sqrt{3x})^2$.

3. $25^{2/3} \cdot 5^{2/3}$.

4. $\sqrt{x^{4n}}$.

5. $\sqrt{z^{1/3}}$.

6. $\sqrt{.49x^9}$.

7. $(2\sqrt[3]{4})^3$.

8. $(a^2)^{5/3}$.

9. $\sqrt[6]{16}$.

10. $y\sqrt[3]{y^7}$.

11. $\sqrt[3]{8a^4}$.

12. $\sqrt[3]{.001w^{-7}}$.

13. $5\sqrt{y}\sqrt{2y^3}$.

14. $\sqrt{\dfrac{4x^5}{a^4}}$.

15. $\dfrac{(10x)^{1/2}}{\sqrt{2x}}$.

16. $\sqrt[4]{\dfrac{16x^9}{81a^8}}$.

17. $\sqrt[3]{-\dfrac{a^5}{8x^9}}$.

18. $\sqrt{z\sqrt{15z^3}\sqrt{5z}}$.

19. $(3^2x^{-6})^{1/4}$.

20. $\sqrt{5x^3} + (\sqrt{5x})^3$.

21. $y\sqrt[3]{ay} - a^{1/3}(y^{2/3})^2$.

22. $\sqrt{16 + 16y^2}$.

23. $\sqrt{\dfrac{a}{2x^2} + \dfrac{3b}{4}}$.

24. $\sqrt[3]{\dfrac{a}{8} - \dfrac{9}{x^3}}$.

25. $\sqrt[3]{27a^3 - 54a^4u^3}$.

26. $\sqrt[3]{-\frac{3}{4}} + 3\sqrt[3]{-162}$.

27. $\sqrt[3]{\frac{1}{4}a} + \sqrt[3]{2a^4}$.

28. Is it true or false that $\sqrt{a} + \sqrt{b} = \sqrt{a + b}$?

Express as a sum and simplify:

29. $(\sqrt{3} - 4\sqrt{5})^2$.

30. $(3\sqrt{2} + \sqrt{3})(\sqrt{2} + 4\sqrt{3})$.

31. $(\sqrt{x} + \frac{1}{2}\sqrt{y})^2$.

32. $\left(\sqrt{a} + \dfrac{1}{\sqrt{b}}\right)\sqrt{2b}$.

33. $(\sqrt{12} - 6\sqrt{3})\left(\dfrac{2}{\sqrt{6}} - \dfrac{1}{\sqrt{3}}\right)$.

Express as a radical or power and simplify:

34. $10\sqrt{5}$.

35. $5\sqrt{2x}$.

36. $2x^{1/3}$.

37. $x^{2/3}y$.

38. $2\left(\dfrac{3x}{2a}\right)^{1/2}$.

39. $2\sqrt[3]{x^2}$.

40. $\frac{1}{3}\sqrt{\dfrac{3a}{7b}}$.

41. $(\sqrt{h^9})^{1/3}$.

42. $\sqrt{3}\sqrt[5]{x^2}$.

43. $\dfrac{\sqrt[3]{2}}{\sqrt{5}}$.

44. $a\sqrt[3]{a^{7/2}}$.

45. $x^{-2}\sqrt{ax^3}$.

46. $x^{-(1/2)}\sqrt{a^2 + x^2}$.

47. $\sqrt[3]{y^5}\sqrt{cy}$.

48. $\dfrac{\sqrt[3]{ax^2}}{\sqrt{2y}}$, $a \geqq 0$.

49. $(-5\sqrt[3]{2x})^2$.

50. $2\sqrt[4]{5(x + y)}$.

51. $x^2(a^2 + x^2)^{-(2/3)}$.

52. $\sqrt[3]{\sqrt[2]{ax^3}}$.

53. $\sqrt{x^5\sqrt[3]{x^2u}}$.

Simplify and express without negative exponents:

54. $\frac{1}{2}(a^2 - x^2)^{-(1/2)}(-2x)$.

55. $\frac{1}{3}(4 - x^2)^{-(2/3)}(-2x)$.

56. $x^{2/3}2(x - 2) + \frac{2}{3}x^{-(1/3)}(x - 2)^2$.

57. $x\frac{1}{2}(a^2 - x^2)^{-(1/2)}(-2x) + (a^2 - x^2)^{1/2}$.

58. $\dfrac{\sqrt{2x - 1} - x\frac{1}{2}(2x + 1)^{-(1/2)} \cdot 2}{2x + 1}$.

59. $\dfrac{x\frac{1}{2}(a^2 + x^2)^{-(1/2)}2x - \sqrt{a^2 + x^2}}{x^2}$.

Express as a product with x (or $|x|$) as one factor:

60. $\sqrt{x + ax^2}$.   61. $\sqrt{6}$.   62. $\sqrt{x^2 + x - 5}$.

Express as a product with $x^{-(2/3)}$ as one factor:

63. $x^{-(2/3)} + x^{1/3}$.

64. $(x^{2/3} - x^{-(4/3)})^{1/2}$.

65. Express $a^{-(1/2)} + a^{-1}b^2 + a^{1/2}b^{-2} + 1$ as a product with a^{-1} as one factor.

66. Express $a^2(x^2 - a^2)^{-(1/3)} + (x^2 - a^2)^{2/3}$ as a product with $(x^2 - a^2)^{-(1/3)}$ as one factor.

Solve the following equations:

67. $2x - 8x^{-3} = 0$.

68. $\frac{1}{3}(b^2 - y^2)^{-(2/3)}(-2\dot{y}) = 0$, $\quad b \neq 0$.

69. $x^2 \frac{1}{2}(9 - x^2)^{-(1/2)}(-2x) + 2x(9 - x^2)^{1/2} = 0$.

*70. Prove that $\sqrt[n]{a}\sqrt[n]{b} = \sqrt[n]{ab}$, $\; n$ a positive integer, $a \geq 0$, $b \geq 0$. Is the theorem ever true for negative a and b?

71. Prove that $\sqrt[m]{\sqrt[n]{a}} = \sqrt[mn]{a}$, $\; m$ and n positive integers, $a \geq 0$.

*72. If n is a positive integer, under what conditions is $\dfrac{\sqrt[n]{a}}{\sqrt[n]{b}} = \sqrt[n]{\dfrac{a}{b}}$?

73. Find all a and b for which $\sqrt{a^2 + b^2} = a + b$.

9.4 Rationalization

A fraction involving radicals or fractional exponents often can be handled more conveniently if it is expressed in a form with no radicals in the denominator.

As an example, consider the problem of finding a decimal approximation of $\dfrac{1}{\sqrt{2}}$. From the table of square roots at the end of the book, we see that $\sqrt{2} \approx 1.414$, where the symbol $\approx$ means "approximately equal" (see the discussion at the beginning of Section 1.4). Hence an approximation to $\dfrac{1}{\sqrt{2}}$ can be found by evaluating $\dfrac{1}{1.414}$, which is .707. Alternatively, one can proceed as follows:

$$\frac{1}{\sqrt{2}} = \frac{\sqrt{2}}{\sqrt{2}\sqrt{2}} = \frac{\sqrt{2}}{2} \approx \frac{1.414}{2} = .707,$$

and a tedious long division has been replaced by a simpler short division. The elimination of the radical in the denominator is called *rationalizing the denominator*. The secret of rationalizing a denominator is to multiply the numerator and denominator of the fraction by a quantity so chosen that the resulting denominator will have no radical.

Illustration 1. Find a decimal approximation of $\sqrt{\dfrac{3}{32}}$.

$$\sqrt{\frac{3}{32}} = \left(\frac{3}{32}\right)^{1/2} = \left(\frac{3 \cdot 2}{32 \cdot 2}\right)^{1/2} = \frac{6^{1/2}}{64^{1/2}}$$

$$= \frac{\sqrt{6}}{8} \approx \frac{2.449}{8} = .306.$$

Illustration 2. Express $\sqrt[3]{\dfrac{x}{8a^2}}$ with no denominator under the radical.

$$\sqrt[3]{\frac{x}{8a^2}} = \left(\frac{x}{8a^2}\right)^{1/3} = \frac{(ax)^{1/3}}{(8a^3)^{1/3}} = \frac{\sqrt[3]{ax}}{2a}.$$

A problem of frequent occurrence is the rationalization of the denominator of an expression such as $\dfrac{4}{3 + \sqrt{6}}$. This can be done by multiplying the numerator and denominator by $3 - \sqrt{6}$:

$$\frac{4}{3 + \sqrt{6}} = \frac{4(3 - \sqrt{6})}{(3 + \sqrt{6})(3 - \sqrt{6})} = \frac{4(3 - \sqrt{6})}{9 - 6} = \frac{4}{3}(3 - \sqrt{6}).$$

One seldom obtains something for nothing. Here we pay the price in the introduction of radicals into the numerator. For some purposes, however, it may be more convenient to have them there than in the denominator.

It is possible to change any fraction with radicals in the denominator to one with no radicals there, but the proof of this is not elementary and cannot be given here.

PROBLEMS

Rationalize the denominator in each of the following:

1. $\dfrac{1}{\sqrt{13}}$.

2. $\dfrac{8}{\sqrt{6}}$.

3. $\dfrac{-10}{\sqrt{15}}$.

4. $\dfrac{-5\sqrt{7}}{2\sqrt{5}}$.

5. $\dfrac{-17}{\sqrt[3]{4}}$.

6. $\dfrac{2}{7^{2/3}}$.

7. $\dfrac{7 - 9^{1/3}}{3^{1/3}}$.

8. $\dfrac{6^{2/3}}{12^{5/3}}$.

9. $\dfrac{3}{\sqrt{9 + x^2}}$.

10. $\dfrac{-2a}{(a^2 - x^2)^{1/3}}$.

11. $\dfrac{-10}{-4 + 3\sqrt{3}}$.

12. $\dfrac{1}{a + \sqrt{b}}$.

13. $\dfrac{\sqrt{2}}{6 + \sqrt{8}}$.

14. $\dfrac{\sqrt{2} - 5}{\sqrt{2} + 5}$.

15. $\dfrac{\sqrt{12} - 4\sqrt{10}}{\sqrt{12} + 3\sqrt{10}}$.

16. $\dfrac{x}{2a - c\sqrt{a}}$.

17. $\dfrac{2}{x + \sqrt{a^2 - x^2}}$.

18. $\dfrac{8\sqrt{x}}{\sqrt{a} - \sqrt{x}}$.

19. $\dfrac{\sqrt{a} + \sqrt{b}}{-2\sqrt{a} + \sqrt{2b}}$.

20. $\dfrac{\sqrt{3}}{8 - 3\sqrt{3} - \sqrt{2}}$.

21. $\dfrac{1}{\sqrt{3} - \sqrt{7} + \sqrt{10}}$.

22. $\dfrac{2}{y^{1/n}}$, n a positive integer.

Use the table of roots at the end of the book to find a decimal approximation of the following:

23. $\sqrt{\dfrac{3}{8}}$.

26. $\sqrt[3]{-\dfrac{4}{49}}$.

29. $\left(\dfrac{12}{5}\right)^{3/2}$.

24. $\sqrt{.24}$.

27. $\sqrt[3]{.128}$.

30. $\dfrac{3}{4 + \sqrt{10}}$.

25. $\sqrt[3]{\dfrac{11}{2}}$.

28. $\sqrt{\dfrac{2}{3} + \dfrac{5}{6}}$.

31. $\dfrac{2}{\sqrt{5} - \sqrt{3}}$.

Express with no denominator under the radical:

32. $\sqrt{12 + \dfrac{5}{3x}}$.

33. $\sqrt{\dfrac{x}{4} - \dfrac{3}{b}}$.

Simplify:

34. $6\sqrt{\dfrac{ax}{3}} - \sqrt{12ax}$.

35. $\sqrt[5]{\dfrac{1}{c^2}} + \sqrt[5]{32c^3}$.

Express as a fraction with a denominator containing only integral exponents:

36. $\left(\dfrac{2x^6}{7b^2z^3}\right)^{1/9}$.

37. $\sqrt[p]{\dfrac{a}{2x^{2p}}}$, p a positive integer.

Rationalize the numerator:

38. $\dfrac{\sqrt{x + a}}{x}$.

41. $\dfrac{\sqrt{3 + h} - \sqrt{3}}{h}$.

39. $\dfrac{\sqrt{19}}{\sqrt{2} + 5}$.

42. $\dfrac{x - \sqrt{x^2 - a^2}}{a}$.

40. $\dfrac{\sqrt{x} - \sqrt{7}}{x - 7}$.

43. $\dfrac{\sqrt{x + a} + \sqrt{x - a}}{a}$.

44. Show that the denominator of $\dfrac{1}{2 - 5^{1/3}}$ can be rationalized by multiplying the numerator and denominator by $4 + 2(5^{1/3}) + 5^{2/3}$.

45. Show that the denominator of $\dfrac{1}{x^{1/3} + y^{1/3}}$ can be rationalized by multiplying the numerator and denominator by $x^{2/3} - x^{1/3}y^{1/3} + y^{2/3}$.

46. Rationalize the denominator of $\dfrac{1}{a + b^{2/3}}$.

9.5 Solution of Equations with Rational Exponents

In Section 3.5 we saw how to solve certain simple equations containing the square root of the unknown. Equations involving higher roots can occasionally be solved, but there is no general procedure. Considerable ingenuity is often required, and since the equation is usually at some time replaced by another not equivalent to it, all solutions should be checked by substitution in the original equation.

Illustration. Solve $\sqrt{3 - x} + \sqrt{2x + 16} = 5$.

Squaring both sides of the equation, we have

$$(1) \qquad\qquad x + 19 + 2\sqrt{3 - x}\,\sqrt{2x + 16} = 25,$$

or

$$(2) \qquad\qquad 2\sqrt{3 - x}\,\sqrt{2x + 16} = 6 - x.$$

Squaring again gives us

$$4(3 - x)(2x + 16) = 36 - 12x + x^2,$$

which reduces to

$$(3) \qquad\qquad 9x^2 + 28x - 156 = 0.$$

The polynomial in (3) has factors over the rational field, but since they are not too easily found by inspection, it is perhaps quicker to solve (3) by the quadratic formula,

$$x = \frac{1}{18}(-28 \pm \sqrt{6400}) = \frac{1}{18}(-28 \pm 80),$$

giving $\frac{26}{9}$ and -6 as the roots of (3). A check shows that both of these are solutions of the original equation. It is essential that the radicals be placed by themselves on one side of the equation, as in (2), before the second squaring, for if one squares (1), the radicals will not be eliminated.

PROBLEMS

Find all real solutions of the following:

1. $\sqrt{y} = y - 6$.

2. $\sqrt{y} = 6 - y$.

3. $\sqrt[3]{x + 10} = 2$.

4. $(4x - 5)^{2/3} = 0$.

5. $\sqrt[4]{6x + 15} - 3 = 0$.

6. $\sqrt{3x + 12} + 3 = 0$.

7. $(9 - x^2)^{1/3} = (x + 4)^{2/3}$.

8. $(8x^2 + 30x + 19)^{1/3} = 3$.

9. $\sqrt{\dfrac{x + 27}{x - 3}} = \dfrac{x + 7}{x - 2}$.

10. $35x^{-2} + 9x^{-1} - 2 = 0$.

11. $x + 3\sqrt{x} - 28 = 0$.

12. $\sqrt{2x - 3} - \sqrt{x + 2} = 1$.

13. $2\sqrt{4x + 11} = 3 + \sqrt{14x}$.

14. $\sqrt{x} - \sqrt{x - 5} = 4$.

15. $\sqrt{4x - 3} - \sqrt{x - 2} = \sqrt{6x - 14}$.

16. $\sqrt{5x + 1} + \sqrt{x + 1} = \sqrt{7x + 15}$.

17. $x^{1/3} - (2x)^{1/3} = 5$.

18. $x^{1/3} - (2x^2)^{1/3} = -4^{1/3}$.

19. $8x^3 - 19x^{3/2} - 27 = 0$.

20. $(3x^3 - x^2 - 2x + 3)^{1/3} = x + 2$.

21. $\frac{1}{3}x^{-(2/3)}(x - 4) + x^{1/3} = 0$.

22. $\dfrac{(x^2 + a^2)^{3/2} - x\frac{3}{2}(x^2 + a^2)^{1/2}2x}{(x^2 + a^2)^3} = 0$, $\qquad a \neq 0$.

23. $\dfrac{\sqrt{a^2 + x^2} - \frac{1}{2}x(a^2 + x^2)^{-(1/2)}2x}{a^2 + x^2} = 0$, $\qquad a \neq 0$.

24. $\dfrac{2x(x^2 - a^2)^{1/3} - x^2\frac{1}{3}(x^2 - a^2)^{-(2/3)}2x}{(x^2 - a^2)^{2/3}} = 0$, $\qquad a \neq 0$.

25. $\dfrac{\frac{1}{3}x^2(x^2 - a^2)^{-(2/3)}2x - 2x(x^2 - a^2)^{1/3}}{x^4} = 0$, $\qquad a \neq 0$.

9.6   Irrational Exponents

Our definitions of powers applied only to rational exponents and so do not cover such powers as $5^{\sqrt{2}}$ or $(\frac{7}{19})^\pi$. If one were to assign a meaning to a^x for irrational x, one would be guided by two considerations in formulating a suitable definition. First, one would like the laws of exponents listed in Theorem 1 to be valid for irrational exponents. Secondly, one intuitively feels that a certain continuity should be preserved in the sense that if r is a rational number near x, then a^r should be near a^x. For example, we should want $5^{\sqrt{2}}$ to be a number such that $5^{1.41}$ is near $5^{\sqrt{2}}$, since 1.41 is near $\sqrt{2}$. We shall not attempt to be precise about the meaning of "near," but say merely that since 1.414 is a rational number still nearer $\sqrt{2}$, one would expect $5^{1.414}$ to be nearer $5^{\sqrt{2}}$ than was $5^{1.41}$.

It is possible to define a^x for irrational x so that it has both of these properties, provided $a > 0$. To do so, however, requires a concept too advanced to be developed in this text. Therefore we shall assume that for $a > 0$ and all real x, a^x is a real number for which (1) the laws of exponents given in Theorem 1 are valid, and (2) if r is a rational number near x, then a^r is near a^x, and moreover, the nearer r is to x, the nearer a^r will be to a^x. It is not possible to give a definition of a^x for negative a such that properties (1) and (2) hold, but we can define $0^x = 0$ for all $x > 0$. As one would expect, it is true that $1^x = 1$ for all x. Also, if $a > 0$, $a^{-x} = \dfrac{1}{a^x}$ for all real x.

The second property provides a means of estimating a^x. Since $\frac{3}{2}$ is near $\sqrt{2}$, $5^{3/2} = (\sqrt{5})^3 \approx 11.180$ is an approximation to $5^{\sqrt{2}}$. A better estimate is given by $5^{1.41} \approx 9.6727$. In Chapter 10 we shall see how logarithms can be used to evaluate such powers.

Illustration 1.

(a) $7^{\sqrt{3}} \cdot 7^{\sqrt{2}} = 7^{\sqrt{3}+\sqrt{2}}$;

(b) $\left(7^{\sqrt{3}}\right)^{\sqrt{2}} = 7^{\sqrt{3}\,\sqrt{2}} = 7^{\sqrt{6}}$;

(c) $(\sqrt{5})^{\pi}(\sqrt{2})^{\pi} = (\sqrt{5} \cdot \sqrt{2})^{\pi} = (10^{1/2})^{\pi} = 10^{\pi/2}$.

Theorem 4.   For all real x, $a^x > 0$ if $a > 0$.

Proof.   If x is rational, it can be expressed in the form $x = m/n$, where m and n are integers and $n > 0$. Now $a^{1/n} > 0$ since $a^{1/n}$ has the same sign as a (see Section 2.19). Since m is an integer, $a^x = (a^{1/n})^m > 0$ by Problem 60 in Section 9.1. The proof when x is irrational depends on the definition of a^x and cannot be given here. The theorem, though, does seem plausible for such powers, since we can choose a rational r near x, making a^r, which is positive, near a^x.

Theorem 5.   Let $x > 0$ and $a > 0$. Then $a^x > 1$ if and only if $a > 1$.

For example, $\sqrt{\pi} > 1$ and $(\tfrac{5}{6})^3 < 1$.

Proof.   If x is rational, let $x = m/n$ for some positive integers m and n. Suppose $a > 1$. Then $a^m > 1$ by Problem 27 in Section 6.1. We must have $a^{m/n} > 1$, for if $a^{m/n} \leq 1$, then by the same problem $a^m = (a^{m/n})^n \leq 1$, a contradiction. Conversely, suppose $a^x > 1$. Then by what we have just shown with a^x in place of a and $1/x$ replacing x, $a = (a^x)^{1/x} > 1$. The proof for irrational x will be omitted.

Theorem 6.   Let $a > 0$, $b > 0$, and $x > 0$. Then $a^x < b^x$ if and only if $a < b$.

In other words, powers of two numbers with the same exponent are in the same relative order as the numbers themselves. Thus since $\tfrac{2}{7} < \tfrac{1}{3}$, we know that $\sqrt{\tfrac{2}{7}} < \sqrt{\tfrac{1}{3}}$.

Proof.   By Theorem 5, $\dfrac{b}{a} > 1$ if and only if $\left(\dfrac{b}{a}\right)^x > 1$. Hence $b > a$ if and only if $b^x > a^x$.

The next theorem will be useful in our discussion of logarithms in the next chapter. It is a companion to the preceding theorem and shows the relation of two powers of a number if the relative order of their exponents is known.

Theorem 7.

(a) Let $a > 1$. Then $a^x < a^y$ if and only if $x < y$.

(b) Let $0 < a < 1$. Then $a^x > a^y$ if and only if $x < y$.

Proof.

(a) Suppose $x < y$. Then $y - x > 0$ and by Theorem 5 $a^{y-x} > 1$. Multiplying both sides of this inequality by the positive number a^x gives us $a^y > a^x$. Conversely, suppose $a^x < a^y$. If $y < x$, then by what we have just shown $a^y < a^x$. If $y = x$, then $a^y = a^x$. Hence $y > x$.

(b) The proof of this part of the theorem will be left to the reader.

Corollary. If $a > 0$ and $a \neq 1$, then $a^x = a^y$ implies $x = y$.

Proof. By the theorem, we can have neither $x < y$ nor $x > y$.

Illustration 2. Solve the equation $2^{x/3} = 32$.

Since $32 = 2^5$, we are to find a number x for which $2^{x/3} = 2^5$. By the corollary, we must have $x/3 = 5$; that is, $x = 15$.

Illustration 3. Which is larger, $3^{-(4/3)}$ or 3^{-2}?

By Theorem 7(a), $3^{-(4/3)} > 3^{-2}$ since $-(4/3) > -2$.

PROBLEMS

Solve the following:

1. $10^x = \dfrac{1}{1000}$.

2. $3^{4x} = 27$.

3. $(\frac{1}{2})^x = \frac{1}{32}$.

4. $(\frac{1}{2})^x = 64$.

5. $14^y = \dfrac{1}{\sqrt{14}}$.

6. $5(10^x) = \frac{1}{2}(10^{3x})$.

7. $16^x = 8$.

Locate x between two consecutive integers if:

8. $7^x = 63.5$.

9. $2^x = \frac{1}{5}$.

10. $10^x = .027$.

11. $(\frac{7}{4})^x = 18$.

Which is the larger number in each of the following pairs?

12. 11^{-3}, 11^0.

13. $(\frac{1}{3})^2$, $(\frac{1}{3})^5$.

14. $(\frac{1}{2})^\pi$, $(\frac{1}{2})^3$.

15. $\pi^{1/3}$, $3^{1/3}$.

16. $2^{2/3}$, $2^{3/4}$.

17. $10^{-\sqrt{2}}$, $10^{-\sqrt{3}}$.

18. 5^{-4}, $(2\pi)^{-4}$.

19. $(1.1)^{-(1/4)}$, $(1.1)^{-(3/7)}$.

20. $\left(\dfrac{1}{3}\right)^{-\sqrt{3}}$, $\left(\dfrac{1}{3}\right)^{-\sqrt{10}}$.

21. $(\sqrt{2} - 1)^{-1}$, $(\sqrt{2} - 1)^2$.

22. $(\pi - 3)^{-(1/2)}$, $(\pi - 3)^{-(1/3)}$.

23. $(\sqrt{2})^{-\sqrt{3}}$, $\left(\dfrac{\pi}{2}\right)^{-\sqrt{3}}$.

24. $(\sqrt[3]{50})^5$, $(\sqrt{13})^5$.

25. 2^5, $10^{3/2}$.

26. $\left(\dfrac{3}{5}\right)^{3/4}$, $\left(\dfrac{2}{3}\right)^{2/3}$. $\left(Hint:\ \text{Consider } \left(\dfrac{2}{3}\right)^{3/4}.\right)$

Estimate roughly the magnitude of:

27. 2^π.

28. $10^{\sqrt{3}}$.

29. $\dfrac{1}{3^{\sqrt{2}}}$.

30. Prove Theorem 7(b). $\left(Hint:\ \text{Apply 7(a) to } \dfrac{1}{a}.\right)$

31. Let $a > 0$, $b > 0$, and $x < 0$. Prove that $a^x > b^x$ if and only if $a < b$.

Chapter 10

Logarithms

10.1 Exponential Functions

In the last chapter we saw that 2^x could be defined for any x as a real number obeying the laws of exponents. Let us sketch the graph of the equation $y = 2^x$. The following table gives values of x and y satisfying the equation:

x	y	x	y
-10	$\frac{1}{1024}$	1	2
-3	$\frac{1}{8}$	1.5	$2^{3/2} \approx 2.83$
-2	$\frac{1}{4}$	2	4
-1	$\frac{1}{2}$	2.5	$2^{5/2} \approx 5.66$
$-.5$	$\frac{1}{\sqrt{2}} \approx .71$	3	8
0	1	4	16
.5	$\sqrt{2} \approx 1.41$	10	1024 .

We have used these to sketch the graph in Figure 10.1.

The graph can be used to illustrate two of the theorems in Section 9.6. First, the graph lies entirely above the x-axis, as it should by Theorem 4 of that section. By Theorem 7(a), if $x_1 < x_2$, then $2^{x_1} < 2^{x_2}$. The geometric interpretation of this is that the curve must be continually rising from left to right. Actually, soon after crossing the y-axis the curve begins to rise very rapidly, and as the equation shows, when x is large, y is enormously large. On the other hand, when x is a large negative number, y is close to zero; the curve as one moves along it to the left comes nearer and nearer, yet never touches, the x-axis.

196

Since 2^x is defined for all x, for each x there is a y such that $y = 2^x$. Geometrically, this means that every line parallel to the y-axis must cut the curve. In our discussion in the last chapter of the definition of a^x for irrational x we pointed out that there is a continuity in the values of a^x in the sense that, referring now to our example, values of x near each other give values of 2^x also near each other. This means that there are no gaps in the graph of $y = 2^x$; it is continuous and can be drawn without lifting the pencil from the paper. Every line parallel to and above the x-axis also cuts the curve.

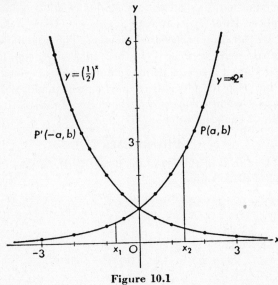

Figure 10.1

There is nothing special about the number 2. The graphs of $y = 3^x$, $y = (\frac{25}{7})^x$, and indeed $y = c^x$ all have the same general characteristics as that of $y = 2^x$ provided $c > 1$. They all rise from left to right, and all cross the y-axis at the point $(0, 1)$.

If $c < 1$, things do look different. Consider, for example, $y = (\frac{1}{2})^x$. If we write this as $y = \dfrac{1}{2^x}$, we see now that when x is large, y is near zero, and the farther out one is on the curve to the right, the closer one is to the x-axis. If $x = -3$, $y = \dfrac{1}{2^{-3}} = 2^3 = 8$. If $x = -5$, $y = \dfrac{1}{2^{-5}} = 2^5 = 32$. It is obvious that as x becomes negatively large, y becomes a very large positive number, and the curve rises steeply as one moves along it to the left. Its graph is also sketched in Figure 10.1. Note that this curve illustrates Theorem 7(b) in Section 9.6.

The graph of $y = (\frac{1}{2})^x$ is typical of those of $y = c^x$ for any c for which $0 < c < 1$. They all fall from left to right, and all cross the y-axis at $(0, 1)$.

The graphs of $y = 2^x$ and $y = (\frac{1}{2})^x$ look somewhat alike. In fact, if one imagines a mirror set along the y-axis perpendicular to the plane of the paper, each is the reflection of the other. This can be verified algebraically by writing the equation of $y = (\frac{1}{2})^x$ in the form $y = 2^{-x}$. Now if $P(a, b)$ is a point on the curve $y = 2^x$, then $b = 2^a$. This can be written $b = 2^{-(-a)}$, which shows that the point $P'(-a, b)$ lies on the curve $y = 2^{-x}$. But P and P' are symmetric with respect to the y-axis.

For any $c > 0$, the graph of $y = c^x$ is continuous and cut by every vertical line and every horizontal line above the x-axis. Since x appears as an exponent, the equation is called an *exponential equation*. The expression c^x assigns a number—namely c^x—to each number x. It thus defines a function f, $f(x) = c^x$, called an *exponential function*. The domain of f is the set of all real numbers, and the range is the set of all positive numbers. Like the polynomial function, it is one of the more important functions not only for mathematics but also for physics, chemistry, and biology. It is used in describing the mathematical aspects of the decay of radioactive substances and the growth of bacterial colonies.

PROBLEMS

Using the table of roots at the end of the book, sketch on the same coordinate plane the graphs of the following:

1. $y = 3^x$.
2. $y = (\frac{1}{3})^x = 3^{-x}$.
3. $y = 1^x$.

4. $y = 5^x$.
5. $y = 5^{-x}$.

Sketch the graphs of:

6. $y = 2^{x/2}$.
7. $y = 3^{x+1}$.
8. $y = -3^x$.
9. $y = (\frac{1}{4})^{-x}$.

10. $y = -10^{-x}$.
11. $y = 2^{|x|}$.
12. $y = 2^{-(x^2)}$.
13. $y = x2^x$.

14. (a) If f is the function defined by $f(x) = 3^x$, find $f(2), f(3), f(5), f(-4), f(0),$ $f(\frac{1}{2})$.

    (b) If $f(x) = c^x$, where $c > 0$, show that $f(u) \cdot f(v) = f(u + v)$ for all u and v.

15. At a certain time a colony of bacteria contains 10,000 members. Observations at the same hour on successive days show that after t days the colony contains $10,000\ (2^t)$ members. How many did it have after five days; after ten days? How many were there two days ago?

16. At a certain time the mass of a radioactive substance is .1 grams. Because of loss by radiation, the mass continually decreases. It is known from the general theory that t years later there will be .1 $(3^{-(t/2)})$ grams remaining. How much will there be after one year; after six years? How much was there one year ago? When will all the substance be gone?

10.2   Logarithms

The graph of $y = 10^x$ is sketched in Figure 10.2. We know that 10^x is defined for all x, and hence for each a, there is a corresponding b such that

$b = 10^a$. Let us now consider the converse problem. Is it true that for each b there is a number a such that $10^a = b$?

If $b \leq 0$, obviously there can be no such number since $10^x > 0$ for all x. If $b > 0$, however, there is an a and only one. It is the x-coordinate of the intersection of the horizontal line b units above the x-axis with the graph of $y = 10^x$. From Figure 10.2 one can see that if $b > 1$, then $a > 0$, but if $0 < b \leq 1$, then $a \leq 0$. It is also clear that as b increases so does a, even for b between zero and one.

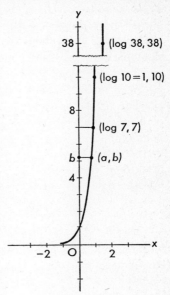

We call a *the logarithm of b to the base 10*, and write $\log_{10} b$ for a when we wish to indicate that the number a is associated with b in this way. Later we shall discuss logarithms to other bases. Since for most of this chapter we shall be using base 10, however, we shall omit the subscript 10 and write $\log b$ for $\log_{10} b$. The reader is warned against thinking of $\log b$ as a product, $(\log)(b)$. Log b is a number and it is derived from b. It is that number a for which $10^a = b$. Since $a = \log b$, we can equally well say $10^{\log b} = b$.

Definition. For each $b > 0$, *$\log b$* (that is, $\log_{10} b$) is that number for which $10^{\log b} = b$.

Figure 10.2

Thus

$$\log 100 = 2, \qquad \text{since } 10^2 = 100;$$

$$\log \frac{1}{1,000} = -3, \qquad \text{since } 10^{-3} = \frac{1}{1,000};$$

$$\log 10 = 1, \qquad \text{since } 10^1 = 10.$$

From the table of roots at the end of the book, we see that $10^{1/2} \approx 3.162$. Hence $\log 3.162 \approx \frac{1}{2}$.

Since $10^{.8451} \approx 7$, $\quad \log 7 \approx .8451$.

The reader should study these examples and the definition until he understands clearly what a logarithm is. He should keep firmly in mind that a logarithm is a number and that it appears as an exponent. Like other numbers, logarithms can be added to each other and multiplied by numbers.

Exercise. Find $\log 1,000$, $\log \frac{1}{10}$, $\log 1$, $\log (10^6)$, $\log .0001$. Why is there no $\log (-3)$ or $\log 0$?

It is easy to find the logarithm of any integral power of 10. For other numbers it is not so simple. For example, to find $\log 38$ we must look for an a for which $10^a = 38$, and it is not at all obvious what a should be. We do know that there is an a (see Figure 10.2). Let us estimate it. Now

$$10^1 = 10,$$
$$10^a = 38,$$
$$10^2 = 100.$$

Since the graph of $y = 10^x$ is rising and $10 < 38 < 100$, we know that $1 < a < 2$. This is about the best we can do now. We shall see later that a is approximately 1.5798 and hence $\log 38 \approx 1.5798$.

PROBLEMS

Find:

1. $\log \sqrt{10}$.

2. $\log \dfrac{1}{\sqrt[3]{10}}$.

3. $\log \sqrt[3]{100}$.

4. $\log (.01\sqrt{10})$.

Find y if:

5. $\log y = 4$.
6. $\log y = -2$.
7. $\log y = 0$.

8. $\log y = \frac{3}{2}$.
*9. Prove that $x = \log (10^x)$.

Locate each of the following between two consecutive integers and give reasons for your answer:

10. $\log 5$.
11. $\log 83$.
12. $\log 263.12$.

13. $\log .7$.
14. $\log .049$.
15. $\log .00031$.

16. Use the table of roots to find approximately (a) $\log 2.154$, (b) $\log 4.642$.

17. If $\log 5 \approx .6990$, find approximately $\log 50$. (*Hint:* Write 50 as $5 \cdot 10$.)

10.3   Properties of Logarithms

The usefulness of logarithms stems in part from three of their algebraic properties. Before stating these, let us clear up some possible misunderstandings in the notation for logarithms.

If the logarithm of a sum is desired, this must be clearly indicated by parentheses, as in $\log (25.1 + 10.03)$, since $\log 25.1 + 10.03$ means $(\log 25.1) + 10.03$. We shall agree that $\log u^r$ means $\log (u^r)$ and not $(\log u)^r$. Thus $\log 15.6^2 = \log (15.6^2)$.

Exercise.   Explain the difference in meaning between $\log (8.71^2)$ and $(\log 8.71)^2$. Compute $\log 10^3$ and $(\log 10)^3$.

Theorem 1.

(a) $\log (uv) = \log u + \log v$,

(b) $\log \dfrac{u}{v} = \log u - \log v$,

(c) $\log (u^r) = r \log u$, where r is any real number.

Let us illustrate these three laws with $u = 100$, $v = 1000$, and $r = 4$. We have

$$\log u = \log 10^2 = 2, \quad \text{and} \quad \log v = \log 10^3 = 3.$$

Now

$$uv = 10^5, \text{ so that } \log (uv) = 5 = \log u + \log v;$$

$$\frac{u}{v} = 10^{-1}, \text{ so that } \log \frac{u}{v} = -1 = \log u - \log v;$$

and

$$u^r = 10^8, \text{ so that } \log (u^r) = 8 = r \log u.$$

To prove (a), we have by definition

$$u = 10^{\log u} \quad \text{and} \quad v = 10^{\log v}.$$

Therefore

$$uv = 10^{\log u} \cdot 10^{\log v} = 10^{\log u + \log v}.$$

On the other hand, by definition, $uv = 10^{\log (uv)}$. If two powers with like bases are equal, then their exponents must be equal (corollary to Theorem 7 in Section 9.6). Hence $\log (uv) = \log u + \log v$. The proof of (b) is similar. To show (c), we have

$$u^r = (10^{\log u})^r = 10^{r \log u}.$$

But by definition, $u^r = 10^{\log(u^r)}$, and therefore $\log(u^r) = r \log u$.

Illustration. If $\log 2 \approx .3010$ and $\log 3 \approx .4771$, find a decimal approximation to $\log 6$ and $\log 8$.

We use the first part of Theorem 1 to find $\log 6$:

$$\log 6 = \log (2 \times 3) = \log 2 + \log 3$$
$$\approx .3010 + .4771 = .7781.$$

By part (c),

$$\log 8 = \log (2^3) = 3 \log 2 \approx 3(.3010) = .9030.$$

Since each real number $x > 0$ has a logarithm, $\log x$ sets up a correspondence that assigns a number, $\log x$, to each positive real number x. It thus defines a function f, $f(x) = \log x$, called a *logarithmic function*. The domain of f is the set of all positive real numbers, and its range is the set of all numbers.

The graph of the equation $y = \log x$ is easily obtained from that of the exponential equation. By the definition of a logarithm, $y = \log x$ means that $10^y = x$. Hence these two equations have identical graphs. The equation $x = 10^y$ is the same as $y = 10^x$ but with x and y interchanged. We can therefore obtain the graph of $x = 10^y$ from that of $y = 10^x$ by replacing each point on the latter by the point with reversed coordinates. Now if $P(a, b)$ and $P'(b, a)$ are two such points, then P' is the reflection of P in a mirror set along the line bisecting the first and third quadrants and perpendicular to the plane of the paper (see Figure 10.3). The graph of $x = 10^y$ will be the reflection in this mirror of the graph of $y = 10^x$. This is the graph of $y = \log x$.

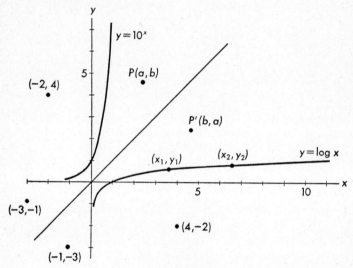

Figure 10.3

Let (x_1, y_1) and (x_2, y_2) be two points on the graph of $y = \log x$ such that $x_1 < x_2$ (see Figure 10.3). Since $x = 10^{\log x}$, $x_1 < x_2$ implies $10^{\log x_1} < 10^{\log x_2}$, which in turn, by Theorem 7 in Section 9.6, implies $y_1 = \log x_1 < \log x_2 = y_2$. In other words, the larger the number, the larger is its logarithm. The graph of $y = \log x$ is then continually rising from left to right. It does, however, rise slowly after crossing the x-axis. The y-coordinate of a point moving along the curve will not reach 1 until the x-coordinate is 10; it will not reach 2 until x is 100. The curve continues to rise more and more slowly the farther out one goes. Note that the graph shows clearly that numbers less than 1 have negative logarithms.

PROBLEMS

If $\log 2 \approx .3010$ and $\log 3 \approx .4771$, use the laws of logarithms to find decimal approximations to:

1. $\log 4$.
2. $\log \frac{2}{3}$.
3. $\log 18$.
4. $\log 1.5$.
5. $\log .5$.
6. $\log \sqrt[3]{2}$.
7. $\log 30$.

8. $\log 300$.
9. $\log 3{,}000$.
10. $\log \frac{1}{3}$.
11. $\log \frac{1}{30}$.
12. $\log \frac{1}{300}$.
13. $\log 5$.

If log 7.83 ≈ .8938, find decimal approximations to:

14. log 78.3.   17. log .783.

15. log 783.   18. log .0783.

16. log 7830.   19. log .000783.

$$20. \ \log \frac{1}{7.83}.$$

Solve the following equations:

21. log x = 0.   24. log $(x + 2)$ = 3.

22. log x = 1.   25. log $(3 - x^2)$ = -2.

23. log x = -2.   26. log $(3 + x^2)$ = -2.

Solve the following inequalities:

27. log x > 2.   29. log $(x - 4)$ < 0.

28. log x ≦ -4.   30. log $|x|$ < -1.

31. Prove log $\dfrac{1}{x}$ = $-$ log x.

32. Give a proof of Theorem 1(b) similar to that used to prove part (a).

33. Prove that log (uvw) = log u + log v + log w.

34. Prove Theorem 1(b) by writing $\dfrac{u}{v}$ as uv^{-1} and using parts (a) and (c).

*35. Show that if log x_1 = log x_2, then $x_1 = x_2$.

36. Prove that if log x_1 < log x_2, then $x_1 < x_2$.

37. If a basic table of logarithms of some integers containing a minimal number of entries were to be constructed and if this were to be sufficient for finding the logarithm of any positive integer, which integers would have to have their logarithms listed? Are there numbers other than integers whose logarithms could be found from this table?

10.4   Logarithm Tables

We have mentioned that there are few numbers whose logarithms are easily found directly from the definition. By advanced methods it is possible to find rational approximations to any desired degree of accuracy of the logarithm of any number. A short table of logarithms is in the back of the book. It lists approximations, correct to four decimal places, of the logarithms of all numbers between 1 and 10 to two decimal places.

There are certain conventions that are standard with almost all tables of logarithms. Any table gives directly the logarithms of numbers only between 1 and 10 (10 not included). The logarithms in the body of the table are then between 0 and 1, since $1 \leqq N < 10$ implies $0 \leqq \log N < 1$. In the interest of simplicity the decimal point in front of each of these logarithms is usually omitted. All numbers in the column headed N lie between 1 and 10. The decimal point between the first and second digit of each of these is also omitted.

To find log 2.74, look for 27 (actually 2.7) in the column headed N. In the row for 27 the entry .4378 in the column headed 4 is the logarithm desired; that is, log 2.74 = .4378. In a similar fashion one finds

$$\log 5.38 = .7308,$$
$$\log 9.35 = .9708,$$
$$\log 1.8 = \log 1.80 = .2553.$$

Since these are only approximations to the logarithms, strictly speaking we should use $\approx$ in place of $=$ here. It is customary, however, to use the equals sign in this connection, and we shall do so, keeping in mind that the numbers are approximations to the true logarithms. For example, $10^{.7308}$ is not exactly equal to 5.38, but is close to it.

Exercise A. Find log 1.02, log 1.20, log 8.87, log 4.

Exercise B. Find N if log N = .5888, log N = .9063, log N = .7404.

Although the table gives directly the logarithms of numbers only between 1 and 10, it can be used to find the logarithms of other numbers. Any positive number a can be expressed as a product of two numbers, the first between 1 and 10 (not including 10) and the second an integral power of 10. That is,

$$(1) \qquad\qquad a = u \times 10^n,$$

where $1 \leqq u < 10$ and n is an integer. For example,

$$13.6 = 1.36 \times 10^1,$$
$$.4093 = 4.093 \times 10^{-1},$$
$$6743 = 6.743 \times 10^3,$$
$$.0078 = 7.8 \times 10^{-3},$$
$$9.3 = 9.3 \times 10^0.$$

This representation, together with the product law of logarithms (Theorem 1(a)), enables us to find the logarithm of any number. For example, to find log 471, we first write 471 in the form (1):

$$471 = 4.71 \times 10^2.$$

Then

$$\log 471 = \log (4.71 \times 10^2)$$
$$= \log 4.71 + \log 10^2. \qquad \text{Theorem 1(a)}$$

Since 4.71 is between 1 and 10, its logarithm can be found in the table, log 4.71 = .6730. From the definition of a logarithm, log 10^2 = 2. Therefore

$$\log 471 = .6730 + 2$$
$$= 2.6730.$$

Illustration 1. Find log .206.

$$\begin{aligned}
\log .206 &= \log(2.06 \times 10^{-1}) \\
&= \log 2.06 + \log 10^{-1} \\
&= .3139 - 1 \\
&= -.6861.
\end{aligned}$$

Since $.206 < 1$, one expects log .206 to be negative. The reader is cautioned against writing $.3139 - 1$ as -1.3139. The latter notation means $-(1 + .3139)$, which is quite different from $-1 + .3139$.

The logarithm of any positive number a can be found similarly. Express a in the form (1):

$$a = u \times 10^n,$$

where $1 \leq u < 10$ and n an integer. Then

$$\begin{aligned}
\log a &= \log u + \log 10^n \\
&= \log u + n,
\end{aligned}$$

and since $1 \leq u < 10$, $\log u$ can be found in the table. The integer n is called the *characteristic* of log a, and the number log u is the *mantissa*. In Illustration 1 the characteristic of log .206 is -1 and the mantissa is .3139.

When working with logarithms, one often encounters the converse problem of finding the number that has a given number as its logarithm; for example, to find a if $\log a = 1.8082$. To solve this, one reverses the steps above. First express 1.8082 as a sum, the first term of which is between 0 and 1 and the second an integer:

$$\begin{aligned}
\log a &= 1.8082 \\
&= .8082 + 1.
\end{aligned}$$

Now each term is the logarithm of some number. From the table, $.8082 = \log 6.43$; from the definition of a logarithm, $1 = \log 10$. Therefore

$$\begin{aligned}
\log a &= \log 6.43 + \log 10 \\
&= \log (6.43 \times 10) \\
&= \log 64.3.
\end{aligned}$$

Since two numbers cannot have the same logarithm unless they themselves are equal, $a = 64.3$. As a rough check, we note that since $1 < \log a < 2$, we should have $10 < a < 100$.

Illustration 2. Find a if $\log a = -2.5166$.

Since $\log a < 0$, we shall expect $a < 1$. Again, we write -2.5166 as $p + n$, where $0 \leq p < 1$ and n is an integer:

$$\begin{aligned}
\log a &= -2.5166 \\
&= .4834 + (-3).
\end{aligned}$$

We must now express .4834 as the logarithm of some number. Since .4834 is not in the body of the table, we shall use instead the number closest to it, .4829, and say that .4834 = log 3.04, introducing thereby a small error. Then, proceeding as before,

$$\log a = \log 3.04 + \log 10^{-3}$$
$$= \log(3.04 \times 10^{-3})$$
$$= \log .00304.$$

Hence $a = .00304$.

The basic principle is the same in all such problems. Log a is expressed as a sum of two numbers,

$$(2) \qquad\qquad \log a = p + n,$$

where $0 \leqq p < 1$ and n is an integer, which may be negative or zero. With the aid of the table, p is expressed as the logarithm of some number u, $p = \log u$. By definition, $n = \log 10^n$. Making these substitutions in (2), we have

$$\log a = \log u + \log 10^n$$
$$= \log (u \times 10^n),$$

and $a = u \times 10^n$.

The number $-.6861$ obtained in Illustration 1 can be expressed in many forms. In addition to $.3139 - 1$ it can be written as $1.3139 - 2$, $14.3139 - 15$, or $9.3139 - 10$. The last form, in which the logarithm is expressed as a positive number minus 10, is favored by many for negative logarithms. Although traditional, usually it is less useful than the simpler form $-.6861$.

PROBLEMS

Express each number in the form $u \times 10^n$, where $1 \leqq u < 10$ and n is an integer:

1. 38.5.
2. 290.
3. .13076.
4. 1.77.
5. .063.

6. 100.
7. 47303.
8. .000551.
9. .001.

Find the logarithms of the following (for numbers of more than three significant digits use the nearest number in the table):

10. 87.6.
11. 340.
12. 13.3.
13. 23.
14. .736.
15. 5.013.

16. 4787.
17. .0567.
18. 123,500.
19. .00398.
20. .000154.

Express each number in the form $p + n$, where $0 \leq p < 1$ and n is an integer:

21. 1.7812.
22. 2.0536.
23. 4.9089.
24. 3.
25. .3452.
26. −.5222.

27. −1.479.
28. −2.2360.
29. 9.2138 − 10.
30. 8.8006 − 10.
31. 19.5431 − 20.

Find a if:

32. $\log a = 1.5539$.
33. $\log a = 1.6880$.
34. $\log a = .3090$.
35. $\log a = 2.9731$.
36. $\log a = .0607$.
37. $\log a = -.1118$.
38. $\log a = 4.8500$.
39. $\log a = -1.1723$.

40. $\log a = -1.0502$.
41. $\log a = -.0068$.
42. $\log a = -2.4949$.
43. $\log a = 2.8125 - 3$.
44. $\log a = 9.7036 - 10$.
45. $\log a = 7.1144 - 10$.
46. $\log a = 14.5694 - 16$.
47. $\log a = 29.2285 - 30$.

48. Make a table of values and sketch the graph of $y = \log x$.

Sketch the graphs of the following: (*Hint:* The properties of logarithms can be used to simplify some of the work.)

49. $y = -\log x$.
50. $y = \log (-x)$.
51. $y = \log (x + 1)$.
52. $y = \log 2x$.

53. $y = \log |x|$.
54. $y = \log x^2$.
55. $y = \log 10^x$.

56. Show that the graph of $y = \log \dfrac{1}{x}$ is falling from left to right.

10.5 Computation with Logarithms

The properties of logarithms given in Theorem 1 can be used to reduce the labor involved in multiplying and dividing numbers with many digits. We illustrate the procedure with a simple example by using logarithms to find the product of 7 and 39. Let $N = 7 \times 39$. Then

$$
\begin{aligned}
\log N &= \log (7 \times 39) \\
&= \log 7 + \log 39 \qquad \text{Theorem 1(a)} \\
&= .8451 + 1.5911 \\
&= 2.4362.
\end{aligned}
$$

We now know the logarithm of the answer. To find N, we must look for the number whose logarithm is 2.4362. It is 273, and so $N = 273$.

It is instructive to carry through the same problem using exponents. To say that $\log 7 = .8451$ means that $7 = 10^{.8451}$. Similarly, $39 = 10^{1.5911}$. Therefore

$$
\begin{aligned}
N &= 7 \times 39 \\
&= 10^{.8451} \times 10^{1.5911} \\
&= 10^{.8451+1.5911} \\
&= 10^{2.4362}.
\end{aligned}
$$

To find N, we must evaluate $10^{2.4362}$; that is, find the number of which 2.4362 is the logarithm. It is 273. We expressed 7 and 39 as powers of 10 and found their product by adding exponents. This is just the reason one adds logarithms when finding products; the numbers have been expressed as powers of 10.

Illustration 1. Compute $84.3 \times .01668$.

Let $N = 84.3 \times .01668$. Then

$$\begin{aligned} \log N &= \log 84.3 + \log .01668 \\ &= 1.9258 - 1.7773 \\ &= .1485. \end{aligned}$$

Therefore $N = 1.41$. Here we replaced .01668 by its nearest three figure equivalent, .0167, in order to be able to use the table in finding its logarithm.

Because the table gives only approximations to logarithms, one must remember that generally results of computations are not exact. In Illustration 1 we introduced an additional error by using .0167 in place of .01668.

Illustration 2. Compute $\dfrac{3 \times 46.50}{7124}$.

Let

$$N = \frac{3 \times 46.50}{7124}.$$

Then

$$\begin{aligned} \log N &= \log (3 \times 46.50) - \log 7124 && \text{Theorem 1(b)} \\ &= \log 3 + \log 46.50 - \log 7124 \\ &= .4771 + 1.6675 - 3.8525 \\ &= -1.7079 \\ &= .2921 + (-2). \end{aligned}$$

Hence $N = .0196$ (approximately).

Desk calculators have long since made logarithms obsolete for computing products and quotients, but logarithms are still useful in finding powers and roots.

Illustration 3. Compute $\sqrt[3]{134.1}$.

Let $N = \sqrt[3]{134.1}$. Then by Theorem 1(c),

$$\log N = \log (134.1^{1/3})$$

$$= \frac{1}{3} \log 134.1 = \frac{1}{3}(2.1271) = .7090.$$

Hence $N = 5.12$ (approximately).

Illustration 4. Compute $\dfrac{(.0264)\sqrt[5]{7.533}}{\sqrt{.0089}}$.

Let

$$N = \frac{(.0264)\sqrt[5]{7.533}}{\sqrt{.0089}}.$$

Then

$$\log N = \log .0264 + \log (7.533^{1/5}) - \log (.0089^{1/2})$$

$$= \log .0264 + \frac{1}{5}\log 7.533 - \frac{1}{2}\log .0089$$

$$= -1.5784 + \frac{1}{5}(.8768) - \frac{1}{2}(-2.0506)$$

$$= -1.5784 + .1754 + 1.0253$$

$$= -.3777$$

$$= .6223 + (-1).$$

Therefore $N = .419$ (approximately).

When computing with logarithms, mistakes can be avoided if one will take the time to organize the material, work carefully, and be neat. All numbers whose antecedents are not immediately obvious should be labeled. Mistakes generally arise because of carelessness and lack of neatness.

Illustration 5. Solve the equation $7^d = 68$ for d.

It is clear that $7^d = 68$ if and only if

$$\log (7^d) = \log 68;$$

that is,

$$d \log 7 = \log 68,$$

or

(1) $$d = \frac{\log 68}{\log 7} = \frac{1.8325}{.8451}.$$

This is a sequence of equivalent equations, the last of which gives the solution to our problem. The evaluation of the quotient $\dfrac{1.8325}{.8451}$ is an entirely separate arith-

metical problem and can be done by any method that is convenient. In particular, logarithms can be used, but this is not essential. The solution is $d = 2.1684$ (approximately). Note that (1) gives d and not $\log d$.

Exercise. Why in (1) can we not say

$$d = \frac{\log 68}{\log 7} = \log 68 - \log 7 = .9874?$$

Although negative numbers have no logarithms, products and quotients involving them can be evaluated by computing as if all factors were positive and then determining the sign by inspection.

Logarithms are of no help in computing a sum, though they may, of course, be used in computing the terms of a sum if these contain products or powers. A typical common error in this connection is

$$\log (13.67 + 56.1) = \log 13.67 + \log 56.1.$$

There is no property of logarithms that justifies such a statement; in fact, it is wrong.

Although the usefulness of logarithms for computational purposes has waned, they are still important. The logarithmic function is one of the most useful in mathematics and science, and appears in the mathematics of many physical theories. This is not surprising considering the importance of its close relative the exponential function.

PROBLEMS

Use logarithms to find the approximate value of the following:

1. $(43.8)(3.28)$.

2. $\dfrac{644}{23.9}$.

3. $(.7104)(.3819)$.

4. $\dfrac{.0793}{.4198}$.

5. $(.86)(234.2)(.0931)$.

6. $\dfrac{1}{6213}$.

7. $(1.80)(-6.44)(.00534)$.

8. $(73.6)\dfrac{.8123}{.5065}$.

9. $\dfrac{6}{(.000883)(.957)}$.

10. $\left(\dfrac{5.06}{361}\right)\left(\dfrac{28.4}{-1.12}\right)$.

11. $\dfrac{(787)(-343)}{(-109)(245)}$.

12. $\dfrac{13 + 18.6}{(.123)(924.1)}$.

13. $\dfrac{(6.4)(-5.8709)(-.0037)}{(156)(-1.93)}$.

Compute the reciprocal of:

14. 17.3.

15. $.03124$.

16. Compute $\log [(52.3)(.176)]$ and $(\log 52.3)(\log .176)$.

17. Compute $\log \dfrac{35}{23.7}$.

18. Compute $\dfrac{\log 35}{\log 23.7}$.

Use logarithms to find the approximate value of:

19. $(.734)^5$.

20. $\sqrt{5.67}$.

21. $\sqrt[3]{100}$.

22. 7^{11}.

23. $(23.9)^{-3}$.

24. $\sqrt[3]{.737}$.

25. $(-.00562)^3$.

26. $(.03574)^{1/2}$.

27. $\sqrt[3]{-1.17}$.

28. $\sqrt[4]{.9068}$.

29. $(1.05)^{-17}$.

30. $(16.37)^{3/2}$.

31. $19^{3/4}$.

32. $(4.36 + 27.1)^{1/2}$.

33. $(.478)^{.36}$.

34. $(3.46)(22.5)^2$.

35. $\dfrac{.0549}{(2.42)^2}$.

36. $\dfrac{15}{\sqrt{493}}$.

37. $\dfrac{(.41)(10^6)}{346^3}$.

38. $\dfrac{(48.1)(6.328)}{26.2\sqrt{477.4}}$.

39. $\sqrt{\dfrac{951}{43.4}}$.

40. $\sqrt{\dfrac{223.4}{(739)(.56)}}$.

41. $\dfrac{\sqrt[3]{-721.4}}{\sqrt{23.68}}$.

42. $\sqrt[3]{\dfrac{(13.1)^2(409)}{1.67}}$.

43. $(12^{1.4})\sqrt{19.33}$.

44. $(10^{1.57})\sqrt{.618}$.

45. $\dfrac{(3.37)^2 + 32.4}{6.87 - \sqrt{90.9}}$.

46. $\dfrac{\sqrt{32} - \sqrt{173}}{(506)(.110)}$.

47. $\log \dfrac{\sqrt{87.1}}{(1.69)(.828)}$.

48. $\dfrac{\log 15}{\log 6 - 4\log 2.87}$.

49. $[(5.34)^2 + (3.27)^2 - 2(5.34)(3.27)(-.4034)]^{1/2}$.

50. $(1)(2)(3)\cdots(10)(11)$.

51. Verify the estimate $5^{\sqrt{2}} \approx 5^{1.41} \approx 9.6727$ given in Section 9.6.

Find the approximate value of:

52. $7^{\sqrt{3}}$.

53. 2^{π}.

54. $8^{-\sqrt{5}}$.

55. $10^{\log 16.1}$.

56. $14^{\log 37}$.

Solve approximately each of the following equations:

57. $2^x = 7$.

58. $3^{-x} = 12$.

59. $6^{2x-1} = 74$.

60. $13.1^x = .0716$.

61. $.92^x = .83$.

62. $.31^x = 5$.

63. $.0638^y = .00252$.

64. $7^{2x} = 7^{x+3}$.

65. $(1.04)^n = 23$.

66. $(\frac{3}{7})^{x-4} = 17$.

67. $3^{(x^2)} = 130$.

68. $3(7^x) = 13^{2x}$.

69. $2^{|x|} = 40$.

70. $\log x^2 = 6\log 3$.

71. $\log(x + 2) - \log 3 = \log 12$.

72. $\dfrac{7(4^x) - 3}{10} = .238$.

73. $2^x + \dfrac{10}{2^x} = 7$.

74. $9^x - 2(3^x) - 35 = 0$.

75. $\log(4x + 12) = 2 + \log x$.

76. If $A = P(1 + r)^n$, find n in terms of A, P, and r.

77. Find the radius of the circle whose area is 874 square inches.
78. The area of a sphere of radius r is $4\pi r^2$. Find the area of the earth if its radius is 3,959 miles.
79. A body falling freely in a vacuum falls in t seconds a distance s feet given by $s = 16.1\ t^2$. How long will it take to fall a distance of 100 feet?
80. The volume of a sphere of radius r is $\frac{4}{3}\pi r^3$. (a) Find the volume of a sphere of radius 6.73 inches. (b) Find the radius of a sphere whose volume is 120 cubic inches.
81. The period of a pendulum is the time required for it to make one complete swing across and back. For a simple pendulum of length l feet swinging through a small arc, the period T (in seconds) is given by

$$T = 2\pi\ \sqrt{\frac{l}{g}},$$

where $g = 32.2$. (a) Find the period of a pendulum 11.7 feet long. (b) How long must the pendulum be if the period is to be 2.25 seconds?
82. It can be shown that if a, b, and c are the lengths of the sides of a triangle, its area A is given by

$$A = \sqrt{s(s - a)(s - b)(s - c)},$$

where $s = \frac{1}{2}(a + b + c)$. Find the area of the triangle whose sides have lengths 27.3, 10.7, and 22.6 feet.
83. In 1940 the population of a certain town was 36,000. Assuming that the growth of the town is such that t years later its population P is given by

$$P = 36{,}000 \left(\frac{5}{4}\right)^{t/10},$$

find the population in 1960. When will the population reach 60,000?
84. A culture of bacteria was started with 1500 bacteria. It is known that the growth of the culture is such that the number N of bacteria present t hours later is given by

$$N = 1500 \left(\frac{23}{15}\right)^{t/12}.$$

Find the number of bacteria present after six, twelve, and eighteen hours. How long will it be before there are ten times as many bacteria as there were originally?
85. The mass of a quantity of radium continually decreases due to loss by radiation. If A_0 is the initial mass—that is, the amount at some particular time—it is known that after t years the mass A of the amount remaining is given by

$$A = A_0 \left(\frac{1}{2}\right)^{t/1600}.$$

(a) If the initial mass is .365 grams, how much is left after 800 years; after 3,200 years? In how many years will the amount be one half of the initial amount?
(b) Show that no matter what the initial amount is, the time required for a quantity of radium to decrease to one half of the initial amount is always the same. This time is called the *half life* of radium.

86. It can be shown that for all positive integers m

$$\frac{2^2 \cdot 4^2 \cdot 6^2 \cdots (2m)^2}{1^2 \cdot 3^2 \cdot 5^2 \cdots (2m+1)^2}(2m+1) < \frac{\pi}{2} < \frac{2^2 \cdot 4^2 \cdot 6^2 \cdots (2m)^2}{1^2 \cdot 3^2 \cdot 5^2 \cdots (2m+1)^2}(2m+2).$$

Verify this for $m = 2$, 5, and 10. It can be shown that for large m the two expressions are almost equal.

10.6   Interpolation

The table of logarithms in the back of the book lists logarithms of numbers with three significant digits. To find the logarithm of a number such as 3.183, we have been using the entry for 3.18 with the realization that this introduced a small error. We can achieve a more accurate result if we observe that log 3.183 must lie between log 3.18 and log 3.19, and use a simple proportion to estimate its value as follows.

From the table, we have log 3.18 = .5024 and log 3.19 = .5038.

$$
\begin{array}{cc}
a & \log a \\
\end{array}
$$

$$.010\left[\begin{array}{c} .003\left[\begin{array}{cc} 3.180 & .5024 \\ 3.183 & \log 3.183 \end{array}\right]d \\ 3.190 \qquad .5038 \end{array}\right].0014$$

Since 3.183 is $\dfrac{.003}{.010}$, or .3, of the way between 3.180 and 3.190, it is reasonable to suppose that log 3.183 will be approximately .3 of the way between .5024 and .5038. Therefore d, the amount we should add to .5024 to obtain log 3.183 (approximately), must be such that

(1) $$\frac{d}{.0014} = \frac{.003}{.010} = .3.$$

From this, $d = (.3)(.0014) = .0004$. There is no point in computing d to more than four decimal places since the logarithms in the table are given to no greater accuracy. Hence log 3.183 = .5024 + d = .5028.

This interpolated value is not as accurate as that obtained from a five place table of logarithms (from such a table, log 3.183 = .50284), but it gives a far better estimate than our former practice of using the value of log 3.18.

We can give a geometric picture of the interpolation process. The graph of $y = \log x$ for x in the vicinity of 3.183 is sketched schematically in Figure 10.4. For purposes of illustration, we have drawn it more curved than it actually is. Let A, M, and B be the points on the graph whose x-coordinates are 3.18, 3.183, and 3.19, respectively. Their y-coordinates are the logarithms of these numbers. We know the y-coordinates of A and B; our problem is to approximate the y-coordinate of M.

The distance $EM = \log 3.183$. Actually, the graph curves only slightly between A and B; and so P, which is on the line joining A and B, is near M, and EP will be a close approximation to $\log 3.183$. By similar triangles,

$$\frac{DP}{CB} = \frac{AD}{AC}, \quad \text{or} \quad \frac{d}{.0014} = \frac{.003}{.010},$$

which is equation (1). $EP = ED + d = .5024 + .0004 = .5028$. The accuracy of the approximation depends on how near P is to M.

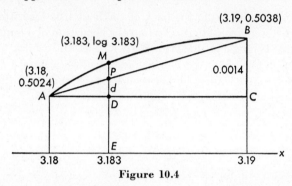

Figure 10.4

By a similar procedure, when given $\log N$, we can find N more accurately than before. For example, let us find N if $\log N = 1.8625$. From the table, we have $\log 72.80 = 1.8621$ and $\log 72.90 = 1.8627$. Let $h = N - 72.80$.

$$.10 \left[h \begin{bmatrix} a & \log a \\ 72.80 & 1.8621 \\ N & 1.8625 \end{bmatrix} .0004 \\ 72.90 \quad 1.8627 \right] .0006$$

Then, as before,

$$\frac{h}{.10} = \frac{.0004}{.0006},$$

and $h = .07$. Therefore $N = 72.80 + .07 = 72.87$ (approximately).

The interpolation method given here is not limited to logarithms; it can be used with any table and is satisfactory if the values of the function are not changing too rapidly. If they are changing rapidly, more sophisticated interpolation methods must be used to obtain good results.

PROBLEMS

Using interpolation, find the logarithm of each of the following:

1. 71.28.
2. .03571.
3. 554.4.
4. .0006895.
5. 23.11.
6. 4.1317.
7. 674.196.

Find N to four significant figures if:

8. $\log N = .9314$.

9. $\log N = 2.0174$.

10. $\log N = -.3006$.

11. $\log N = -1.7888$.

12. $\log N = 1.9947$.

Evaluate:

13. $\dfrac{(87.36)(.1717)}{(9.039)(11.14)}$.

14. $\sqrt{65.85}$.

15. $\sqrt[3]{.8231}$.

16. $(107.46)^{2/5}$.

10.7 Logarithms to Other Bases

Although the number 10 plays a central role in logarithms, nowhere is it really essential. Neither in the definition nor in the proofs of the properties of logarithms were any particular properties of 10 used. This suggests that one might just as well have selected 7 rather than 10 and, instead of asking for a number a such that $10^a = 68$, have asked for a number d such that

$$(1) \qquad\qquad 7^d = 68.$$

Such a d might with equal propriety be called a "logarithm" of 68, and this we shall do. To distinguish between the two, we write

$$d = \log_7 68, \quad \text{and} \quad a = \log_{10} 68 = \log 68,$$

7 or 10 being the *base* of the systems of logarithms in each case. In Illustration 5 in Section 10.5 we solved (1) for d. We have then

$$\log_7 68 = 2.1684, \quad \text{and} \quad \log_{10} 68 = 1.8325.$$

Any positive number c other than 1 can be used as a base for a system of logarithms, since for each $b > 0$, the equation $c^a = b$ has a unique solution for a. We call a the *logarithm of b to the base c*, and write $a = \log_c b$.

Definition. Let c be a positive number different from 1. For each $b > 0$, $log_c\, b$ is that number for which $c^{\log_c b} = b$.

For example,

$$\log_2 16 = 4, \qquad \text{since } 2^4 = 16;$$
$$\log_5 \tfrac{1}{125} = -3, \qquad \text{since } 5^{-3} = \tfrac{1}{125};$$
$$\log_{10} .1 = -1, \qquad \text{since } 10^{-1} = .1;$$
$$\log_8 2 = \tfrac{1}{3}, \qquad \text{since } 8^{1/3} = 2.$$

The properties of logarithms in Theorem 1 are valid for logarithms to any base, the proof being the same as that given there with c in place of 10.

For $c > 1$, the graph of $y = \log_c x$ has the same general characteristics as the graph of $y = \log_{10} x$, as one can see by considering the graph of the related equation $y = c^x$. If $0 < c < 1$, it has the general shape of the reflection in the x-axis of the graph of $y = \log_{10} x$.

Exercise A.   Using the graphs of $y = c^x$ for $c > 1$ and $0 < c < 1$, show that for each $b > 0$ there is just one a such that $c^a = b$.

Exercise B.   Verify Theorem 1 for base 2 with $u = 64$, $v = 16$, $r = \frac{1}{2}$.

Exercise C.   Why is 1 not suitable as a base for logarithms?

If s and t are two bases, the logarithms of all numbers to the base s are a fixed multiple of those to the base t. That is, $\log_s b = k \cdot \log_t b$ for all b, where k depends only on s and t. We shall prove this and determine the number k. By the definition of a logarithm, $b = s^{\log_s b}$. Take the logarithm to the base t of both sides and use Theorem 1(c):

$$\log_t b = \log_t (s^{\log_s b}) = (\log_s b)(\log_t s).$$

Therefore

$$(2) \qquad\qquad \log_s b = \frac{1}{\log_t s} \log_t b,$$

and we have shown that $k = \dfrac{1}{\log_t s}$.

Although any positive number except 1 is a legitimate base for a system of logarithms, in practice only one other number besides 10 is used. It is an irrational number, commonly denoted by the letter e, which cannot be defined here, but is approximately 2.71828. Relation (2) with $s = 10$ and $t = e$ shows that for all b

$$(3) \qquad\qquad \log_{10} b = \frac{1}{\log_e 10} \log_e b \approx .43429 \log_e b.$$

Because 10 is the basis of our number system, logarithms to the base 10 are the most convenient for computational purposes. In the calculus and its applications that use the logarithmic function, $f(x) = \log_e x$, certain formulas derived from this become appreciably simpler if e is chosen as the base. For this reason, e is used as the base for all mathematical work other than computing. Logarithms to the base e are called *natural logarithms*, and tables of them can be found in any handbook of mathematical tables. Logarithms to the base 10 are called *common logarithms*. Strange as it may seem, natural logarithms are easier to compute than common logarithms. In practice, tables of common logarithms are constructed by making first a table of natural logarithms. These are then converted to common logarithms, according to (3), by multiplying each by $\dfrac{1}{\log_e 10} \approx .43429$.

PROBLEMS

Find:

1. $\log_2 8$.

2. $\log_2 \frac{1}{2}$.

3. $\log_6 6$.

4. $\log_{10} .001$.

5. $\log_{100} .001$.

6. $\log_e e^3$.

7. $\log_2 \sqrt{2}$.

8. $\log_3 \sqrt[5]{3}$.

9. $\log_5 .2$.

10. $\log_3 \dfrac{1}{\sqrt{27}}$.

11. $\log_{10} 1,000,000$.

12. $\log_4 1$.

13. $\log_9 3$.

14. $\log_{1/2} 32$.

15. $\log_{\sqrt{7}} 7$.

16. $\log_2 \frac{1}{32}$.

17. $\log_8 16$.

18. $\log_{16} 8$.

Find N if:

19. $\log_{10} N = 4$.

20. $\log_{10} N = -2$.

21. $\log_3 N = 2$.

22. $\log_8 N = \frac{1}{3}$.

23. $\log_4 N = 0$.

24. $\log_e N = \frac{1}{2}$.

Find c if:

25. $\log_c 36 = 2$.

26. $\log_c 2 = \frac{1}{3}$.

27. $\log_c 9 = -1$.

28. $\log_c e = 1$.

29. $\log_c \frac{16}{25} = 2$.

30. $\log_c 1 = 0$.

Without actually finding the logarithm, locate each of the following between two consecutive integers:

31. $\log_{10} 26$.

32. $\log_3 15$.

33. $\log_2 19.42$.

34. $\log_2 \frac{1}{3}$.

35. $\log_2 \sqrt[3]{2}$.

36. $\log_e 10$.

37. $\log_5 4$.

38. $\log_7 .001$.

39. $\log_e .206$.

40. Prove that for every base c, $\log_c 1 = 0$ and $\log_c c = 1$.

41. Prove Theorem 1(a) for logarithms to any base.

By solving the appropriate exponential equation, find the following:

42. $\log_2 10$.

43. $\log_3 134$.

44. $\log_2 28.3$.

45. $\log_3 28.3$.

46. $\log_{10} 28.3$.

47. $\log_3 \sqrt{3}$.

48. $\log_e 10$.

49. $\log_7 .154$.

50. $\log_e 1.75$.

51. $\log_e 56$.

52. $\log_e .7861$.

53. $\log_2 .0403$.

54. $\log_e e^2$.

55. $\log_e \dfrac{1}{e}$.

By considering the graph of the related exponential equation, sketch the graph of:

56. $y = \log_2 x$.

57. $y = \log_e x$.

58. $y = \log_{1/3} x$.

59. Prove that $\log_{10} e = \dfrac{1}{\log_e 10}$.

60. It can be shown that when n is large, $\left(1 + \dfrac{1}{n}\right)^n$ is near e, and that the larger n is, the nearer it will be to e. Find an approximation to e by evaluating the expression for $n = 10$. Find a better approximation by choosing $n = 100$.

61. Solve the equation $\frac{1}{2}(e^x - e^{-x}) = 3$.

Chapter 11

Approximate Solution
of Equations

11.1 Approximations to Roots

In applications of mathematics it is a problem of some importance to find the solution or solutions of a numerical equation. As we have pointed out, there are relatively few equations whose exact solutions can be found by algebraic methods. For most equations one must be content with approximations to the solutions. Typical examples are

$$(1) \qquad\qquad \begin{aligned} x^3 - 3x^2 &= x - 5, \\ x + \log x &= 0, \\ 2^x - 3x &= 2. \end{aligned}$$

There are many methods for approximating the real roots of equations, some being better adapted to certain types of equations than others. Unfortunately, all of them involve computing, the amount of which increases markedly as greater accuracy is obtained. The procedure we shall describe is simple, works with any equation likely to be encountered in practice, and is capable of approximating a root to any desired degree of accuracy. It is, however, applicable only to real roots, is not too efficient, and can be laborious.

Using the notation for functions, we can write any equation containing x in the form $f(x) = 0$ by moving to the left side all terms to the right of the equals sign. If we were solving (1), we should let

$$f(x) = x^3 - 3x^2 - x + 5.$$

The solutions of (1) are the zeros of f; that is, those numbers r for which $f(r) = 0$.

If $f(x)$ is any such expression, consider the graph of the equation $y = f(x)$. It might look something like the sketch in Figure 11.1. Let $A(a, f(a))$ and

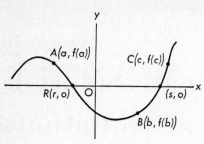

B(b, f(b)) be two points on the curve for which $f(a) > 0$ and $f(b) < 0$. Then A is above the x-axis and B below, and at some point R between A and B the curve must cross the x-axis. If r is the x-coordinate of R, then $f(r) = 0$. Of course, the curve may cross the x-axis more than once between A and B. Similarly, if $f(c) > 0$, we should know there is a root s between b and c.

Figure 11.1

The above argument seems very plausible, especially when one looks at Figure 11.1. It does depend, however, on the continuity of the graph between A and B. If there had been a gap in the graph at the point where the curve would normally have crossed the x-axis at R, then no root r would have existed there. For example, let

$$f(x) = -\frac{x+1}{x}.$$

The graph of $y = f(x)$ is sketched in Figure 11.2. We see that $f(-\frac{1}{2}) = 1$ and $f(1) = -2$, yet there is no r, $-\frac{1}{2} < r < 1$, for which $f(r) = 0$. The graph is not continuous between A and B; that section cannot be drawn without lifting the pencil from the paper. Between $C(-3, -\frac{2}{3})$ and $A(-\frac{1}{2}, 1)$ the graph is continuous.

Since $f(-3) < 0$ and $f(-\frac{1}{2}) > 0$, we should know that f had at least one zero between -3 and $-\frac{1}{2}$ even if we could not recognize it immediately from the equation.

We shall say that a function f is continuous if its graph, $y = f(x)$, is continuous. Though not sufficiently precise for rigorous proofs, this definition furnishes an intuitive picture adequate for our purposes. Translating the concept illustrated in Figure 11.1 from geometric to algebraic terminology, we have:

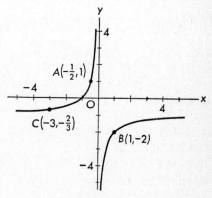

Figure 11.2

Theorem 1. If a function f is continuous in the interval $a \leq x \leq b$ and if $f(a) > 0$ and $f(b) < 0$ (or $f(a) < 0$ and $f(b) > 0$), then there is at least one r, where $a < r < b$, such that $f(r) = 0$.

The proof of this theorem is too advanced to be given here. It is an existence theorem, and the proof gives no indication of where the zero is, other than that it lies between a and b. This does not mean that the theorem is of no practical value; it is the basis of our method.

Theorem 2.   A polynomial is continuous everywhere.

The proof of this cannot be given here either. It enables us to use Theorem 1 in approximating the zeros of polynomials, as we shall now illustrate.

Let us approximate the roots of

(2) $$x^3 - 3x^2 - x + 5 = 0.$$

We let

$$f(x) = x^3 - 3x^2 - x + 5,$$

and wish to find approximately numbers r such that $f(r) = 0$. First we locate the roots between consecutive integers by making a table of values of x and $f(x)$:

x	$f(x)$
-2	-13
-1	2
0	5
1	2
2	-1
3	2 .

By Theorem 2, f is continuous for all x. Since $f(-2) < 0$ and $f(-1) > 0$, by Theorem 1 there is a root between -2 and -1. There is another between 1 and 2, and a third between 2 and 3. As a third degree polynomial, $f(x)$ cannot have more than three zeros, and so we know there are no others. Using the table, we have sketched the graph of $y = x^3 - 3x^2 - x + 5$ in Figure 11.3.

We shall now find a better approximation to the root r that lies between 1 and 2 by locating it between consecutive tenths. In Figure 11.4 we have sketched roughly on an enlarged scale that section of the curve between $A_1(1, 2)$ and $B_1(2, -1)$. One could, starting with 1.1, evaluate f at each of 1.1, 1.2, etc. until two num-

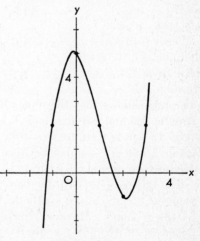

Figure 11.3

bers were found between which the graph crossed the x-axis, but this would seem to entail unnecessary calculation. Instead, let us try to estimate where it will cross.

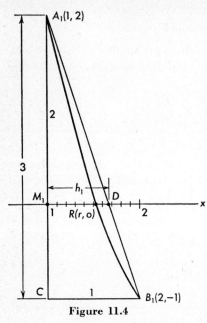

Figure 11.4

Since the graph is not curving very much between A_1 and B_1, the point R at which it crosses the x-axis will be near the point of intersection D of the x-axis and the line joining A_1 and B_1. We can find h_1, the distance between M_1 and D, by similar triangles. We have

$$\frac{M_1 D}{CB_1} = \frac{M_1 A_1}{CA_1}; \quad \text{that is,} \quad \frac{h_1}{1} = \frac{2}{3},$$

and $h_1 = \frac{2}{3}$. The x-coordinate of D is $1 + h_1 = \frac{5}{3} \approx 1.7$. How near this number is to r will depend on how curved the graph is in the section between A_1 and B_1. Essentially, we are interpolating between 1 and 2 by the same method we used to find N when given $\log N$.

Having estimated that the curve crosses the x-axis in the vicinity of 1.7, we shall compute $f(x)$ first for x's near that number, hoping to find quickly two values of $f(x)$ of opposite sign:

x	$f(x)$
1.5	.125
1.6	−.184
1.7	−.457 .

The table shows that the root r lies between 1.5 and 1.6. The difference between 1.5 and r is less than .1, so we can say that 1.5 is an approximation of r that is accurate to within .1 of a unit. We could equally well have taken 1.6 or any number between 1.5 and 1.6 as an approximation of r. Any of these would be accurate to within .1.

The table of powers in the back of the book is helpful in computing the values of $f(x)$. So also is synthetic division. For a polynomial $f(x)$, we know by the remainder theorem (Section 5.5) that $f(a)$ is the remainder obtained upon dividing $f(x)$ by $x - a$. For a's other than simple integers, often $f(a)$ can be computed most quickly by using this theorem and synthetic division.

A still better approximation of r can be found by locating r between consecutive hundredths. A sketch of the section of the curve between $A_2(1.5, .125)$ and $B_2(1.6, -.184)$ is shown in Figure 11.5. Again, to avoid unnecessary computation, we make a preliminary estimate of the location of R by a simple proportion:

$$\frac{h_2}{.1} = \frac{.125}{.309}, \quad \text{or} \quad h_2 = \frac{.125}{.309}(.1) \approx .04.$$

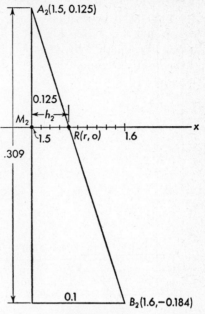

Hence $r \approx 1.5 + h_2 \approx 1.54$. Computing $f(x)$ for values of x near 1.54, we have

x	$f(x)$
1.53	.028877
1.54	$-.002536$.

Therefore $1.53 < r < 1.54$, and 1.53 (or 1.54) is an approximation of r to within .01 of a unit.

Figure 11.5

By continuing the process, we can find an approximation to any desired degree of accuracy, but the work does become laborious.

The other two roots of (2) can be approximated similarly. Note that the graph of the polynomial curves markedly between $(2, -1)$ and $(3,2)$ (Figure 11.3). Hence an estimate of the root lying between 2 and 3 obtained by simple proportion would be so much in error as to be useless.

As another example, we approximate the roots of the equation

$$\log x = -x.$$

Let $f(x) = x + \log x$. We shall assume, as can be shown, that f is continuous for all $x > 0$, permitting us to use Theorem 1. We make a table of values to find the approximate location of the zeros of f:

x	$\log x$	$f(x) = x + \log x$
.001	-3	-2.999
.01	-2	-1.99
.1	-1	$-.9$
1	0	1
2	.3010	2.3010 .

There is a zero r of f between .1 and 1. It is not difficult to show this is the only one.

We shall now locate r between consecutive tenths. Since the graph of $y = \log x$, and hence that of $y = x + \log x$, is curving rapidly between $x = .1$ and $x = 1$ (see Figure 10.3 in Section 10.3), there is no point in trying to estimate r by a simple proportion. We compute $f(x)$ at intervals of one tenth, beginning with .1:

x	$\log x$	$f(x)$
.1	-1	$-.9$
.2	$-.6990$	$-.4990$
.3	$-.5229$	$-.2229$
.4	$-.3979$	$.0021$.

We see that $.3 < r < .4$.

Let us estimate r to within .01. From Figure 11.6,

$$\frac{h}{.1} = \frac{.2229}{.2250}.$$

Therefore $h \approx .10$ and $r \approx .3 + h \approx .40$.

Figure 11.6

x	$\log x$	$f(x)$
.39	$-.4089$	$-.0189$
.40	$-.3979$	$.0021$

Therefore $.39 < r < .40$, and .39 is an approximation of r to within .01.
The next step gives

x	$\log x$	$f(x)$
.399	$-.3990$	0
.400	$-.3979$	$.0021$.

It looks as if we were fortunate enough to have found r exactly, but this is an illusion. Our logarithm table gives values only to four decimal places. Using a five place table, we have

x	$\log x$	$f(x)$
.399	$-.39903$	$-.00003$
.400	$-.39794$	$.00206$,

and $.399 < r < .400$. With the aid of a seven place table of logarithms, we can show that $.39901 < r < .39902$ and say that $r = .39901$ to within $.00001$.

For some equations the initial approximation to a solution can be found more quickly by graphing two related equations rather than by making a table of values as we did in the example above. If in that example we graph the equations $y = \log x$ and $y = -x$, the x-coordinates of their points of intersection will be the solutions of $\log x = -x$. The two graphs are shown in Figure 11.7, and we see that the point of intersection is approximately $(.4, -.4)$.

This method is especially useful in determining the number of solutions and their magnitudes. For this, rough sketches, which can be quickly drawn, usually suffice. From even a much cruder sketch than that in Figure 11.7 we could have seen that there is only one solution and that it lies between .1 and 1.

When finding the roots of a polynomial equation with integral coefficients, it sometimes pays to check first for rational roots and, if there are any, to remove the corresponding factors. For example, if solving

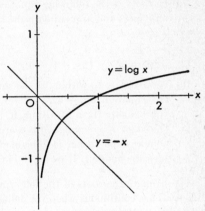

Figure 11.7

$$(3) \qquad 3x^4 - 2x^3 + 3x^2 - 11x + 6 = 0,$$

one would first check for possible rational roots using Theorem 3 in Section 5.7. Such a root is $\frac{2}{3}$, and (3) can be written

$$3(x - \tfrac{2}{3})(x^3 + x - 3) = 0.$$

The remaining roots of (3) must be the roots of $x^3 + x - 3 = 0$, which, being of lower degree, is easier to work with than (3).

PROBLEMS

1. Approximate to within .01 the other two roots of the equation $x^3 - 3x^2 - x + 5 = 0$ discussed in the text.

2. Use the method of the text to approximate the positive root of $x^2 = 5$ to within .001.

3. Approximate to within .01 the root between -1 and -2 of the equation $2x^3 - 9x^2 - 12x + 8 = 0$. Check your result by finding a rational root and hence all the roots.

4. The equation $x^3 + 5x + 2 = 0$ has only one real root. Approximate it to within .01.

Each of the following equations has exactly one root in the indicated interval. Approximate this root to within .1.

5. $x^3 - 2x^2 + x + 1 = 0$; between -1 and 0.
6. $x^3 - 4x^2 + 2x - 2 = 0$; between 3 and 4.
7. $x^3 + 2x^2 + 4x + 5 = 0$; between -2 and -1.
8. $x^4 - 2x^2 + x - 6 = 0$; between 1 and 2.
9. $x^4 - 6x^3 + 2x^2 + 30x - 35 = 0$; between 1 and 2.
10. $x^4 - 6x^3 + 2x^2 + 30x - 35 = 0$; between 2 and 3.

All the roots of the following equations are real. Locate each root between consecutive integers and approximate the largest to within .01:

11. $x^3 - 2x + 1 = 0$.
12. $x^3 - 4x + 1 = 0$.
13. $-2x^3 + 3x^2 + 12x + 1 = 0$.
14. $x^4 + 2x^3 - 10x^2 - 14x + 21 = 0$.
15. $x^3 - 2.36x - 1.05 = 0$.

16. Approximate to within .01 the single real root of $x^3 - 2.13x = 4.7$.
17. The equation $8x^3 - 8x + 1 = 0$ has three real roots between -2 and 2. Approximate them to within .1.
18. The edges of a rectangular box are 4, 5, and 7 inches. A larger box containing 30 more cubic inches is to be made by increasing the length of each edge by the same amount. How much is this increase?

Approximate the roots of the following to within .01. You may assume that all functions are continuous wherever defined.

19. $\log x = x - 2$.
20. $\log_{\frac{1}{2}}(x + 2) = \frac{1}{2}x$.
21. $\log x = \dfrac{1}{x}$.
22. $2^x = -x + 2$.
23. $2^{-x} + x^2 - 3 = 0$.
24. $\dfrac{(1 + j)^4 - 1}{j} = 4.3$.
25. $e^{(-x^2)} = x$.

11.2 Sets of Equations

Occasionally, the method of the last section can be used to approximate the real solutions of pairs of equations in two unknowns, giving us an algebraic alternative to the graphical method of Section 8.3.

As an example, let us approximate the real solutions of the pair of equations in Illustration 1 of that section:

$$(1) \qquad y^2 = \frac{2}{x}, \quad x^2 + y^2 = 4.$$

If we substitute $\dfrac{2}{x}$ for y^2 in the second of these, we have

$$x^2 + \frac{2}{x} = 4$$

or

$$\frac{x^3 - 4x + 2}{x} = 0.$$

The roots of this are those of

$$(2) \qquad x^3 - 4x + 2 = 0.$$

The roots of (2) lie between -3 and -2, 0 and 1, and 1 and 2. The first of these is not of interest since it does not give a real value for y. Using our method of successive approximations, we find that the second root lies between .539 and .540 and the third between 1.675 and 1.676. Corresponding to .539, the values of y as determined from the equation $y^2 = \dfrac{2}{x}$ are ± 1.926. Those corresponding to 1.675 are ± 1.092. The approximate real solutions of (1) are $(.539, \pm 1.926)$ and $(1.675, \pm 1.092)$.

PROBLEMS

Using algebraic methods, approximate to within .1 the real solutions of the following pairs of equations:

1. $y = \dfrac{1}{x}$, $x^2 + y^2 = 3$.

2. $y = \frac{1}{4}x^3$, $y = 2x - 1$.

3. $x^2 + y = 1$, $x + y^2 = 2$.

4. $y = \dfrac{2}{x^2 + 1}$, $x^2 + y^2 = 7$.

5. $y = \log x$, $y = \dfrac{1}{x^2}$.

6. $y = 2^{-x}$, $y^2 = x$.

ANSWERS TO ODD-NUMBERED PROBLEMS

Section 1.1

5. $2, 1\frac{1}{2}$.
7. All $\subset R$, $A \subset P$, $A \subset B$, $B \subset P$, $C \subset P$, $D \subset P$, $D \subset A$, $D \subset B$, $D \subset C$.
15. $T \subset S$, $T \subset F$; all multiples of 12.

Section 1.2

1. Addition: A; multiplication: A, C.
3. No.
5. No.
7. Yes.
9. No.

Section 1.3

1. $\pm (1, 2, 4, 8, 17, 34, 68, 136)$.
3. 24, 48, 72, 96.
5. 4, 126, 1, 0, -9, -1.
13. 2, 3; 3, 5; 5, 7; 11, 13; 17, 19; 29, 31; 41, 43; 59, 61; 71, 73; 101, 103; 107, 109; 137, 139; 149, 151; 179, 181; 191, 193; 197, 199.
15. $990 = 2 \cdot 3^2 \cdot 5 \cdot 11$, $729 = 3^6$, $9016 = 2^3 \cdot 7^2 \cdot 23$, $4155 = 3 \cdot 5 \cdot 277$.
17. No.

Section 1.4

9. 1.5.
11. $.111\cdots$, 1.
13. $.2857142\cdots$, 285714.
15. $.3636\cdots$, 36.
17. $.7692307\cdots$, 769230.

Section 1.5

1. No.
3. 25. Rational.
5. All.

Section 2.1

1. $C2$.
3. $D2$.
5. $D2$.
7. $C1, C1$.
9. $C1, D1$.
11. $C2, A2$.
13. $D2, D1$.
15. $D2$.
17. $7xy$.
19. $2zx + 3z$.

Section 2.3

1. $-3, 7$.
3. $5, -7u, a(x + y), w$.
5. $\frac{10}{8} + b, a - b$.
7. $2, -8$.
9. $\frac{1}{4}, x, y$.
11. $-5, -x + y + z$.
13. $5x + 5y + 5z; 5x + 5(y + z)$.
15. $6 \cdot 2; 2 \cdot 3 \cdot 2$.
17. $\frac{1}{3}(x + b), \frac{x}{3} + \frac{b}{3}$.
19. Sum.
21. Sum.
23. Product.
25. Product.
27. Product.
29. Sum.

Section 2.4

1. 5^6.
3. 6^6.
5. $(\frac{2}{7})^5$.
7. a^7b^7.
9. a^{15}.
11. $5a^3b$.
13. $2y^2(1 + y^2)$.

15. $x(2 + 9x)$.
17. $3x^7y^5$.
21. $2x^6(2 + x^6)$.
23. $x(8xy^2 + 16y + 15)$.

Section 2.5

1. $7x^2 + 4x + 6$.
3. $6x^2 + 3xy + 4y^2$.
5. $x(53 + 11x + 52x^2)$.
7. $4x^2 + 10a^2x + 34a^2$.

Section 2.6

1. $x^2 + 16x + 60$.
3. $ax + \frac{2}{5}a + \frac{3}{2}x + \frac{3}{5}$.
5. $x^3 + 3x^2 + x$.
7. $x^3 + ax^2 + (4a + 7)x + a(4a + 7)$.
9. $3x^4 + 7x^3 + 25x^2 + 21x + 40$.
11. $x^3 + 3x^2y + 3xy^2 + y^3$.
13. $x^3 + 2ax^2 + 2a^2x + a^3$.
17. $6x^3 + 7x^2 + 67x + 25$.
19. $5y^3 + 8y^2 + 15y + 27$.

Section 2.7

1. Z.
3. I.
5. I.
7. I.
9. N.
11. $C1, Z$.
13. $C2, C1, N$.
15. I, Z.
17. $Z, C1, N$.

Section 2.9

3. 0.
5. 0.
7. 5.
9. 25.
11. $-\frac{75}{16}$.
13. -27.
19. $10b^2$.
21. $(b + c)^2$.
23. $-a(b + 11)^2$.
25. x^3b^8.
27. $-16b^6z^9$.
29. $-15abd$.

31. $-(x - y)^2$.
33. $ab + cd$.

Section 2.10

15. $5x - y + 4x^2$.
17. $-7x^3 + 31x^2 - x$.
19. $5x^2 + \frac{25}{2}x$.
21. $5y^2 + 7y - \dfrac{10}{y}$.
23. $2x^4 + x^3y - 6x^2y^2 - 4y^4$.
25. $3x^2 - 19x + 28$.
27. $x^2 - y^2$.
29. $-3y^2 + 4y + 4$.
31. $-acx^2 + (bc + ad)x - bd$.
33. $4s^2t^2 - 20st^3 + 25t^4$.
35. $a^2 - b^2 + 2a + 1$.
37. $u^2 + 2uv + v^2 - w^2$.
39. $12x^4 - 18x^3 - 30x^2$.
41. $x^3 + a^3$.
43. $x^4 - 2x^2y^2 + y^4$.
45. $-4(x^2 - 2x + 2)$.
47. $2(3x^2 + x^2y - 3xy - 3xy^2 + y^2)$.
49. $-7x + 5$.
51. $8x(7x + 4)$.
53. $2x - 3$.
55. $10x + z - \frac{9}{2}$.
57. $b^{12} - a^{12}$.
59. $(x - 5)(5x^3 - 23x^2 + 11x + 15)$.
61. 3.
63. -9.
65. $x - 3 - b, y + b + 3$.

Section 2.11

1. $y(y + 3)$.
3. $ab(a + b)$.
5. Impossible.
7. Impossible.
9. $\left(\dfrac{1}{a} + \dfrac{1}{y}\right)\left(\dfrac{1}{a} - \dfrac{1}{y}\right)$.
11. $(x + \sqrt{5})(x - \sqrt{5})$.
13. $x(3x^2 - 5x + 4)$.
15. $(2x + 5)(-x + 3)$.
17. $a(2 - 5b)(1 - 3b)$.
19. $(a - 5)(a - 13)$.
21. $(a + 13)(a + 5)$.

Section 2.11—continued

7. $3y, \frac{1}{3}x$.

23. $(x + 2y + z)(x + 2y - z)$.

15. (a) 0; (b) none; (c) none; (d) 1; (e) none.

25. $(3 - 4t)(-7 + 2t)$.

27. $c(6a + b)(a - b)$.

19. 0.

29. $(5u - 2)(x - y)$.

21. -7.

31. $(ax - 7)(ax + 4)$.

23. No solution.

33. $5(x - 1)^3(x - 5)$.

25. (b) No.

35. $(2x^2 + 5)(x^2 + 6)$.

37. $(y + 1)(y - 1)(y + 4)$.

Section 2.15

39. $x^2(x^2 + 1)(x + 3)$.

3. (a) $\dfrac{-7}{2}$; (b) $-\dfrac{-(a + x)}{5}$; (c) $\dfrac{-1}{-4}$.

41. $(7a - b)(1 - x)$.

43. $(2x + 1)(4x^2 - 2x + 1)$.

11. 2.

45. $(x + 1)^2(x - 1)$.

13. Not possible.

47. $(x + a)(x - a + 1)$.

15. Not possible.

49. $(-x + 2y)(3a + b)$.

17. $-\frac{1}{4}$.

51. $d(a - c)$.

19. 20.

53. $-3(x - 1)(x - 3)$.

21. $-7(a + c)(x + y)$.

55. $(x^2 - y^2)^2$.

23. Yes, if $a \neq 0, b \neq -c$.

57. $-4x^7(-14x^2 + 1)^2(49x^2 - 2)$.

25. $\frac{7}{5}$.

27. $\frac{3}{2}, a \neq 0, a \neq b$.

Section 2.12

29. $-\frac{5}{3}x^3a, a \neq 0, x \neq 0$.

31. Not possible; $x \neq -y$.

1. $x^2 + x + 1 = (x + 3)(x - 2) + 7$.

3. $3x^4 + x^2 = (x^2 + 1)(3x^2 - 2) + 2$.

33. $\dfrac{1}{a^{n-1}}, a \neq 0, x \neq 0$.

5. $x^4 + 8x^3 + 5x^2 - 39x + 10$
    $= (x+6)(x^3+2x^2-7x+3) - 8$.

35. $\dfrac{6}{-7 + 2a}, a \neq 0, a \neq \dfrac{7}{2}$.

7. $x^4 + 3x^3y - 11x^2y^2 + 3xy^3 - 2y^4$
    $= (x - 2y)(x^3 + 5x^2y - xy^2 + y^3)$.

37. $\dfrac{z - w}{a^3}, a \neq 0, z \neq w$.

9. $x^2 + (-2y + 3)x - 3y^2 - 13y - 4$
    $= (x - 3y - 1)(x + y + 4)$.

39. $-\dfrac{x + 2}{x}, x \neq 0, \dfrac{1}{3}$.

13. $x^n - a^n = (x - a)(x^{n-1} + ax^{n-2} + a^2x^{n-3} + \cdots + a^{n-2}x + a^{n-1})$.

41. $\dfrac{x - 2a}{x + a}, x \neq -a, -\dfrac{a}{3}$.

Section 2.13

43. $\dfrac{x + 2}{x + a}, x \neq 2, -a$.

5. (a) 2; (b) 3.

9. Theorem 3.

45. Not possible; $x \neq \sqrt[7]{-c}$.

11. If $a = 0$, b can be any number.

15. -4.

47. $\dfrac{x^3 - 16}{x^3}$.

17. 0.

23. $\frac{5}{3}, -\frac{5}{3}$.

49. $\dfrac{2}{(x + 1)^2}$.

25. a, b.

27. $c, -c$.

51. $\frac{39}{8}$.

29. $1, -1, -17$.

53. $\frac{1}{2}$.

Section 2.14

3. 8.

5. 3.

55. $\dfrac{ax}{4y}, y \neq 0$.

57. $\dfrac{5x}{b}$, $b \neq 0$.

59. $\dfrac{y(a^2 - b)}{x(a^2 - b^2)}$, $x \neq 0$, $y \neq 0$, $a \neq \pm b$.

61. $\dfrac{(d + w)5a}{c}$, $c \neq 0$, $w \neq d$.

63. 1, $x \neq -y$.

65. $\dfrac{a}{3y - 2x}$, $x \neq \dfrac{3}{2}y$.

67. $\dfrac{(25x^2 - 1)a}{(4 - a)(6x - 2)}$, $a \neq \pm 4$, $x \neq \dfrac{1}{3}$.

69. $\dfrac{-(2a - c)ac(c + a)}{a + 2c}$, $a \neq c$, $-2c$.

71. $\dfrac{-12(9x^2 - 1)}{(x + 4)(x + 1)^2}$, $x \neq \pm 1$, -4.

73. $\dfrac{5a(x + 3)}{3(a - b)x^2(2x + 3)}$, $x \neq 0$, 7, $-\dfrac{3}{2}$;

$a \neq \pm b$.

75. $\left(\dfrac{1}{a} + \dfrac{1}{y}\right)^2$.

Section 2.16

1. 24.
3. 120.
5. $a(x + 2)(x + 3)$.
9. (a) $\frac{13}{8}$; (c) $\frac{34}{35}$; (e) 0; (g) $\frac{41}{1960}$;

(i) $\dfrac{2(x + 1)}{x(x + 2)}$; (k) $\dfrac{y^2 + 2by - b^2}{(y - b)^2(y + b)}$;

(m) $\dfrac{4x^3 - x^2 - 10x + 50}{(x + 5)^2(2x + 5)}$.

10. (a) $\dfrac{-7}{32}$; (c) $\dfrac{8}{35}$; (e) $-\dfrac{3}{48}$;

(g) $\dfrac{3}{27,440}$; (i) $\dfrac{1}{(x + 2)x}$;

(k) $\dfrac{by}{(y + b)(y - b)^3}$;

(m) $\dfrac{x(2x - 7)(3x + 10)}{(2x + 5)(x + 5)^3}$.

11. $\frac{101}{42}$.

13. $\frac{25}{36}$.
15. $-\frac{3}{10}$.

17. $\dfrac{-2x + 6}{x^3}$.

19. $\dfrac{8b - ac}{a^2b}$.

21. $\dfrac{1 + xy}{x}$.

23. $\dfrac{2b - a}{2ab}$.

25. $\dfrac{1}{x - 1}$.

27. $\dfrac{x}{b + x^2}$.

29. $\dfrac{10 - 3x}{3x(x + 3)}$.

31. $\dfrac{x^2}{x - 1}$.

33. $\dfrac{-4}{(b - 1)(b + 4)}$.

35. $\dfrac{1}{1 + x}$.

37. $\dfrac{-6x^3 - 19x^2 + 2x + 3}{(x^2 + 3x + 1)(x - 1)}$.

39. $\dfrac{3x^2 + 12x + 13}{x + 2}$.

41. $\dfrac{2x^2 + 5x + 14}{2(x - 5)(x + 2)(x - 1)}$.

43. $\dfrac{-9}{x^2(x^2 - 9)}$.

45. $\dfrac{a^2 - 11ab - 7b^2 + 3a^2b + ab^2}{(3a + b)(2a - b)(a - 4b)}$.

47. $\dfrac{-1}{x + a}$.

49. $\dfrac{(x - y)(x^2 + y^2)}{x + y}$.

51. 2.

53. $\dfrac{7(7x + 4)(4x^2 + 17x - 2)}{(x + 3)^2}$.

Section 2.16—continued

55. $\dfrac{4(x-1)}{(x+1)^3}.$

57. $a = 2,\ b = 1.$

59. $\dfrac{-1}{5(x+5)} + \dfrac{1}{5(x-5)}.$

Section 2.17

3. $\frac{20}{13}.$

5. $\frac{35}{2}.$

7. $x + y.$

9. $\frac{4}{3}.$

11. $\dfrac{2+a^2}{7ab}.$

13. $\dfrac{b+c}{2b}.$

15. $(x+y)^2.$

17. $\dfrac{b+a}{b-a}.$

19. $2.$

21. $3x(3x-2).$

23. $z.$

25. $\dfrac{x+1}{x+3}.$

27. $\dfrac{10+3x}{7+2x}.$

29. $-\dfrac{3(u-6)}{8(u-3)}.$

31. $-\dfrac{14}{x},\ x \neq 0,\ \pm 7.$

Section 2.18

1. No.

3. Any m not a perfect square.

5. No.

Section 2.19

1. 20.

3. $\sqrt{17}.$

5. 6.

7. $\frac{5}{6}.$

9. Not real.

11. $2 + 7\sqrt{5}.$

13. $-1.$

15. $-2.$

17. .1.

19. $\frac{1}{5}.$

21. 19.

23. 3.

25. Not real.

27. 9.

29. $-\dfrac{3b}{x^2}.$

31. $7ax^2.$

33. Yes.

35. Yes.

37. $10, -10.\ 10{,}000^{1/4} = 10.$

39. $\sqrt{15},\ -\sqrt{15}.$

43. No. $a = b$ if a and b are both positive or both negative or both zero.

45. Yes.

49. $-\frac{5}{4}.$

51. 16.

53. 6.

55. $y^2\sqrt{5}.$

57. $\frac{1}{2}.$

59. $a.$

61. $5 + \sqrt{5}.$

63. $21 + 7\sqrt{2}.$

Section 3.1

1. True.

3. True.

5. False.

7. True.

9. True.

11. False.

13. True.

15. False.

17. True.

19. If $x = 5$, $x + 1 = 6.$

21. If $x = 12$, $\dfrac{x}{x(x+1)} = \dfrac{1}{x+1}.$

23. For all $x \neq -5$, $\dfrac{x^2 - 25}{x+5} = x - 5.$

25. $x^2 + 5x + 4 = (x+2)^2 + x.$

27. $3x + \dfrac{3}{2} = \dfrac{4x+3}{2} + x.$

Section 3.2

11. $-4.$
13. $0, -1.$
15. $b, -b.$
17. $12 - 2a.$
19. $0, a^2.$
21. $-1, -3.$
23. $-\frac{5}{4}.$

Section 3.3

3. No.
7. 4.
9. None.
11. $3a + 5.$
13. $\frac{13}{60}.$
15. $0.$
17. All numbers.
19. $-\frac{1}{14}.$
21. $\frac{36}{13}.$
23. Yes.
25. Yes.
27. Yes.
29. No.
31. $\frac{7}{6}u - 3.$
33. $2 + \frac{y}{3}; -6 + 3x.$
35. $\frac{1}{m}(y - b), m \neq 0; \frac{1}{x}(y - b), x \neq 0.$
37. $\frac{1}{8}y^2.$
39. If $m \neq 3, x = -2;$
    if $m = 3, x =$ any number.
41. If $a \neq 1, y = \frac{a + 1}{5};$
    if $a = 1, y =$ any number.
43. $\frac{1}{27}(9 + 2y^2).$
45. $\frac{b^2}{a^2}(a^2 + x^2), a \neq 0.$
47. $\frac{3(b + 2)}{2 - b}, b \neq 2.$
49. $\frac{9}{2}.$
51. $\frac{b}{a}x.$
53. $-\frac{15}{2}.$
55. $\frac{f}{m}, m \neq 0.$

57. $\frac{gl^2}{4\pi^2}.$
59. $-\frac{x}{y}, y \neq 0.$ $\frac{3}{4}.$ No solution.
61. $-\frac{1 + 2xy}{x^2 + 6y^2}, x \neq 0, y \neq 0.$
63. $-\frac{5}{6}.$
65. $x = \frac{5}{3}.$
67. $x = 0; y = 3.$
69. $V = \frac{r}{2}(10 - \pi r^2), r \neq 0.$

Section 3.4

1. $-7, 2.$
3. $0, -\frac{3}{2}.$
5. $3, -3.$
7. $a, b.$
9. $4, -4.$
11. $\sqrt{5}, -\sqrt{5}.$
13. $0, -3, 2.$
15. $-1 - \sqrt{17}, -1 + \sqrt{17}.$
17. $c, -\frac{3}{2}c.$
19. $3, -3, 2, -2.$

Section 3.5

1. 2.
3. $\frac{-1}{b}(ax + c).$
7. No.
9. 5.
11. $2\sqrt{3}, -2\sqrt{3}.$
13. $3, 5.$
15. 0 if $a \neq 0;$ any number except 1
    or -1 if $a = 0.$
17. Any number except zero.
19. No solution.
21. $\frac{1}{2}, 6.$
23. 6.
25. No solution.
27. 8, 9.
29. $-2, -\frac{34}{9}.$
31. $0, \sqrt{\frac{2}{3}}, -\sqrt{\frac{2}{3}}.$
33. $r^2 = \frac{mM}{F}, F \neq 0; M = \frac{r^2 F}{m}, m \neq 0.$

Section 3.5—continued

35. $\frac{a}{b}(a+b)$ if $a \neq 0$, $b \neq 0$; no solution if $a \neq 0$, $b = 0$ or $a = 0$, $b \neq 0$; any number except 0 if $a = 0$, $b = 0$.

37. All $c \neq 0$, -2, $-\frac{4}{3}$; $u = \dfrac{c(4c+5)}{3c+4}$.

39. $\frac{1}{9}(5x_1 + 4x_2)$, $x_1 \neq x_2$.

41. $y \neq 1$, -1; $x = \frac{1}{4}(y - 11)$.

43. (13) $b \neq 0$, $a \neq 0$, $b \neq -c$;
　　(20) $a \neq 0$, $x \neq -a$;
　　(21) $x \neq 0$, $-\frac{2}{3}$;
　　(22) $a \neq 0$, $\dfrac{5b}{2}$; $b \neq 0$;
　　(23) $y \neq 0$, -1;
　　(24) $x \neq 2$, -2; (26) $x \neq 0$;
　　(29) $u \neq 0$, 3, 6, -6.

45. 16 and 18, -16 and -18.

Section 4.1

1. $1 - \frac{1}{2}i$.
3. $-45 - 28i$.
5. -1.
7. 1.
9. $19 - 8i$.
11. $4 + 18i$.
13. 0.
15. $-i$.
17. $\frac{1}{2} + 7\sqrt{2}i$.
19. $0 + 2i$.
21. $16 + 0 \cdot i$.
23. $(\sqrt{3} - 2) + 1 \cdot i$.
25. $-4a + 7i$.
27. $\frac{20}{17} + (-\frac{5}{17})i$.
29. $\frac{63}{452} + \frac{267}{452}i$.
31. $-\frac{11}{5} + (-\frac{3}{5})i$.
33. $-3 + 1 \cdot i$.
35. $5 + \frac{5}{4}i$.
37. $(a_1a_2 - b_1b_2) + (a_1b_2 + b_1a_2)i$.
39. 2, 6, 10, 14, $\cdots$.
43. $i\sqrt{17}$, $-i\sqrt{17}$.
45. $i\sqrt{12}$, $-i\sqrt{12}$.
55. $6i$, $-6i$.
57. 6, -6.
59. $2i$, $-2i$.

61. $9x^2 + 4$.
63. $x^2 + 2\sqrt{2}x + 38$.
65. $2x^3 + ix^2 + 18x - 18i$.
67. $(x + i)(x - i)$.
69. $(2x + 5i)(2x - 5i)$.
71. $(x + \frac{1}{2} + \sqrt{12})(x + \frac{1}{2} - \sqrt{12})$.
73. $(\sqrt{3}x + i\sqrt{8})(-\sqrt{3}x + i\sqrt{8})$.

Section 4.2

1. -3, $\frac{3}{5}$.
3. $\frac{6}{5}$, $-\frac{1}{5}$.
5. 0, 2.
7. $\frac{8}{53}$, $\frac{28}{53}$.
9. 5, 7.
11. 0, 4.
13. 0, 0.
15. $\frac{1}{10} + 7i$.
17. $-5i$.
19. $2 + 2i$.
21. $a^2 - b^2 - 2abi$.
23. $\frac{4}{5} - \frac{7}{5}i$.
29. (a) $\bar{\alpha} = 2 - 3i$, $\bar{\beta} = 1 + i$,
　　　$\overline{\alpha + \beta} = 3 - 2i$.

Section 4.3

1. $(3x - 5)^2$.
3. $(x + 2 + \sqrt{3})(x + 2 - \sqrt{3})$.
5. $(\frac{4}{3}x + 6i)(\frac{4}{3}x - 6i)$.
7. $(x - 4 + 5i)(x - 4 - 5i)$.
9. $-4\left(y - \dfrac{3}{4} + \dfrac{\sqrt{37}}{4}\right)\left(y - \dfrac{3}{4} - \dfrac{\sqrt{37}}{4}\right)$.
11. $-1 + \sqrt{2}$, $-1 - \sqrt{2}$.
13. $\frac{3}{2} - \sqrt{5}$, $\frac{3}{2} + \sqrt{5}$.
15. $i\sqrt{7}$, $-i\sqrt{7}$.
17. $-\frac{1}{2}(1 + \sqrt{1 - 4c})$,
　　$-\frac{1}{2}(1 - \sqrt{1 - 4c})$.
19. 0.
21. $-\frac{1}{4}$.
23. $-2a$, $-c$.
25. $\frac{1}{2}(3 + \sqrt{5})$, $\frac{1}{2}(3 - \sqrt{5})$.
27. $\left(1 + \sqrt{\dfrac{5}{2}}\right)x$, $\left(1 - \sqrt{\dfrac{5}{2}}\right)x$.

29. $x - 1 + \sqrt{x+4}, x - 1 - \sqrt{x+4}.$

31. $0, -8.$

33. $5.$

35. (a) $b^2 - 4ac \geq 0$; (b) $b^2 - 4ac < 0.$
One solution if $b^2 - 4ac = 0.$

39. 15 and $16, -15$ and $-16.$

41. $-\frac{5}{2} + \frac{1}{2}\sqrt{5}, -\frac{5}{2} - \frac{1}{2}\sqrt{5}.$

43. $-3 + \sqrt{2}, -3 - \sqrt{2}.$

Section 4.4

1. $(3 + i)x^2 + (3 + i)x - 7.$

3. $x^2 + x + \frac{5}{4}.$

5. $5x^2 + 20ix - 25.$

7. $x^3 + (-7 + 4i)x^2 + (7 - 26i)x$
$+15 + 30i.$

13. $-\frac{1}{2} + 2i.$

15. $-5, i.$

17. $\frac{1}{4}(1 + \sqrt{33})i, \frac{1}{4}(1 - \sqrt{33})i.$

19. $(x + 7)(x - 7).$

21. $(x + \sqrt{17}i)(x - \sqrt{17}i).$

23. $(x - 3)(x + i).$

25. $(x + 4i)(x + 2i).$

27. $-1, -3i.$

29. $\dfrac{1}{\sqrt{2}} + \dfrac{1}{\sqrt{2}}i, -\dfrac{1}{\sqrt{2}} - \dfrac{1}{\sqrt{2}}i.$

Section 4.5

1. (a) $(\frac{9}{2}, -2).$

3. (a) $(-4, \frac{11}{2}).$

5. (a) $(35, 0).$

11. $(-5, 3).$

Section 5.1

1. Domain is set of all real numbers.
Range is $-2.$

3. $g(1) = \dfrac{5}{2}, g(0) = 3, g(-a) = 3 + \dfrac{a}{2},$
$g(-4)$ is undefined. Domain is set
of all $t \geq 0$; range is set of all real
numbers $\leq 3.$

5. $f(2) = \frac{4}{3}, f(0) = -4, f(-5) = \frac{1}{6}.$
No.

7. (b) No.

9. $f(x) = x^3.$

Section 5.2

1. $\dfrac{1 + \sqrt{7}}{8}; \dfrac{3}{2}.$

3. 3, rational.

5. 4, complex.

7. 2, rational.

9. $q(2) = 17 - 12i,$
$q(1 - i) = -10 - 5i,$
$q(\overline{1 - i}) = 2 + 5i,$
$\overline{q(1 - i)} = -10 + 5i.$

Section 5.3

1. $x^2 - 5x - 6 = (x - 6)(x + 1).$

7. $x^3 - 1 = (x - 1)(x^2 + x + 1).$

9. $x - \sqrt{3}, \sqrt{3}.$

11. $(x - 2i)(x + 3 + i).$

13. $(x + 1 + \sqrt{7})(x + 1 - \sqrt{7}).$

15. $(x + 3 + \sqrt{12})(x + 3 - \sqrt{12}).$

17. $3x^2 + 8.$

19. $(x + \sqrt{8}i)(x - \sqrt{8}i).$

21. $(x + 1 + \sqrt{7})(x + 1 - \sqrt{7}).$

23. $x(x + \sqrt{20}i)(x - \sqrt{20}i).$

25. $2(x + \sqrt{5})(x - \sqrt{5}).$

27. $(x - 4)(x + 3).$

29. $0, 2i, -2i.$

31. (a) $r(x) = x^2 - 2x + 3,$
$\deg r(x) = 2.$
$s(x) = -3x^3 - x^2 - x + 2,$
$\deg s(x) = 3.$
(b) $p(2) = 7, q(2) = -4,$
$r(2) = 3, s(2) = -28.$

33. $\text{Deg } (p(x) \cdot q(x)) = n + m;$
$\deg (p(x) + q(x)) \leq$ larger of
m and $n.$

Section 5.4

1. $2x^2 + 9x + 32, 128.$

3. $x^2 + \frac{7}{2}x + \frac{17}{4}, \frac{27}{8}.$

5. $x^3 - 3x^2 + 9x - 27, 87.$

7. $(x - 1)(x + 1)(x + 3).$

9. $(x - 1)(x + 1)(x^2 - x + 1).$

11. $x^8 - 1 = (x-1)(x+1)(x^2+1)(x^4+1).$

Section 5.5

1. $p(x) = (x+1)(-x^2 + 5x - 6) + 8$, $a = -1$.
3. 7.
5. $p(1) = 8$, $p(2) = 0$, $p(-2) = 56$.
7. $q(2) = 7$, $q(2.7) = 24.976$, $q(2.744) = 26.560557568$.
9. $(x - 2)(3x + 5)$, $-\frac{5}{3}$.
11. $(x - 4)(x + 1)(x - 3)$, 4, -1, 3.
13. $(x - 3 - \sqrt{2})(x - 3 + \sqrt{2})$.
15. $n - 1$.
17. $-1 - \sqrt{45}$, $-1 + \sqrt{45}$.
19. $0, 3, 10$.
21. $-5, 5$.
23. $0, -3, -\frac{5}{2}$.
25. $-\frac{1}{2}, \frac{1}{2}$.
27. $0, -\frac{3}{4}$.
29. $(x - 3i)(x + i)(x - 1)$.
31. $(3x + 2)^2(x^2 + x + 2)$.
33. $x^5 - a^5 = (x - a)(x^4 + ax^3 + a^2x^2 + a^3x + a^4)$.
35. n odd.
37. $x^2 - 14x + 44$.

Section 5.6

1. True; false.
3. False; false.
5. False; true.
7. False; true.
9. False; true.
11. True.
13. False.
15. False.
17. True.
19. True.

Section 5.7

1. $\frac{3}{2}$.
3. -1.
5. $2, -2, -3$.
7. $-\frac{1}{2}, \frac{1}{4}, \frac{1}{3}$.
9. $(x - 5)(x + 5)(x + 3)^2$.
11. $(2x - 5)(4x - 1)(x + \sqrt{3}i)(x - \sqrt{3}i)$.
13. $2, 3, 4$.
15. $\frac{3}{2}(1 + \sqrt{3}i)$, $\frac{3}{2}(1 - \sqrt{3}i)$.

Section 5.8

1. deg 3; -10(mult. 1), 1(mult. 2).
3. deg 7; 4(mult. 6), 0(mult. 1).
5. deg 2; $3i - 7$(mult. 1), $3i + 7$(mult. 1).

7. deg 7; $\frac{3}{7}$(mult. 1), $-\frac{7}{3}$(mult. 3), $-\pi$(mult. 2), $3 - i\sqrt{6}$(mult. 1).
9. deg 2; if $a \neq 0$, a(mult. 1), $-a$(mult. 1); if $a = 0$, 0(mult. 2).

11. $2\left(y + \frac{3}{2} + \frac{i}{2}\right)\left(y + \frac{3}{2} - \frac{i}{2}\right)$.

13. $(x + 2)(x - 2)(x - 3)$.
15. $3x - 15$.
17. $(x + 3\sqrt{2}i)(x - 3\sqrt{2}i)$.
19. $(x + \frac{1}{2})(x - \frac{3}{2})$.

21. $-8\left(x - \frac{1}{2}\right)\left(x + \frac{1}{4} + \frac{\sqrt{3}}{4}i\right)$
$\left(x + \frac{1}{4} - \frac{\sqrt{3}}{4}i\right)$.

23. $(y + \frac{7}{2})^4$.
25. $i(x + 3)(x - 2)$.
27. $z(z + 1)(z - 3i)$.

29. $2\left[x - \frac{1 + \sqrt{33}}{4}i\right]\left[x - \frac{1 - \sqrt{33}}{4}i\right]$.

31. $(x + 2a)(x - a)$.

35. $-\dfrac{1}{\sqrt{2}} - \dfrac{1}{\sqrt{2}}i$. No.

37. There are n n^{th} roots.
39. $c = 3$.

Section 5.9

1. $x^2 + 1$. $p(x) = (x^2 + 1)(3x - 3)$.
3. $x^2 + 4$. $p(x) = (x^2 + 4)(x^4 + 9x^2 + 20)$.
5. $b^2 - 4ac < 0$.
7. $(x - 3)(x^2 + 2)$, $(x - 3)(x + \sqrt{2}i)(x - \sqrt{2}i)$.
9. $(x - 2)(x^2 + 4x + 5)$, $(x - 2)(x + 2 + i)(x + 2 - i)$.
11. $3(x + 1)(x - 2)(x + \sqrt{2})(x - \sqrt{2})$.
13. $x(x^2 + 3)^2$, $x(x + \sqrt{3}i)^2(x - \sqrt{3}i)^2$.
15. $(x - 3)(x + 1 + \sqrt{5})(x + 1 - \sqrt{5})$.
17. $(x - 1)^3(x - 2)^2$.
21. $(x^2 - \sqrt{2}x + 1)(x^2 + \sqrt{2}x + 1)$.

Section 6.1

1. $\frac{9}{13} > \frac{7}{11}$.

3. $\frac{1}{\sqrt{2}} > \frac{3}{5}$.

5. $-5 < -\frac{1}{2} < 10$.

7. $-1 < 0 < \frac{2}{3} < \frac{3}{4}$.

9. $-16 < -7 < 0 < \frac{1}{5} < 1 < \frac{10}{3}$.

13. $a < c$.

15. $b = 1$. No.

19. $c \geqq 0$.

31. If $a < b < 0$, $a^2 > b^2$ and $a^3 < b^3$.

33. $\frac{a}{b} < \frac{2a}{b}$ if $a > 0$, $\frac{2a}{b} < \frac{a}{b}$ if $a < 0$,

$\frac{a}{b} = \frac{2a}{b}$ if $a = 0$.

35. $\frac{7}{16}; \frac{15}{-78}$.

37. (a) $x < 1$; (b) $x \leqq 1$.

39. $x > 4$.

41. $x > -\frac{23}{7}$.

47. $1.732 < \sqrt{3} < 1.733$.

49. $3.162 < \sqrt{10} < 3.163$.

51. $1.259 < \sqrt[3]{2} < 1.260$.

53. $1.144 < \sqrt[3]{1.5} < 1.145$.

Section 6.2

3. $n > 1$.

11. $a = \sqrt{2}$. Trichotomy.

13. 4 is the least upper bound of S; it is not an element of S.

15. Set of all even integers.

Section 6.3

5. $0, \frac{1}{2}, 3, \sqrt{2}, -\frac{1}{4}$.

7. (a) $\frac{3}{8} \leqq x \leqq 15$; (b) $-\frac{4}{5} < x \leqq 7$;
   (c) $-5 < x < -4.9$.

9. 3.

11. $\frac{16}{5}$.

13. $\sqrt{2}$.

15. $\frac{10}{4}$.

17. $\frac{1}{2}$.

19. $\frac{1}{16}$.

21. $\sqrt{3} - \frac{1}{2}$.

23. $2\pi - \frac{58}{7}$.

25. $|a| = a$ if $a \geqq 0$;
    $|a| = -a$ if $a \leqq 0$.

29. (a) No. (b) Yes.

31. $x < -2$ or $x > 2$. Neither a largest nor a least element.

33. $|w| \leqq 7.1$.

35. $1.7, -1.7$.

37. None.

41. $x \leqq -\frac{5}{2}$ or $x \geqq \frac{3}{2}$.

45. $a \geqq 0$.

49. $a \geqq 0$ and $b \geqq 0$, or
    $a \leqq 0$ and $b \leqq 0$.

53. $|x - y|$.

55. $-1.6 < -\frac{\pi}{2} < -1.5$;

$-1.58 < -\frac{\pi}{2} < -1.57$;

$-1.571 < -\frac{\pi}{2} < -1.570$.

57. $-\sqrt{2} < x < \sqrt{2}$. No.

59. (a) $-\frac{1}{2} \leqq x \leqq 1$; (b) $-4 \leqq x < 2$.

61. (a) $\left[\frac{9}{2}\right] = 4$, $[12] = 12$,

$\left[-\frac{3}{4}\right] = -1$, $\left[\frac{\pi}{2}\right] = 1$.

(b) Domain is set of all real numbers; range is set of all integers.

Section 6.4

1. $x < 7$.

3. $x \leqq -2$.

5. $x \geqq \frac{21}{2}$.

7. All real numbers.

9. $x > \frac{1}{4}$.

11. $x \geqq 6 - a$.

13. $-10 < x < -5$.

15. $0 < x < \frac{7}{2}$.

17. -1.

19. $-3 \leqq x \leqq 3$.

21. 5.

23. $-2 < x < 6$.

25. $0 \leqq x \leqq \frac{1}{2}$.

27. No solution.

29. $-19 \leqq x \leqq 21$.

Section 6.4—continued

31. $1 < x < 4$.
33. $1 \leqq x < 22$.
35. $\frac{15}{4} \leqq x \leqq 4$.
37. $\frac{1}{2}$.
39. $x > 2$.
41. $x < -2$ or $6 < x \leqq 9$.
43. (a) $c \geqq -5$; (b) $c < -5$.

Section 6.5

1. $x < -3$ or $x > 2$.
3. $x \leqq 0$ or $x \geqq 4$.
5. $-\frac{1}{2} \leqq x \leqq 5$.
7. $x < -\sqrt{7}$ or $x > \sqrt{7}$.
9. $\frac{1}{2}(3 - \sqrt{5}) \leqq x \leqq \frac{1}{2}(3 + \sqrt{5})$.
11. -3.
13. All real numbers.
15. All real numbers.
17. $x < 1$.
19. $x \leqq -3$ or $0 \leqq x \leqq 3$.
21. $4 < x < \frac{21}{5}$.
23. $x > -2$.
25. $-2 < x < 1$ or $x \geqq \frac{5}{2}$.
27. $-2 < x < 0$ or $x > 6$.
29. $x < -\frac{3}{2}$ or $-1 < x < 2$.
31. $c > -7$.

Section 7.1

3. 4.
5. 5.
7. $\sqrt{113}$.

Section 7.2

1. (a) Rises; falls. (b) Yes; yes.
   (c) Does not change.
3. (a) Rises; falls. (b) Yes; yes.
   (c) Does not change.
5. Graph is horizontal line through point $(0, 9)$.
7. Graph is x-axis.
9. (a) Rises; x cannot be negative.
   (b) No; no. (c) Decreases.
11. (a) x cannot be positive; rises.
    (b) No; no.
13. (a) Falls; rises. (b) Yes; yes.
    (c) Does not change.

15. (a) Falls; falls. (b) Yes; no.
    (c) Increases.
17. (a) Rises; falls. (b) Yes; yes.
    (c) Increases.
19. (a) Falls; rises. (b) No; no.
    (c) Decreases.
21. $(1, 3)$; $(4, -12)$, $(-4, -12)$; $(2, 0)$, $(-2, 0)$, $(0, 4)$.
23. $(5, 0)$, $(-2, 0)$, $(0, -10)$.
25. Once; once.

Section 7.3

1. $y = x$.   5. $x^2 + y^2 = 49$.
3. $x = 0$.   7. $y = 2x$.

Section 7.4

1. $(-5, 0)$, $(0, 5)$.
3. $(-\frac{13}{6}, 0)$, $(0, -\frac{13}{5})$.
5. $(0, -\frac{12}{5})$.
7. $(\frac{12}{5}, 0)$.
9. Nonlinear.
11. Linear; $a = 3$, $b = \frac{1}{2}$, $c = 0$.
13. Nonlinear.
15. Nonlinear.
17. Linear; $a = 6$, $b = -1$, $c = 0$.
19. $(-4, 0)$, $(5, 9)$.
21. (b) All lines pass through $(-1, 3)$.
    (c) $y = -3x$. (d) $y = 3$.

Section 7.5

1. One real zero. Polynomial positive if $x > \frac{5}{3}$.
3. Two real zeros. Polynomial positive if $-\sqrt{3} < x < \sqrt{3}$.
5. No real zeros. Polynomial negative for all x.
7. Two real zeros. Polynomial positive if $x < \frac{4}{5}$ or $x > 5$.

Section 8.1

1. $(7, 4)$.
3. $(-3, \frac{5}{2})$.
5. No solution.
7. $(0, 0)$.
9. $(0, -\frac{3}{10})$.
11. $(\frac{181}{39}, \frac{28}{39})$.

13. $(\frac{9}{38}, \frac{1}{19})$.

15. $\left(\dfrac{1-b}{a-b}m, \dfrac{1-a}{a-b}m\right)$.

17. $(\frac{13}{9}, 13)$.

19. $\left(\dfrac{b_2c_1 - b_1c_2}{a_1b_2 - a_2b_1}, \dfrac{a_1c_2 - a_2c_1}{a_1b_2 - a_2b_1}\right)$.

21. $(-1, -\frac{1}{3})$.

23. $(1, 1, 2)$.

25. No solution.

27. No solution.

29. $(2 - t, -1 - 2t, t)$, t any number.

31. $(-2 + 4s - 3t, s, t)$, s and t any numbers.

33. $(-2, -5, 12)$.

Section 8.2

1. $(6, 4), (4, -6)$.

3. $(1, 3), (1, -3), (-1, 3), (-1, -3)$.

5. $(0, -3)$.

7. $(0, 0), (4, 16), (-4, -16)$.

9. $(2\sqrt{5}i, 1 + \sqrt{5}i)$,

   $(-2\sqrt{5}i, 1 - \sqrt{5}i)$.

11. $(0, 0), (2, 8)$,

   $(-1 + \sqrt{3}i, -4 - 4\sqrt{3}i)$,

   $(-1 - \sqrt{3}i, -4 + 4\sqrt{3}i)$.

13. No solution.

15. $(0, 0), (1,1)$,

   $[\frac{1}{2}(-1 + \sqrt{3}i), \frac{1}{2}(-1 - \sqrt{3}i)]$,

   $[\frac{1}{2}(-1 - \sqrt{3}i), \frac{1}{2}(-1 + \sqrt{3}i)]$.

17. $(3, \sqrt{6})$.

Section 8.3

1. $(1.7, 1.3)$.

3. $(2.6, .3), (-2.6, .3)$.

5. No solution.

7. $(\frac{27}{13}, \frac{8}{13})$.

9. $(0, 0), (\frac{25}{8}, \frac{5}{2})$.

Section 8.4

1. All points below line.

3. All points on or below line.

5. All points inside circle.

7. All points above upper part or below lower part of curve.

9. All points on or to left of curve.

11. All points.

13. All points on or below graph.

15. Below.

19. All points on or inside circle and on or below line.

21. All points above curve and above line.

23. All points between the two circles.

25. No solution.

27. All points inside triangle or on upper side.

29. All points inside triangle.

31. All points on or inside rectangle.

33. All points on line.

35. The point $(9, 3)$.

Section 9.1

1. $0^1 = 0$, $1^0 = 1$, 0^{-5} is undefined.

3. $\frac{1}{9}$.

5. $\frac{1}{4}$.

7. $10{,}000$.

9. $\frac{1}{49}$.

11. 64.

13. 64.

15. $\dfrac{y^4}{x^3}$.

17. $\dfrac{a}{x}$.

19. $\dfrac{3x^2}{y^3}$.

21. $7u^7$.

23. $\dfrac{-1}{6a^2}$.

25. $\dfrac{x^3}{c^3}$.

27. $\frac{1}{9}b^5x$.

29. $\dfrac{-2}{x + y}$.

31. $\dfrac{a^2}{b^2}$.

33. $-3(5^{-1})ax^{-2}$.

Section 9.1—continued

35. $3(20^{-1})$.

37. $7(1.03^{-10})$.

39. $3(4^{-1})x^{-2}y^3z^6$.

41. a^5.

43. y^{-6}.

45. x^8y^{-4}.

47. y^{-4}.

49. $\dfrac{64b^{21}}{a^3}$.

51. $\dfrac{1 + a^6}{a^3}$.

53. $\dfrac{-(a + b)}{a^2b^2}$.

55. $\dfrac{1}{(x + y)^2}$.

57. $\dfrac{a^2b}{b + 3a^2}$.

Section 9.2

1. $\frac{7}{3}\sqrt[4]{x}$.

3. $(\sqrt[5]{b})^{-7}$.

5. $-w^{3/2}$.

7. $\sqrt{2x}$.

9. $-(\sqrt[3]{u})^7$.

11. $(ay)^{5/2}$.

13. $(x + y)^{2/3}$.

15. $\sqrt{a}\,\sqrt[3]{b^2}$.

17. $\frac{1}{81}$.

19. 128.

21. $.1$.

23. $-\frac{1}{3}$.

25. $\dfrac{a}{2w^3}$.

27. $\dfrac{9}{16x^5y^2}$.

29. 10^{-1}.

31. $2x^{3/2}y^{1/2}$.

33. $a(a + b)^{-1}$.

35. $\dfrac{1}{\sqrt{7}}$.

37. $x^{5/6}$.

39. $9z^4$.

41. $a^{-(2/3)}$.

43. $b^{-(3/5)}$.

45. $\dfrac{1}{\sqrt{2}x^{5/6}y^{4/3}}$.

47. $\dfrac{a^{3/2}x}{-8y^{3/2}}$.

49. $-(c + d)$.

51. $\dfrac{1}{2}\left|\dfrac{x}{b}\right|$.

53. $b^{2/3} + 2b^{1/3}a + a^2$.

55. $x - y$.

57. $r^8 - 4r^4s^{-1} + 4s^{-2}$.

59. $a^{-3} + 3a^{-2}y + 3a^{-1}y^2 + y^3$.

61. $x^{-1}y^2 + 3xy + 2 + 3x^2y^{-1} + xy^{-2}$.

63. $a^{2/3} + a^{1/3}b^{1/3} + b^{2/3}$.

Section 9.3

1. $6\sqrt{5}$.

3. 25.

5. $z^{1/6}$.

7. 32.

9. $\sqrt[3]{4}$.

11. $2a^{4/3}$.

13. $5\sqrt{2}y^2$.

15. $\sqrt{5}$.

17. $-\dfrac{a^{5/3}}{2x^3}$.

19. $\dfrac{\sqrt{3}}{|x|^{3/2}}$.

21. 0.

23. $\dfrac{1}{2|x|}\sqrt{2a + 3bx^2}$.

25. $3a\sqrt[3]{1 - 2au^3}$.

27. $\left(\dfrac{a}{4}\right)^{1/3}(1 + 2a)$.

29. $83 - 8\sqrt{15}$.

31. $x + \sqrt{x}\,\sqrt{y} + \frac{1}{4}y$.

33. $4 - 4\sqrt{2}$.

35. $\sqrt{50x}$.

37. $(x^2 y^3)^{1/3}$.

39. $(8x^2)^{1/3}$.

41. $h^{3/2}$.

43. $\left(\frac{4}{125}\right)^{1/6}$.

45. $\sqrt{\dfrac{a}{x}}$.

47. $(c^3 y^{13})^{1/6}$.

49. $(4 \cdot 5^6 x^2)^{1/3}$.

51. $\left[\dfrac{x^6}{(a^2 + x^2)^2}\right]^{1/3}$.

53. $(x^{17} u)^{1/6}$.

55. $\dfrac{-2x}{3(4 - x^2)^{2/3}}$.

57. $\dfrac{a^2 - 2x^2}{\sqrt{a^2 - x^2}}$.

59. $\dfrac{-a^2}{x^2 \sqrt{a^2 + x^2}}$.

61. $|x| \sqrt{\dfrac{6}{x^2}}$.

63. $x^{-(2/3)} (1 + x)$.

65. $a^{-1}(a^{1/2} + b^2 + a^{3/2} b^{-2} + a)$.

67. $\sqrt{2},\ -\sqrt{2},\ i\sqrt{2},\ -i\sqrt{2}$.

69. $0,\ \sqrt{6},\ -\sqrt{6}$.

73. $a = 0$ and $b \geqq 0$, or $b = 0$ and $a \geqq 0$.

Section 9.4

1. $\dfrac{\sqrt{13}}{13}$.

3. $-\frac{2}{3}\sqrt{15}$.

5. $\dfrac{-17}{2} \sqrt[3]{2}$.

7. $\frac{1}{3}[7(3^{2/3}) - 3^{4/3}]$.

9. $\dfrac{3\sqrt{9 + x^2}}{9 + x^2}$.

11. $-\frac{10}{11}(4 + 3\sqrt{3})$.

13. $\dfrac{3\sqrt{2} - 2}{14}$.

15. $\dfrac{-66 + 7\sqrt{30}}{39}$.

17. $\dfrac{2(x - \sqrt{a^2 - x^2})}{2x^2 - a^2}$.

19. $\dfrac{2a + (2 + \sqrt{2})\sqrt{ab} + 2b^2}{2(b - 2a)}$.

21. $\frac{1}{42}(7\sqrt{3} - 3\sqrt{7} + \sqrt{210})$.

23. $.612$.

25. 1.765.

27. $.504$.

29. 3.718.

31. 3.968.

33. $\dfrac{1}{2|b|} \sqrt{b(bx - 12)}$.

35. $c^{3/5}\left(\dfrac{1}{c} + 2\right)$.

37. $\dfrac{\sqrt[p]{2^{p-1} a}}{2x^2}$.

39. $\dfrac{19}{(\sqrt{2} + 5)\sqrt{19}}$.

41. $\dfrac{1}{\sqrt{3 + h} + \sqrt{3}}$.

43. $\dfrac{2}{\sqrt{x + a} - \sqrt{x - a}}$.

45. $\dfrac{x^{2/3} - x^{1/3} y^{1/3} + y^{2/3}}{x + y}$.

Section 9.5

1. 9.

3. -2.

5. 11.

7. $-2 + \dfrac{1}{\sqrt{2}},\ -2 - \dfrac{1}{\sqrt{2}}$.

9. $5,\ \frac{17}{4}$.

11. 16.

13. $\frac{7}{2},\ \frac{175}{2}$.

Section 9.5—continued

15. 2.

17. $\dfrac{125}{-1 + 3(-2^{1/3} + 2^{2/3})}$.

19. $\frac{9}{4}$.
21. 1.
23. No solution.

25. $a\sqrt{\dfrac{3}{2}}, \; -a\sqrt{\dfrac{3}{2}}$.

Section 9.6

1. -3.
3. 5.
5. $-\frac{1}{2}$.
7. $\frac{3}{4}$.
9. $-3 < x < -2$.
11. $5 < x < 6$.
13. $(\frac{1}{3})^2$.
15. $\pi^{1/3}$.
17. $10^{-\sqrt{2}}$.
19. $(1.1)^{-(1/4)}$.
21. $(\sqrt{2} - 1)^{-1}$.
23. $(\sqrt{2})^{-\sqrt{3}}$.
25. 2^5.
27. 8.
29. .2.

Section 10.1

15. 320,000 after 5 days; 10,240,000 after 10 days; 2,500 2 days ago.

Section 10.2

1. $\frac{1}{2}$.
3. $\frac{2}{3}$.
5. 10,000.
7. 1.
11. $1 < \log 83 < 2$.
13. $-1 < \log .7 < 0$.
15. $-4 < \log .00031 < -3$.
17. 1.6990.

Section 10.3

1. .6020.
3. 1.2552.

5. $-.3010$.
7. 1.4771.
9. 3.4771.
11. -1.4771.
13. .6990.
15. 2.8938.
17. $-.1062$.
19. -3.1062.
21. 1.
23. $\frac{1}{100}$.
25. $\dfrac{\sqrt{299}}{10}, \; \dfrac{-\sqrt{299}}{10}$.
27. $x > 100$.
29. $4 < x < 5$.
37. List logarithms of all positive prime integers. Logarithms of all powers of positive rational numbers with rational exponents could be found.

Section 10.4

1. 3.85×10.
3. 1.3076×10^{-1}.
5. 6.3×10^{-2}.
7. 4.7303×10^4.
9. 1×10^{-3}.
11. 2.5315.
13. 1.3617.
15. .6998.
17. -1.2464.
19. -2.4001.
21. $.7812 + 1$.
23. $.9089 + 4$.
25. $.3452 + 0$.
27. $.521 + (-2)$.
29. $.2138 + (-1)$.
31. $.5431 + (-1)$.
33. 48.8.
35. 940.
37. .773.
39. .0672.
41. .984.
43. .649.
45. .0013.
47. .169.

Section 10.5

1. 144.
3. .271.
5. 18.7.
7. −.0619.
9. 7,100.
11. 10.1.
13. −.000462.
15. 32.0.
17. .1694.
19. .213.
21. 4.64.
23. .0000732.
25. -1.77×10^{-7}.
27. −1.05.
29. .436.
31. 9.10.
33. .767.
35. .00938.
37. .00990.
39. 4.68.
41. −1.84.
43. 142.
45. −16.4.
47. .8241.
49. 13.4.
53. 8.82.
55. 16.1.
57. 2.81.
59. 1.70.
61. 2.23.
63. 2.17.
65. 80.0.
67. 2.10, −2.10.
69. 5.32, −5.32.
71. 34.
73. 1, 2.32.
75. $\frac{1}{8}$.
77. 16.7 in.
79. 2.49 sec.
81. (a) 3.79 sec. (b) 4.14 ft.
83. 56,200 in 1960. Will reach 60,000 in 22.9 years.
85. .258 grams after 800 years; .091 grams after 3200 years. After 1600 years one half of original amount remains.

Section 10.6

1. 1.8530.
3. 2.7438.
5. 1.3638.
7. 2.8288.
9. 104.1.
11. .01626.
13. .1489.
15. .9372.

Section 10.7

1. 3.
3. 1.
5. $-\frac{3}{2}$.
7. $\frac{1}{2}$.
9. −1.
11. 6.
13. $\frac{1}{2}$.
15. 2.
17. $\frac{4}{3}$.
19. 10,000.
21. 9.
23. 1.
25. 6.
27. $\frac{1}{9}$.
29. $\frac{4}{5}$.
31. $1 < \log_{10} 26 < 2$.
33. $4 < \log_2 19.42 < 5$.
35. $0 < \log_2 \sqrt[3]{2} < 1$.
37. $0 < \log_5 4 < 1$.
39. $-2 < \log_e .206 < -1$.
43. 4.459.
45. 3.043.
47. $\frac{1}{2}$.
49. −.9612.
51. 4.025.
53. −4.633.
55. −1.
61. 1.818.

Section 11.1

1. −1.21, 2.68.
3. −1.46.
5. −.5.
7. −1.5.
9. 1.6.
11. Between −2 and −1, 0 and 1; 1.
13. Between −2 and −1, −1 and 0; 3.34.
15. Between −2 and −1, −1 and 0; 1.72.
17. −1.1, .1, .9.
19. .01, 2.38.
21. 2.51.
23. −1, 1.64.
25. .65.

Section 11.2

1. (.6, 1.6), (−.6, −1.6), (1.6, .6), (−1.6, −.6).
3. (−1.7, −1.9), (1.3, −.8).
5. (1.9, .3).

Four-Place Common Logarithms

N	0	1	2	3	4	5	6	7	8	9
10	0000	0043	0086	0128	0170	0212	0253	0294	0334	0374
11	0414	0453	0492	0531	0569	0607	0645	0682	0719	0755
12	0792	0828	0864	0899	0934	0969	1004	1038	1072	1106
13	1139	1173	1206	1239	1271	1303	1335	1367	1399	1430
14	1461	1492	1523	1553	1584	1614	1644	1673	1703	1732
15	1761	1790	1818	1847	1875	1903	1931	1959	1987	2014
16	2041	2068	2095	2122	2148	2175	2201	2227	2253	2279
17	2304	2330	2355	2380	2405	2430	2455	2480	2504	2529
18	2553	2577	2601	2625	2648	2672	2695	2718	2742	2765
19	2788	2810	2833	2856	2878	2900	2923	2945	2967	2989
20	3010	3032	3054	3075	3096	3118	3139	3160	3181	3201
21	3222	3243	3263	3284	3304	3324	3345	3365	3385	3404
22	3424	3444	3464	3483	3502	3522	3541	3560	3579	3598
23	3617	3636	3655	3674	3692	3711	3729	3747	3766	3784
24	3802	3820	3838	3856	3874	3892	3909	3927	3945	3962
25	3979	3997	4014	4031	4048	4065	4082	4099	4116	4133
26	4150	4166	4183	4200	4216	4232	4249	4265	4281	4298
27	4314	4330	4346	4362	4378	4393	4409	4425	4440	4456
28	4472	4487	4502	4518	4533	4548	4564	4579	4594	4609
29	4624	4639	4654	4669	4683	4698	4713	4728	4742	4757
30	4771	4786	4800	4814	4829	4843	4857	4871	4886	4900
31	4914	4928	4942	4955	4969	4983	4997	5011	5024	5038
32	5051	5065	5079	5092	5105	5119	5132	5145	5159	5172
33	5185	5198	5211	5224	5237	5250	5263	5276	5289	5302
34	5315	5328	5340	5353	5366	5378	5391	5403	5416	5428
35	5441	5453	5465	5478	5490	5502	5514	5527	5539	5551
36	5563	5575	5587	5599	5611	5623	5635	5647	5658	5670
37	5682	5694	5705	5717	5729	5740	5752	5763	5775	5786
38	5798	5809	5821	5832	5843	5855	5866	5877	5888	5899
39	5911	5922	5933	5944	5955	5966	5977	5988	5999	6010
40	6021	6031	6042	6053	6064	6075	6085	6096	6107	6117
41	6128	6138	6149	6160	6170	6180	6191	6201	6212	6222
42	6232	6243	6253	6263	6274	6284	6294	6304	6314	6325
43	6335	6345	6355	6365	6375	6385	6395	6405	6415	6425
44	6435	6444	6454	6464	6474	6484	6493	6503	6513	6522
45	6532	6542	6551	6561	6571	6580	6590	6599	6609	6618
46	6628	6637	6646	6656	6665	6675	6684	6693	6702	6712
47	6721	6730	6739	6749	6758	6767	6776	6785	6794	6803
48	6812	6821	6830	6839	6848	6857	6866	6875	6884	6893
49	6902	6911	6920	6928	6937	6946	6955	6964	6972	6981
50	6990	6998	7007	7016	7024	7033	7042	7050	7059	7067
51	7076	7084	7093	7101	7110	7118	7126	7135	7143	7152
52	7160	7168	7177	7185	7193	7202	7210	7218	7226	7235
53	7243	7251	7259	7267	7275	7284	7292	7300	7308	7316
54	7324	7332	7340	7348	7356	7364	7372	7380	7388	7396
N	0	1	2	3	4	5	6	7	8	9

Four-Place Common Logarithms (Continued)

N	0	1	2	3	4	5	6	7	8	9
55	7404	7412	7419	7427	7435	7443	7451	7459	7466	7474
56	7482	7490	7497	7505	7513	7520	7528	7536	7543	7551
57	7559	7566	7574	7582	7589	7597	7604	7612	7619	7627
58	7634	7642	7649	7657	7664	7672	7679	7686	7694	7701
59	7709	7716	7723	7731	7738	7745	7752	7760	7767	7774
60	7782	7789	7796	7803	7810	7818	7825	7832	7839	7846
61	7853	7860	7868	7875	7882	7889	7896	7903	7910	7917
62	7924	7931	7938	7945	7952	7959	7966	7973	7980	7987
63	7993	8000	8007	8014	8021	8028	8035	8041	8048	8055
64	8062	8069	8075	8082	8089	8096	8102	8109	8116	8122
65	8129	8136	8142	8149	8156	8162	8169	8176	8182	8189
66	8195	8202	8209	8215	8222	8228	8235	8241	8248	8254
67	8261	8267	8274	8280	8287	8293	8299	8306	8312	8319
68	8325	8331	8338	8344	8351	8357	8363	8370	8376	8382
69	8388	8395	8401	8407	8414	8420	8426	8432	8439	8445
70	8451	8457	8463	8470	8476	8482	8488	8494	8500	8506
71	8513	8519	8525	8531	8537	8543	8549	8555	8561	8567
72	8573	8579	8585	8591	8597	8603	8609	8615	8621	8627
73	8633	8639	8645	8651	8657	8663	8669	8675	8681	8686
74	8692	8698	8704	8710	8716	8722	8727	8733	8739	8745
75	8751	8756	8762	8768	8774	8779	8785	8791	8797	8802
76	8808	8814	8820	8825	8831	8837	8842	8848	8854	8859
77	8865	8871	8876	8882	8887	8893	8899	8904	8910	8915
78	8921	8927	8932	8938	8943	8949	8954	8960	8965	8971
79	8976	8982	8987	8993	8998	9004	9009	9015	9020	9025
80	9031	9036	9042	9047	9053	9058	9063	9069	9074	9079
81	9085	9090	9096	9101	9106	9112	9117	9122	9128	9133
82	9138	9143	9149	9154	9159	9165	9170	9175	9180	9186
83	9191	9196	9201	9206	9212	9217	9222	9227	9232	9238
84	9243	9248	9253	9258	9263	9269	9274	9279	9284	9289
85	9294	9299	9304	9309	9315	9320	9325	9330	9335	9340
86	9345	9350	9355	9360	9365	9370	9375	9380	9385	9390
87	9395	9400	9405	9410	9415	9420	9425	9430	9435	9440
88	9445	9450	9455	9460	9465	9469	9474	9479	9484	9489
89	9494	9499	9504	9509	9513	9518	9523	9528	9533	9538
90	9542	9547	9552	9557	9562	9566	9571	9576	9581	9586
91	9590	9595	9600	9605	9609	9614	9619	9624	9628	9633
92	9638	9643	9647	9652	9657	9661	9666	9671	9675	9680
93	9685	9689	9694	9699	9703	9708	9713	9717	9722	9727
94	9731	9736	9741	9745	9750	9754	9759	9763	9768	9773
95	9777	9782	9786	9791	9795	9800	9805	9809	9814	9818
96	9823	9827	9832	9836	9841	9845	9850	9854	9859	9863
97	9868	9872	9877	9881	9886	9890	9894	9899	9903	9908
98	9912	9917	9921	9926	9930	9934	9939	9943	9948	9952
99	9956	9961	9965	9969	9974	9978	9983	9987	9991	9996
N	0	1	2	3	4	5	6	7	8	9

Powers and Roots

n	n^2	n^3	$\sqrt{n}$	$\sqrt[3]{n}$	n	n^2	n^3	$\sqrt{n}$	$\sqrt[3]{n}$
0	0	0	0.000	0.000	50	2 500	125 000	7.071	3.684
1	1	1	1.000	1.000	51	2 601	132 651	7.141	3.708
2	4	8	1.414	1.260	52	2 704	140 608	7.211	3.733
3	9	27	1.732	1.442	53	2 809	148 877	7.280	3.756
4	16	64	2.000	1.587	54	2 916	157 464	7.348	3.780
5	25	125	2.236	1.710	55	3 025	166 375	7.416	3.803
6	36	216	2.449	1.817	56	3 136	175 616	7.483	3.826
7	49	343	2.646	1.913	57	3 249	185 193	7.550	3.849
8	64	512	2.828	2.000	58	3 364	195 112	7.616	3.871
9	81	729	3.000	2.080	59	3 481	205 379	7.681	3.893
10	100	1 000	3.162	2.154	60	3 600	216 000	7.746	3.915
11	121	1 331	3.317	2.224	61	3 721	226 981	7.810	3.936
12	144	1 728	3.464	2.289	62	3 844	238 328	7.874	3.958
13	169	2 197	3.606	2.351	63	3 969	250 047	7.937	3.979
14	196	2 744	3.742	2.410	64	4 096	262 144	8.000	4.000
15	225	3 375	3.873	2.466	65	4 225	274 625	8.062	4.021
16	256	4 096	4.000	2.520	66	4 356	287 496	8.124	4.041
17	289	4 913	4.123	2.571	67	4 489	300 763	8.185	4.062
18	324	5 832	4.243	2.621	68	4 624	314 432	8.246	4.082
19	361	6 859	4.359	2.668	69	4 761	328 509	8.307	4.102
20	400	8 000	4.472	2.714	70	4 900	343 000	8.367	4.121
21	441	9 261	4.583	2.759	71	5 041	357 911	8.426	4.141
22	484	10 648	4.690	2.802	72	5 184	373 248 ·	8.485	4.160
23	529	12 167	4.796	2.844	73	5 329	389 017	8.544	4.179
24	576	13 824	4.899	2.884	74	5 476	405 224	8.602	4.198
25	625	15 625	5.000	2.924	75	5 625	421 875	8.660	4.217
26	676	17 576	5.099	2.962	76	5 776	438 976	8.718	4.236
27	729	19 683	5.196	3.000	77	5 929	456 533	8.775	4.254
28	784	21 952	5.292	3.037	78	6 084	474 552	8.832	4.273
29	841	24 389	5.385	3.072	79	6 241	493 039	8.888	4.291
30	900	27 000	5.477	3.107	80	6 400	512 000	8.944	4.309
31	961	29 791	5.568	3.141	81	6 561	531 441	9.000	4.327
32	1 024	32 768	5.657	3.175	82	6 724	551 368	9.055	4.344
33	1 089	35 937	5.745	3.208	83	6 889	571 787	9.110	4.362
34	1 156	39 304	5.831	3.240	84	7 056	592 704	9.165	4.380
35	1 225	42 875	5.916	3.271	85	7 225	614 125	9.220	4.397
36	1 296	46 656	6.000	3.302	86	7 396	636 056	9.274	4.414
37	1 369	50 653	6.083	3.332	87	7 569	658 503	9.327	4.431
38	1 444	54 872	6.164	3.362	88	7 744	681 472	9.381	4.448
39	1 521	59 319	6.245	3.391	89	7 921	704 969	9.434	4.465
40	1 600	64 000	6.325	3.420	90	8 100	729 000	9.487	4.481
41	1 681	68 921	6.403	3.448	91	8 281	753 571	9.539	4.498
42	1 764	74 088	6.481	3.476	92	8 464	778 688	9.592	4.514
43	1 849	79 507	6.557	3.503	93	8 649	804 357	9.644	4.531
44	1 936	85 184	6.633	3.530	94	8 836	830 584	9.695	4.547
45	2 025	91 125	6.708	3.557	95	9 025	857 375	9.747	4.563
46	2 116	97 336	6.782	3.583	96	9 216	884 736	9.798	4.579
47	2 209	103 823	6.856	3.609	97	9 409	912 673	9.849	4.595
48	2 304	110 592	6.928	3.634	98	9 604	941 192	9.899	4.610
49	2 401	117 649	7.000	3.659	99	9 801	970 299	9.950	4.626
					100	10 000	1 000 000	10.000	4.642

Index